REFERENCE SERIES

Post-World War II Fighters

1945–1973

Marcelle Size Knaack

New Imprint by
OFFICE OF AIR FORCE HISTORY
UNITED STATES AIR FORCE
WASHINGTON, D.C., 1986

Library of Congress Cataloging-in-Publication Data

Knaack, Marcelle Size (Date)
Post-World War II fighters, 1945–1973.

(Reference series / Office of Air Force History)
Bibliography: p. 336.
Includes index.
Originally published as v. 1 of the author's Encyclopedia of US Air Force aircraft and missile systems.
1. Fighter planes—United States. 2. United States. Air Force—History. 3. Aeronautics, Military—United States. I. Title. II. Title: Post-World War 2 fighters, 1945–1973. III. Title: Post-World War Two fighters, 1945–1973. IV. Series: Reference series (United States. Air Force. Office of Air Force History)
UG1242.F5K57 1985   358.4'3'0973   85–18822
ISBN 0–912799–19–6

For sale by the Superintendent of Documents, U.S. Government Printing Office
Washington, D.C. 20402

FOREWORD

The first in a series of U.S. Air Force aircraft and missile systems, this volume deals with the development, deployment, and operations of fighter aircraft between 1945 and 1973, commencing with the F-80 *Shooting Star* and ending with the F-15 *Eagle*. Many of these aircraft were employed during the Korean War, the war in Southeast Asia, and during cold war crises throughout the world. Additional volumes to be published in this series will cover Air Force bombers, transports, trainers, other military aircraft, and missile systems.

JOHN W. HUSTON
Major General, USAF
Chief, Office of Air Force History

PREFACE

This volume contains basic information on all Air Force fighters developed between World War II and 1973, including all configurations. It is based primarily on US Air Force sources. The origin of each aircraft is noted as well as its most troublesome development, production, and operational problems. Also covered are significant modifications, most of which can be attributed to ever-changing aeronautical technology. Production totals, delivery rates, unit costs, phaseout dates, and other important milestones are provided, as well as a brief description of each version's new features.

The book begins with the first postwar American jet fighter—the F–80 Shooting Star. It ends with Northrop's F–5 Freedom Fighter. Complete consistency of data on each fighter was not always available, but each section describes the aircraft's basic development, production decision dates, program changes, test results, procurement methods, and the like. Technical data and operational characteristics also are provided.

Many people contributed to this work, in particular members of the Historical Office, Aeronautical Systems Division, of the Air Force Systems Command (AFSC), and the Historical Office, Air Force Logistics Command (AFLC), both located at Wright-Patterson AFB, Ohio. The author also owes a special debt to Colonel Monte D. Montgomery, a former staff officer in the Allocations Division, Deputy Chief of Staff, Programs and Resources, Headquarters USAF; and to Dr. Thomas G. Belden, former Chief Historian of the Air Force, who strongly encouraged publication of such an encyclopedia. Finally, she is indebted to her office colleagues, Max Rosenberg, Deputy Chief Historian, Office of Air Force History; Carl Berger, Chief, Histories Division; Bernard C. Nalty, Clyde R. Littlefield; and several other colleagues; members of the Editorial Branch, particularly Eugene P. Sagstetter; and Eleanor C. Patterson, who typed the entire manuscript without faltering.

Marcelle Size Knaack

TABLE OF CONTENTS

Page

Page

Page

POST-WORLD WAR II FIGHTERS

1945–1973

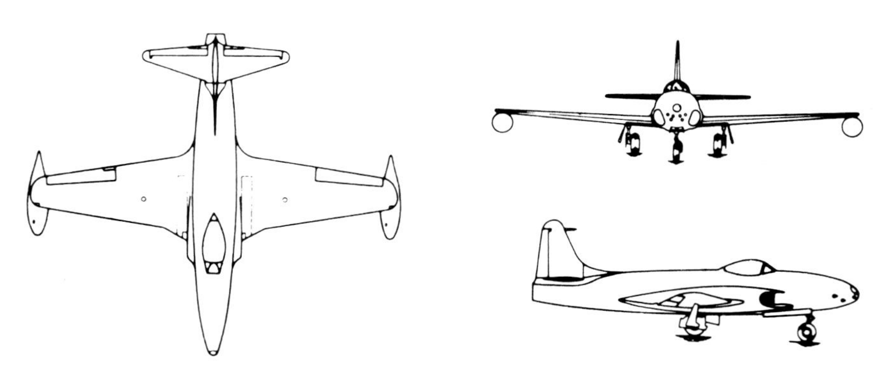

LOCKHEED F–80 SHOOTING STAR—First True American Jet Fighter

F–80B: featured underwing rocket launchers that were added to the F–80A.

TF–80C: had extended fuselage (38.5 inches more) to fit extra seat under lengthened canopy. Became T–33, commonly known as the T-Bird.

LOCKHEED F-80 SHOOTING STAR

Manufacturer's Model 80

Basic Development **May 1943**

The Army Air Forces (AAF) requested Lockheed Aircraft Company to design a jet-propelled airplane using the British DeHavilland-built Halford engine. This followed the Advanced Development Objectives (ADO) of July 1941, soon after the British had flown their first jet—a Gloster plane powered by a Whittle jet-propelled engine of an entirely new design. Germany's first jet, the Messerschmitt 262, had been flight-tested by the Luftwaffe early in 1941, a few months ahead of the British aircraft. Lockheed's 1943 design yielded an experimental plane that gave way to the F-80. Known as the P–80 until mid-1948,[1] the F–80 was the first true American jet fighter—even though Bell's P–59A Airacomet preceded it by 2 years.[2]

General Operational Requirements (GOR) **17 June 1943**

This GOR called for development of a jet-propelled plane of superior performance.

Go-Ahead Decision **June 1943**

During a conference (16–19 June) at Wright Field, Ohio, Lockheed proposed to build one airplane around the Halford engine in just 180 days. Backing its proposal with solid performance data, Lockheed secured immediate approval.

Development Contract **1943**

A letter contract (LC) on 24 June (6 days after the Wright Field conference) let Lockheed begin work without delay. The formal contract, signed on 16 October, provided for one XP–80, to be delivered within 180 days of the LC date. Total cost of $515,000

---

[1] The United States Air Force, established 26 July 1947 (when the National Security Act of 1947 became law) as a separate service, coequal with Army and Navy, came into being on 18 September 1947. In the ensuing months the Air Force revised its duty prefix letter, in the designation given to fighter aircraft, from "P" for Pursuit to "F" for Fighter. The actual date for the revision of designation letters was 11 June 1948.

[2] The XP–59A Airacomet (ordered in September 1941 to take advantage of early British work on gas turbine engines) flew on 1 October 1942. It was powered by 2 General Electric I–A turbojets, developed from the Whittle jet. Bell's experimental Airacomet and 13 subsequent prototypes were followed by 20 productions (designated P–59A) that were equipped with better but still underpowered J–31–GE–3 turbojets. The P–59As were single-seaters. They carried nose armament of one 37-mm cannon, three .50-cal machineguns, and bomb racks under the outer wings, but were utilized to train jet pilots. Entering service a year before the war ended, they were all in use in the summer of 1945. Their performance, however, was disappointing—top speed (359.5 knots per hour) at 30,000 feet was slower than that of the conventional P–47 and P–51.

included a 4 percent fixed fee of $19,800. Two other experimental planes (XP–80As) were ordered under similar provisions in February 1944. In March, the AAF also ordered 13 prototypes (YP–80As)—more than usual, to speedup testing.

Mockup Inspection **20–22 July 1943**

Except for the engine (not yet available), the XP–80 mockup was complete. The sleek low-wing-airframe was so simple it elicited few immediate changes.

First Flight (XP–80) **8 January 1944**

Even though delayed by engine problems, the flight was on schedule. Lockheed actually produced the first XP–80 in 145 days. However, the Halford H–1 engine, held up abroad for 2 months, still did not work. A second imported engine arrived in December 1943—only a few weeks ahead of the first flight.[3] During flight tests in the spring of 1944, the XP–80 became the first AAF airplane to exceed 500 mph in level flight. Nevertheless, the XP–80 was discarded in favor of an airframe having the more powerful General Electric I–40 engine (later designated the J33–11). After brief pilot transition with the Fourth Air Force, the XP–80 in November 1946 went to the Museum Storage Depot of Orchard Park, Illinois.

First Flights (XP–80A) **1944**

The two XP–80As, ordered early in 1944, were first flight tested on 1 June and 1 August. The AAF continued testing the first XP–80A's flight characteristics[4] until the plane crashed on 20 March 1945 and was completely destroyed. The second XP–80A differed from the first by featuring an additional seat, behind the pilot's. This XP–80A was primarily flown to test the new J33–11 engine performance.[5]

First Flight (YP–80A) **13 September 1944**

The AAF accepted the first of the 13 P–80 prototypes on 18

---

[3] Production of the British Halford engine was assumed by the Allis-Chalmers Manufacturing Company, Milwaukee, Wisconsin. The Navy monitored production of the new engines, plagued by endless maintenance difficulties. The AAF received only 3 Allis-Chalmers H–1 engines, and turned them over to the Navy in January 1947.

[4] The XP–80A was heavier and had a slightly bigger wing than the XP–80. Testing showed that its stability, maneuverability, and the like excelled that of the best fighters then in use.

[5] The General Electric Company, Schenectady, New York, was the original manufacturer of the I–40 (J33–11) engine, adopted for the P–80 over the troublesome Allis-Chalmers H–1 (J36) engine. However, production slippage at the Schenectady plant prompted the opening of a second engine source. Hence, the Allison Division of the General Motors Corporation, Indianapolis, Ind., entered the engine program in the spring of 1944.

September (5 days after its first flight). The plane was given more instruments and transferred to the National Advisory Committee for Aeronautics (NACA) for high-speed experiments. The second YP–80A was completed as the XF–14, a reconnaissance version of the basic prototype (later to become the RF–80). Despite late engine deliveries, all YP–80As (including the XF–14) had left the Lockheed plant by the end of February 1945 to engage in usual prototype operations. An exception was four prototypes allocated to tactical duty under "Extraversion," a European/Mediterranean Theater project that ended in May 1945. Two of the four Extraversion planes (one, re-equipped with a Rolls Royce B–41 engine) were lost. The others returned to a remote control research program in the United States.

F-80A

Production Decision **1944**

The AAF definitively endorsed the P–80 on 4 April (2 months ahead of the XP–80A's first flight) with a LC that introduced the first production contract. This contract, as approved in December, called for two lots of P–80s (500 in each). Delivery of the first 500 was to be completed by the end of 1945; the rest, by February 1946.[6] Each of the first 500 P–80s would cost $75,913; the later ones, $20,000 less per aircraft. A second production contract in June 1945 raised the P–80 procurement above 3,500—most of them subsequently cancelled.[7]

First Acceptance (Production Aircraft) **February 1945**

Despite major problems, the AAF received its first P–80A on schedule. The P–80 actually attained quantity production in March (only 21 months from its design), even though precision tools were lacking and the engines were either in short supply or unacceptable.

Testing **October-November 1945**

Accelerated service tests showed that with proper maintenance the P–80A was safe for flight. Many mechanical "bugs" were found, however. An engineering inspection of the 126th P–80A in mid-November (delayed for months because the first planes were practically handmade and hardly typical of later ones) also disclosed a number of deficiencies.

---

[6] Germany's growing use of jet fighters (and the North American P–51's inability to measure up) underlined the P–80's urgency. In January 1945, the P–80 production got the same high priority as the B–29. This came after concluding that a slowdown of P–38 production would not solve the manpower, space, and part shortages preventing Lockheed from speeding up the P–80 production.

[7] An additional 1,000 P–80s were to be built by North American and labeled P–80Ns to distinguish them from the Lockheed productions. They too were cancelled.

Program Changes **1945-1949**

The close of WW II brought a sharp curtailment of the P–80 procurement. The second production contract (June 1945) was completely cancelled on 5 September; the first went through several changes before settling for a total of 917 airplanes, against the 1,000 originally contracted for. Moreover, the P–80's cost climbed some $19,000 per unit, due to reduced procurement, readjusted delivery schedules, and more particularly, required configuration changes. Nevertheless, postwar procurement through fiscal year 1950 raised the entire program to 1,731 P–80s (by then redesignated F–80s) of one model or another.[8]

Enters Operational Service **1946**

Months after many of the P–80s had been accepted, the aircraft were assigned to the 412th Fighter Group.[9] In the spring of 1946 the AAF had 301 P–80s, hardly any of them overseas. The main reason was the same shortage of parts and engines that had kept the P–80 out of WW II. All P–80As using J33–9 engines had been grounded in 1945, while a General Motors strike the following year further complicated the engine situation. Furthermore, the P–80 had the highest accident rate in the AAF[10]—36 crashes alone between March and September 1946. Here, low pilot experience played a part.

Production Modifications **1946**

Beginning with the 346th production, Lockheed put the Allison J33–17 engine in the P–80A. The GE J33–11 and Allison J33–9 engines, used interchangeably by earlier P–80As, would be reconfigured along the lines of the new J33–17.[11]

Modernization **1947-1948**

The AAF paid Lockheed $8.5 million to give the P–80As some features of the next model (P–80B). This took roughly 1 year. By March 1948, all P–80As in service had received under-wing rocket

---

[8] This Air Force Logistics Command (AFLC) figure included all experimental and prototype planes, some 60 P–80s bought for the Air National Guard (ANG), and 128 F–80Cs converted to TF–80Cs (also referred to as T–33s). Lockheed reported F–80 production to be below 1,700. Headquarters AAF/USAF showed 1,552 F–80s bought for the active forces. All three sets of figures were correct, being based on different accounting methods.

[9] After testing the aircraft, this unit had reported in mid-1945 that the P–80 "was the only fighter airplane with sufficient speed to escort proposed jet-propelled bombers." The 412th also thought the P–80 well-suited for other tactical roles—counter air and ground support.

[10] More than twice that of any other fighter, excluding the P–59 which was seldom flown.

[11] There was no money for Allison to do the work. It would be handled over several years during regular depot engine overhauls.

launchers, and all but a few got an engine water-alcohol injection system to ease takeoff. To cure canopy problems at high speed, Lockheed installed newly-developed canopy remover kits on many of the P–80As as part of the $8.5 million modernization deal. Oversea units did their own canopy work. The same fund shortages that kept Allison from improving the engines of the early P–80As slowed other postproduction modifications. Faulty aileron boost pumps (the cause of several accidents) and hydraulic pressure losses still existed. These, like upgrading the original engines, would eventually be corrected during regular depot overhauls.

End of Production **December 1946**

Production terminated with delivery of 12 last aircraft.

Total P–80As Accepted

525

Acceptance Rates

The AAF accepted 33 P–80As in FY 45, 311 in FY 46, and 181 in FY 47.

Flyaway Cost Per Production Aircraft

Approximately $95,000[12]

Subsequent Model Series

P–80B

Other Configurations—RF–80A

FP–80A. A P–80A, with a longer and deeper nose to house cameras in place of the six M–2 guns, initially on the basic aircraft. The FP–80A's prototype (the XF–14) was flown in the fall of 1944. It was followed by the XFP–80A, a reconnaissance version of the production P–80A. The AAF earmarked 152 of the 917 P–80s procured under the first production contract for conversion to photographic models. These FP–80As were all accepted in FY 47 (between July 1946 and April 1947) at a flyaway cost per production aircraft of $107,796—airframe, $75,967; engine (installed), $21,584; electronics, $4,195; ordnance, $2,335; other (including armament), $3,715.[13] The Air Force in 1951 converted 70 of the redesignated F–80As to the reconnaissance type. To better fit these RF–80As for Korean operations, they were given improved photographic equipment.[14] In 1953, 98 RF–80As exchanged their J33–A–11 engines for the more powerful J33–A–35s of yet another F–80 version (the famed

[12] Average cost of the various P–80s ordered under the first production contract of December 1944. If included, research and development costs boosted the aircraft's average price to over $110,000.

[13] Average aircraft costs in Air Force Technical Order (T.O.) 00–25–30 did not reflect engineering change and modification costs after basic contract approval.

[14] Redesignated 94th Fighter-Interceptor Squadron (FIS) on 16 April 1950.

and most produced T–33). This upped performance and prolonged aircraft service life. The Air Force flew a few RF–80s until late 1957.

Oversea Deployments **1948–1949**

In July 1948, 16 F–80s of the 56th Fighter Group, Strategic Air Command (SAC), departed Selfridge AFB, Mich., on a pioneer journey. The planes left Bangor AFB, Maine, on the 20th and made refueling stops in Labrador, Greenland, and Iceland. They landed in Scotland 9 hours and 20 minutes after leaving the United States. This first west-east transatlantic jet flight, on the heels of the Soviet land blockade of Berlin, was followed by a similar F–80 crossing in the summer of 1949. After that, use of the North Atlantic route became routine—saving time, money, and bolstering European security.

War Commitments **1950**

F–80As never directly took part in the Korean conflict. In 1950 they were used in the United States for training. Production of jet fighter pilots was too important to be curtailed—even temporarily. This fact rather than the aircraft's obsolescence was the reason they were kept at home.[15]

Phaseout **1951**

The F–80A began leaving the Air Force in October 1951.

Milestones **19 June 1947**

The AAF as early as 1945 wanted to achieve a world speed record with the P–80A. When minor modifications failed, the AAF spent $35,000 to devise a speedier, slimmed down version (the P–80R).[16] Piloted by Colonel Albert Boyd, Chief of the Wright Field's Flight Test division, the P–80R on 19 June 1947 set an official record of 623.73 mph over a 3-kilometer course at Muroc, Calif. This broke the British Gloster twin-jet Meteor IV's 616 mph record of 7 September 1946. Colonel Boyd's record speed was an average—on one of the four runs, the tiny plane streaked across the course at 632.5 mph.

---

[15] The Air Force filled most early F–80 requisitions from the Far East Air Force (FEAF) with the only planes immediately available in large numbers. These were older F–51s, retrieved from the Air National Guard or withdrawn from storage. FEAF fighter pilots knew the F–51 and needed no transitional training—a crucial factor at the time.

[16] The P–80R had a J33–A–23 engine, with water-alcohol injection, clipped wings, a smaller cockpit canopy, and a high-speed sleek finish.

F-80B

Previous Model Series

F-80A

New Features

Thinner wings with thicker skin; stronger nose bulkheads to support greater fire power (six M-3 .50-in machine guns); stainless steel armored compartment containing the new Allison J33-21 engine, with water-alcohol injection and fitted for jet-assisted take-off (JATO).[17] The F-80B also featured underwing rocket launchers (added to the F-80A), cockpit cooling and canopy anti-frosting systems, and a jettisonable pilot seat (designed, manufactured, and installed by Lockheed).

Basic Development **1945**

The P-80B got its start in early 1945, when Lockheed presented plans for the P-80Z—an advanced P-80 type. The Lockheed's sophisticated P-80Z plans were unrealistic. To follow them would amount to building a whole new aircraft. Instead, the AAF settled for a much simpler model. This aircraft also bore the P-80Z designation until the spring of 1947. A March engineering inspection found that after 65 changes the P-80Z still differed little from the P-80A. The P-80Z accordingly became the P-80B 1 month later.

Procurement **1946**

A December 1946 letter contract ordered 60 P-80Bs (still known as P-80Zs); an amendment on 31 January 1947 raised the order to 140. This included 60 for the ANG, reduced to 54 in March due to a shortage of funds. In the end a grand total of 240 P-80Bs was purchased under the several-time altered production contract of 1944.

First Acceptance (Production Aircraft) **7 March 1947**

It was accepted after 3 days of engineering inspection and 1 month before the aircraft became the P-80B.

End of Production **March 1948**

Production terminated with delivery of the 765th P-80 (525 P-80As, then 240 P-80Bs).

Total P-80Bs Accepted

240

Flyaway Cost Per Production Aircraft

The AAF in May 1947 set the P-80B's unit cost below $75,000. In

---

[17] Those F-80As with the 4,000-lb-thrust J33-17 engine (600 pounds weaker than the J33-21) were given water-alcohol injection systems. All F-80As were fitted for jet-assisted takeoff. This minor modification was directed in March 1947.

the long run, the F–80A and the similar F–80B were priced under a single tag—around $95,000 per plane.

Subsequent Model Series

P–80C (F–80C on 11 June 1948).

Other Configurations

None

Phaseout **1951**

In practice F–80Bs and F–80As were usually considered the same aircraft. Both models began USAF phaseout in late 1951.

F-80C

Previous Model Series

F–80B

New Features

A more powerful engine and better armament.[18]

Contractual Arrangements **1948-1949**

The AAF used fiscal year 1947 funds to order the first P–80Cs, but the definitive contract was not signed until 2 February 1948. Procurement of the last increment (F–80Cs) was authorized in fiscal year 1950.

Enters Operational Service **1948**

Still little more than an improved P–80, the F–80C's early days achieved scant recognition. Yet, it was this aircraft that introduced the jet fighter into the Korean conflict.

Oversea Deployments **1949-1950**

Most FEAF fighter wings had F–80Cs months before the Korean war. In May 1950, 365 of the 553 aircraft in FEAF operational units were F–80Cs.

War Commitments **1950-1953**

Because of FEAF's defensive mission, F–80Cs on 25 June 1950 (when the war broke out) had only .50-caliber machineguns. As counter air interceptors, they were equipped with mid-wing rocket posts for carrying up to 16 5-inch high-velocity rockets. Designed as fighters, none of them were fitted with pylon bomb racks. The F–80C used the least fuel at 15,000 feet, but its range at that altitude was still quite short. Yet, before they knew it, the F–80Cs were tapped for all types of jobs—from escorting B–29s to flying

[18] Early F–80Cs had the J33–A–23 engine of the P–80R; later productions, the J33–A–35 (5,400-pound-thrust with water injection). All F–80Cs were armed with the F–80B's M–3 guns. The improvement lay in an increase of the gun's rate of fire.

interdiction and close air support.[19] As fighter-bombers, they stood down on 1 May 1953, but a few remained committed to the interceptor role until the truce on 27 July.

Special Modifications **1950**

The F–80C's radius of action was around 100 miles. With two Lockheed external 165-gallon tanks (and a full rocket load) it was only 225 miles. Lieutenants Edward R. Johnston and Robert Eckman of the 49th Fighter-Bomber Wing at Misawa Air Base in Japan came up with one answer. Two center sections of a standard disposable tank were inserted in the middle of each of the two external tanks. These modified "Misawa" tanks each held 265 gallons—enough fuel for 1 extra hour of flight and a 350-mile radius of action, depending on the type of combat mission. Every FEAF F–80C would get a pair of Misawa tanks, even though they might overstress the wing tips.[20]

Appraisal

As early as March 1951, pilots realized the F–80C's shortcomings as escort. The MIGs were able to fly through bomber formations before the F–80Cs (100-mph-slower at 25,000 feet) could engage them.[21] The F–80Cs proved excellent fighter-bombers and stood up well under rough field conditions. The strain of combat flying, however, caused them to deteriorate faster than they could be repaired. In 1952, they already required more routine maintenance for each hour flown than any other fighter, including the F–51 of WW II note.[22] In air-to-air combat, the F–80C's success was short lived.[23] Soon, these aircraft relied on F–86 support to keep them out of MIG–15 gunsights. In the long run, enemy aircraft downed only 14 F–80Cs. Still, operational losses were high—277, 113 of them due to ground fire. The 277 represented almost one-half of the entire F–80C production.

---

[19] Pre-1950 economy programs prevented the building of longer and stronger runways at temporary air installations in Japan, where conventional aircraft were being replaced by jets. This postponed deployment of the F–84E (specifically adapted for air-ground operations) and severely pared FEAF flight training. Too, fund shortages back home added to the problems of the new F–84 and F–86 jets.

[20] The F–80C's radius of action reverted to 100 miles, when bombs replaced the external fuel tanks.

[21] F–80C production was barely ended when the Korean war started, but the aircraft were already behind the times, as more advanced jets came onto the scene.

[22] In the spring of 1952, an average of 7,500 manhours per aircraft would be needed to recondition some of the 49th Wing's F–80Cs after only 4 months of flying.

[23] Nevertheless, an F–80C on 8 November 1950 destroyed a MIG–15 in what was believed to be the first conclusive air combat between jet fighters.

Total F–80Cs Accepted

The Air Force accepted 670, against 798 ordered. The last 128 were completed as TF–80Cs (redesignated T–33As on 5 May 1949). By 30 June 1950, all but a few of the 798 F/TF–80Cs had been accepted.

Flyaway Cost Per Production Aircraft (F/TF–80C)

$93,456.00—airframe, $62,050; engine (installed), $21,192; electronics, $5,536; armament, $4,678.

Subsequent Model Series

None

TF–80C

Other Configurations

A P–80C fuselage, taken off the production line in August 1947, was extended by 38.5 inches to fit an extra seat under the lengthened canopy. This prototype trainer was first flown on 22 March 1948. Redesignated TF–80C in June, it became the T–33A within a year. The TF–80C first had the J33–A–23 engine, then the more powerful –25. The trainer also retained 2 of the F–80C's .50-caliber machineguns that were optional in the T–33A. Commonly called the T-Bird, the T–33 was produced in larger quantities than any other F–80. Eventually, given a still better engine (the J33–A–35), the T–33 served as the Air Force's standard jet trainer for almost two decades.

Phaseout **1954–1955**

Discontinuance of the last USAF tactical F–80C squadron—some 8 months after the Korean war—foretold the F–80C phaseout from the regular forces. Yet, several F–80Cs lingered in the active inventory until October 1955.[24] The Air National Guard still flew a mix of F–80 day fighters in 1956, shelving the last ones in mid-1958.

Other Countries

Around 100 F–80Cs went to allied nations under the Military Assistance Program (MAP).

Other Uses

A number of F–80s ended up as drones. Designated QF–80s, they collected fallout samples from radioactive clouds. They served in addition as missile targets. The Air Force Missile Development Center at Holloman AFB, N. Mex., was still using them in late 1963.

---

[24] The Air Force Reserve (AFR) also got F–80Cs—a few in mid-1953 and 175 by mid-1955. After switching some F–80Cs for more modern fighters, the AFR in November 1957 dropped all its fighters and became a troop carrier force.

PROGRAM RECAP

The Air Force accepted a grand total of 1,731 F–80s—counting all prototypes and P–80 deliveries actually received by the AAF. The program consisted of 1 XF–80, 2 XF–80As, 13 YF–80As, 525 F–80As, 240 F–80Bs, 670 F–80Cs, 152 RF–80As,[25] and 128 TF–80Cs (redesignated T–33As in 1949).

---

[25] All other RF–80As in the inventory were converted F–80As.

TECHNICAL DATA

F–80A/B, F–80C, and T–33A

Manufacturer	(Airframe)	Lockheed Aircraft Corporation, Burbank, Calif.
	(Engine)	Allison Division of General Motors Corporation, Kansas City, Mo.
Nomenclature		F–80, fighter; T–33, subsonic jet trainer.
Popular Name		Shooting Star/T-Bird

Characteristics	*F–80A/B*	*F–80C*	*T–33A*
Engine, Number & Designation	1 J33–A–11 or 1 J33–A–17; F–80B, 1 J33–A–21	1 J33–A–23 or 1 J33–A–35	1 J33–A–23 or 1 J33–A–25 or 1 J33–A–35
Length/Span	34.6 ft/39.11 ft	34.6 ft/39.11 ft	37.9 ft/38.11 ft
Weight (empty)	7,920 lb	8,240 lb	8,084 lb
Max. Gross Weight	14,500 lb	16,856 lb	11,965 lb
Max. Speed	484.5 kn (sea level)	503.6 kn (7,000 ft)	471.5 kn (25,000 ft)
Cruise Speed	356.0 kn	381.2 kn	
Rate of Climb (sea level)	4,580 fpm	6,870 fpm	6.5 min. to 25,000 ft
Service Ceiling	45,000 ft	42,750 ft	47,500 ft
Range	360 nm	920 nm	3.12 hours
Armament	6.50-in machine guns	6.50-in machine guns	None (2.50-in machine guns in TF–80C)
Ordnance	up to 2,000 lb	up to 2,000 lb	
Rockets	8 5-in HV	16 5-in HV	
Crew	1	1	2

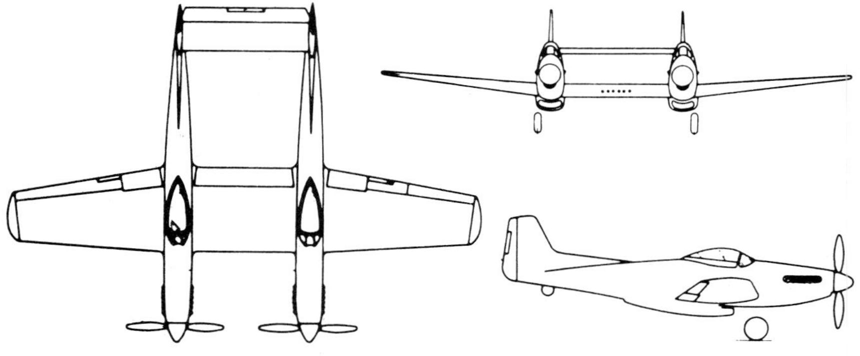

NORTH AMERICAN F–82 TWIN MUSTANG—All F–82s Were Much the Same.

F–82E: long-range escort fighter; first truly operational model (F–82As and Bs went to testing).

F–82F/G/H: featured a nacelle beneath the center-wing to house radar equipment. They were used as all-weather fighter interceptors.

NORTH AMERICAN F-82 TWIN MUSTANG

Manufacturer's Model NA-123

Basic Development **January 1944**

As a double-fuselaged P–51 Mustang, the post-World War II P–82 in reality reached back to October 1940, when the P–51 prototype first flew.[1] Since North American used some Curtiss P–40 technical data to quickly develop the YP–51, the P–82's ancestry may even be traced to 1937, when the experimental P–40 Warhawk was ordered.[2]

Advanced Development Objective **20 February 1942**

A special escort plane was needed. The ADO of 1942 responded to the AAF's 1941 air war plans that "urged development of special escort planes [even though] bombers for the moment could rely on current interceptor-type models for support, especially the P–47." Since Republic's incoming P–47s also served as fighter-bombers, these plans suggested employment of a modified bomber type for the escort role.[3]

General Operational Requirements **January 1944**

With even longer range than the latest P–51 then in production,[4]

---

[1] The North American P–51 Mustang was developed in record time to satisfy British WW II requirements for a fighter that would take into account the early lessons of aerial combat over Europe. Among the aircraft's most notable features were a laminar-flow wing section, aft-mounted ventral radiator for minimum drag, and simple lines to ease the production that began in late 1941. A year later, the Army Air Forces adopted the P–51 for its own use. It ordered some 2,000 P–51Bs, a ground attack version of the Royal Air Force P–51 single-seat fighter.

[2] During May 1939, in competition with other pursuit prototypes, the Curtiss Warhawk was evaluated at Wright Field. This plane was immediately selected for procurement under a first contract of nearly $13 million—largest at the time for a US fighter. The first P–40s (of 12,302 produced) were delivered in May 1940.

[3] The 1941 air war plans sounded a discordant note at a time of overwhelming faith in the bomber's supremacy. Moreover through the late summer of 1942, WW II experience tended to confirm that escorts were only necessary to support bombers past enemy fighters along the coasts of France and Belgium. Once the "fighter belt" was crossed, little if any German opposition would be met.

[4] This P–51D, like the later P–51H and P–51K, closely resembled the P–51B and P–51C, both of which could carry 184 gallons of fuel internally, 150 gallons in external tanks, and remain in the air 4 hours and 45 minutes. In November 1943 (1 month before the first P–51Bs entered service with the British-based Eighth Air Force), the AAF chose the P–51B and P–51C for escort duty over the battle-tested P–47 and Lockheed's slightly older P–38. This step was meant to stop the soaring bomber losses due to escorts being too short-ranged even with extra fuel tanks. (The use of extra fuel tanks for longer range dated back to WW I, when it first proved a definite fire hazard. It was also long resisted on the grounds that interceptor-type fighters weighted with fuel would be more vulnerable to enemy aircraft.)

the new plane was to penetrate deep into enemy territory.[5] Its immediate role would be to escort the B–29 bombers used in the Pacific against Japan.

Initial Procurement **February 1944**

On 7 January North American presented a bold design based on the successful P–51.[6] This design promised range, reliability, and less pilot fatigue (the two pilots could spell one another). The AAF endorsed it at once. In fact, a February letter contract to construct and test three experimental P–82s gave way in the same month to an order for 500 productions.

First Flight (XP-82) **6 July 1945**

The AAF accepted this XP–82 in August and a second one in September. Both were equipped with Packard Merlin V–1650–23 and –25 engines.[7] The third experimental plane, designated XP–82A, had two Allison V–1710–119 engines. It was accepted in October.

F-82B

Program Changes **1945-1950**

Germany's surrender on 7 May 1945 and Japan's on 1 September caused the cancellation or the drastic cutback of many military contracts. Conversely, the AAF had to confront new requirements and problems.[8] In the process, the P–82 program fared pretty well. Against the 500 P–82Bs initially planned, overall procurement was finalized on 7 December 1945 at 270 P–82s. Included were 20 P–82Zs (P–82Bs, actually), already on firm order and later allocated to testing. The rest would be long-range P–82E escorts (P–82Bs, equipped with new Allison engines). The definitive contract (W33–038 ac–13950), signed on 10 October 1946, spelled out delivery dates for the 250 P–82Es. But this schedule was never met. Moreover, by

---

[5] A requirement learned the hard way. Two 1943 missions (17 August and 14 October) over Schweinfurt, Germany, had resulted in the loss of 120 B–17s (more than 25 percent of those engaged) and death or capture of 1,200 airmen. In the P–51's case, this had prompted the AAF to rush modification of the plane's fuselage to insert an extra tank that would extend range to more than 800 miles.

[6] North American's idea of joining two standard, well-proven, P–51 fuselages (complete with engine) was not unique. It was reminiscent of the Heinkel–111Z transport and glider tug, a "Siamese Twin" arrangement of two Heinkel–111 bombers, built by the Germans earlier in the war. In any case, North American's plane proved to be the sole American example.

[7] British Rolls Royce-type engines built in the United States.

[8] The need existed to perfect an American liquid-cooled engine and to make use of government-owned war surplus engine parts. Then too, so-called "Z" airplanes had to be procured in lots of 20 to keep some major aircraft companies going until new production requirements were firmed up.

January 1950, some 90 change orders and supplemental agreements had pared the 250 F–82Es[9] to 100; the remaining 150 becoming night fighters to cope with rising air defense demands.

First Acceptance (Production Aircraft) **January 1946**

With delivery of 2 P–82Bs—formerly known as P–82Zs. All P–82B productions were used for testing, as initially planned.

Total P–82Bs Accepted

The Air Force accepted 19—against 20 ordered.

End of Production **March 1946**

With the AAF acceptance of 13 last P–82Bs.

Acceptance Rates

The AAF accepted all P–82Bs in fiscal year 1947—2 in January 1946, 4 in February, and 13 in March.

Flyaway Cost Per Production Aircraft

$140,513

Other Configurations

P–82C. A P–82B, modified in late 1946, for testing as a night interceptor. The P–82C featured a new nacelle (under the center wing section) housing an SCR–720 radar.
P–82D. This modified P–82B was a P–82C with a different radar—the APS–4. The two modified planes (P–82C and P–82D) had radar operators in lieu of copilots.

Subsequent Model Series

P–82E

Phaseout **1949**

By December, no P–82Bs (by then redesignated F–82Bs) remained in the Air Force inventory.

F–82E

Previous Model Series

F–82D, technically. But in effect, the F–82E followed the F–82B, which it so closely resembled.

New Features

Two Allison liquid-cooled engines, V–1710–143 and V–1710–145.[10] Otherwise, the twin-fuselage (joined by a center-wing panel and

---

[9] The newly-formed United States Air Force had renamed all pursuit aircraft as fighters on 11 June 1948.

[10] Each of these 12-cylinder engines developed 1,600 horsepower at takeoff; each of the F–82B's Packard-built V–1650 engines, only 1,380.

tailplane) low-wing, long-range, F–82E escort was similar to the F–82B.[11]

Contractual Arrangements **1946**

The $35 million procurement contract of October 1946 covered 250 F–82Es plus tools and spare parts. $17 million was for the first 100 planes, $14.5 million for the remaining 150, and $3.5 million for special tools and ground-handling equipment. Delivery of the first F–82Es was scheduled for November 1946, and the contract would be reviewed after completion of 100 airplanes. However, these plans fell through. Overall procurement of F–82s remained intact, but total costs rose to more than $50 million, and the number of E models was quickly reduced by more than one-half.

Program Slippage

Malfunctions of government-furnished, Allison-built engines plagued the shrunken F–82E program from the start.[12] While waiting for acceptable engines, North American had to bear the expense of storing unequipped F–82 airframes.[13] The situation grew so bad that the contractor requested and was granted in December 1947 greater partial payments, even though only four planes had been delivered.

First Flight (Production Aircraft) **April 1947**

Although the engine had passed its 150-hour teststand test in

[11] The wing had a NACA low-drag, laminar flow air foil section and could haul external fuel tanks, bombs, or rockets. Both the F–82B and E could be provided with jettisonable canopies, hydraulic boost controls for all movable surfaces, thermal anti-icing, anti-G suits, adequate cabin heating and ventilation, low-pressure oxygen system, and armorplating to protect the two pilots.

[12] The government had always wanted to give its Twin Mustang F–82 a purely American and stronger engine than the foreign-born P–51's V–1650 (built at Packard plants, dismantled after the war). It therefore negotiated in August 1945 with the Allison Division of the General Motors Corporation for a new version of the V–1710. Various models of this engine had equipped the P–38, P–39, and P–40 of WW II fame, and Allison promptly agreed to buy surplus government V–1710 parts for the new project. Even so, the F–82 program's new V–1710 engines proved costly in the long run—reaching $18.5 million after many amendments. The airplane-engine combination was never satisfactory. Yet, no damages could be assessed against Allison, because the engines has passed the 150-hour qualification tests and met procurement specifications. Nonetheless, the contract was cut back in early 1948, and the Air Force made Allison store special engine tools for 2 years at no cost to the government.

[13] The planes were kept at the Consolidated Vultee Aircraft Corporation, Downey, Calif. Assembly lines were set up at Downey to install the engines and deliver the F–82s, rather than taking them back to the North American plant in Inglewood, Calif. Storage costs, paid by North American, included rent, plant protection, maintenance and insurance. Many F–82s stayed at Downey for nearly 2 years, exposing their electrical and radar equipment to damage from moisture. Special precautions had to be taken to prevent corrosion. The Air Force figured this alone raised costs by more than $2 million.

October 1946, troubles appeared on the first flight. Hence, this F–82E and three later ones underwent special engine tests at once. By year's end, the Air Force had accepted and restricted to testing these four F–82Es, redesignating them F–82As.[14]

Engine Problems **1947-1948**

Spark plug fouling, auxiliary stage super-charger failure, oil loss by spewing, backfiring at high and low power, plus engine oil leakage, roughness, and surging were but a few of the V–1710–143 and V–1710–145 deficiencies. Spark plug fouling was an early and most difficult problem. Oil accumulation required a new set of plugs for nearly every flight. By December 1947, North American was about ready to give up flight-testing the F–82. But the combined efforts of Allison, North American, and the Air Force were beginning to pay off. Nonetheless, extensive engine flight-tests continued through June 1948—months after the first F–82Es entered service.[15]

Enters Operational Service **May 1948**[16]

Three months after the Strategic Air Command had received the first B–50 bomber[17] the aircraft entered operational service. By 31 December, SAC counted 81 F–82E long-range escorts among its tactical aircraft.

Total F-82Es Accepted

96 (excluding the 4 that were booked as F–82As).

End of Production **December 1948**

With delivery of the last F–82E.

Acceptance Rates

The Air Force accepted 72 F–82Es in fiscal year 1948 (between January and June 1948), and 24 in fiscal year 1949 (22 in July 1948, 1 in October, and 1 in December).

Flyaway Cost Per Production Aircraft

The cost amounted to $215,154. Except for the F–82B, every F–82 carried the same price tag.

Other Configurations

None

---

[14] One was accepted in September 1947, one in November, and two in December.

[15] The first 200 engines could only be operated at lower than the specified power rating. They were accepted to avoid further F–82 slippage, after Allison promised to later align them to specification.

[16] The F–82 program (as twice revised after the war) slipped about 1 year, but the North American storage problem lasted almost 2.

[17] The Boeing B–50 was basically an improved B–29 Superfortress—the Twin Mustang had been programmed to escort the B–29, back in 1944.

Subsequent Model Series

F–82F

Phaseout **1950–1951**

F–82Es (last piston-engined fighters to enter Air Force service) quickly disappeared from the SAC inventory. The first sizeable lot was declared surplus in March 1950.

F-82F, F-82G, F-82H

Previous Model Series

F–82E

New Features

A nacelle beneath the center-wing that housed radar equipment (F–82F's AN/APG–28 and F–82G's SCR–720C[18]); automatic pilot; and a radar operator replacing the second pilot. When winterization was added to the F or G, it became an F–82H.[19]

Go-Ahead Decision **1946–1947**

The LC of February 1946 covered 250 P–82Es, but the October contract gave the AAF the option to adjust requirements after completion of 100 planes. Moreover, the P–82 in November 1945 was already linked to an all-weather role, "assuming that yet-to-be held tests would show it to be adequate for that purpose." Testing soon showed that the P–82 was hard to maneuver, decelerated slowly, and had poor pilot visibility. Still, the night fighter survived in early 1947, because there was little choice. If the year-old Air Defense Command (ADC) did not get the P–82, it would have nothing better than the P–61 while awaiting the P–87 and the P–89.

Program Slippage

Slippage of F–82F and G deliveries was slight, since interceptor production was not due to start until the 100 F–82Es were completed. When the engine impasse was broken in early 1948, F–82s of all types started flowing in.[20]

Enters Operational Service **September 1948**

By the end of the month, ADC had 29 F–82Fs. Five squadrons of the 52d and 325th All-Weather Wings flew F–82s in late 1949, but

---

[18] The SCR–720 radar was not new, having been used by the Northrop P–61 Black Widow in WW II.

[19] In late 1946, modification of two P–82Bs to C and D night interceptors had confirmed that all P–82s were much the same. All it took to convert the long-range escort into a single-place interceptor was to remove the controls and canopy from the right-hand cockpit. Adding interceptor components virtually completed the transformation.

[20] All 250 F–82s were shop-completed by 30 April 1948, exactly 1 year after F–82s (minus engines) started piling up in storage.

the combat capability of ADC (under the newly formed Continental Air Command (CONAC) since December 1948) was not much improved.[21]

End of Production **April 1948**

Total F-82s Accepted

150[22]—91 F-82Fs, 45 F-82Gs, and 14 F-82Hs.

Acceptance Rates

One F-82G was accepted in fiscal year 1948 (February 1948), all other F-82s (F, G, and H models) in fiscal year 1949. The last F-82G and 6 winterized F-82Hs were received in March 1949.

Flyaway Cost Per Production Aircraft

Same as the F-82E—$215,154.

Other Configurations

None

Subsequent Model Series

None

Oversea Deployments **December 1948**

The Caribbean Air Command was the first to receive F-82s—15 by year's end. Fifth Air Force was next, with one squadron (the 68th) soon flying F-82s out of Itazuke Air Base in Japan. Another squadron (the 4th) was in place at Kadena Air Base, Okinawa, before the Korean war. It was part of the Twentieth Air Force, which once had directed the worldwide operations of all B-29 Superfortresses.

War Commitments **1950-1952**

Few of the 40 F-82s available to the Far East Air Forces in mid-1950 were combat-ready. In July, Fifth Air Force[23] spared three F-82s of the 68th Fighter All-Weather Squadron for operations over Korea, but the planes proved of little value except against known and fixed targets. In addition, FEAF's F-82 operations (like ADC's)[24] were hampered by parts shortages and maintenance troubles. If Fifth Air Force continued to use F-82s over Korea,

---

[21] In mid-December 1949, the Air Force began classifying its airplanes into first and second-line categories. The stipulated first-line life was 3 years from the time of delivery. Hence, the F-82E (available since the spring of 1948) would reach second-line status in 1951. This criterion was not applied to other F-82s. Based on Air Proving Ground's suitability tests, all F-82 interceptors were immediately relegated to second-line category.

[22] This was in addition to the 100 F-82 escorts.

[23] The Fifth was the largest air force under FEAF.

[24] ADC resumed major air command status in January 1951.

only 60 days of extra supply support could be expected.[25] Hence, although a few of SAC-surplus F–82Es went to FEAF, all F–82s were withdrawn from combat in February 1952. Despite limited use, the F–82s managed to leave a pretty good war record. They destroyed 20 enemy planes (4 in air fights, 16 on the ground). They scored the first aerial victory in Korea on 27 June 1950, downing a Soviet-built Yakovlev–11.

Phaseout **1950-1953**

In mid-1950 Air Defense units began trading F–82s for F–94s,[26] and in early 1951 the few Twin-Mustangs remaining in ADC were towing targets. The F–82s coming out of Korean combat in February 1952 lingered a bit longer in the inventory. After June 1953, no F–82s appeared on Air Force, Air National Guard, or Air Reserve Forces rolls.

PROGRAM RECAP

The Air Force accepted a grand total of 272 F–82s (including 22 prototype, test, and early productions received by the AAF). Specifically, the F–82 program consisted of 2 XF–82s, 1 XF–82A, 19 F–82Bs (known for a while as P–82Zs and all allocated to testing), 4 F–82As, 96 F–82Es, 91 F–82Fs, 45 F–82Gs, and 14 F–82Hs.

---

[25] When F–82 production ceased in 1948, no provision had been made for an adequate supply of spare parts. Further, the Air Force did not have many F–82s to begin with. It could ill afford to weaken the F–82 units committed to the Pacific Northwest's defense or to draw from the 14 F–82Hs in Alaska.

[26] The F–94 was the first USAF jet interceptor.

TECHNICAL DATA

F–82E, F–82F, and F–82G

Manufacturer	(Airframe)	North American Aviation, Inc., Inglewood, Calif.
	(Engine)	Allison Division of General Motors Corporation, Indianapolis, Ind.
Nomenclature	(F–82E)	Long-Range Escort Fighter
	(F–82F/G)	All-Weather Fighter Interceptor
Popular Name		Twin-Mustang

Characteristics (Basic Mission)	*F–82E*	*F–82F*	*F–82G*
Engine, Number & Designation	1 V–1710–143 (left) & 1 V–1710–145 (right)	same	Same
Length/Span	39.11 ft/51.2 ft	42.2 ft/51.6 ft	42.2 ft/51.6 ft
Max. Takeoff Weight	24,864 lb	26,208 lb	25,891 lb
Weight (empty)	14,914 lb	16,309 lb	15,997 lb
Takeoff Ground Run (sea level)	1,865 ft	2,135 ft	2,060 ft
Average Cruise Speed	261 kn	250 kn	250 kn
Combat Speed (max. power)	400 kn	396 kn	396 kn
Combat Range	2,174 nm	1,920 nm	1,945 nm
Service Ceiling	29,800 ft	27,700 ft	28,300 ft
Combat Ceiling (max. power)	38,400 ft	36,800 ft	37,200 ft
Rate of Climb (max.)	4,020 fpm	3,690 fpm	3,770 fpm
Combat Radius (sea level)	976 nm	870 nm	882 nm
Crew	2	2	2
Ordnance Max.[27]	4,000 lb	4,000 lb	4,000 lb
Guns (Internal)[28]	6	6	6

---

[27] Four 1,000-lb bombs, or two 2,000-lb bombs, or twenty-five 5-inch rockets.

[28] Six 0.5-inch Browning MG 53–2 machineguns in center wing section.

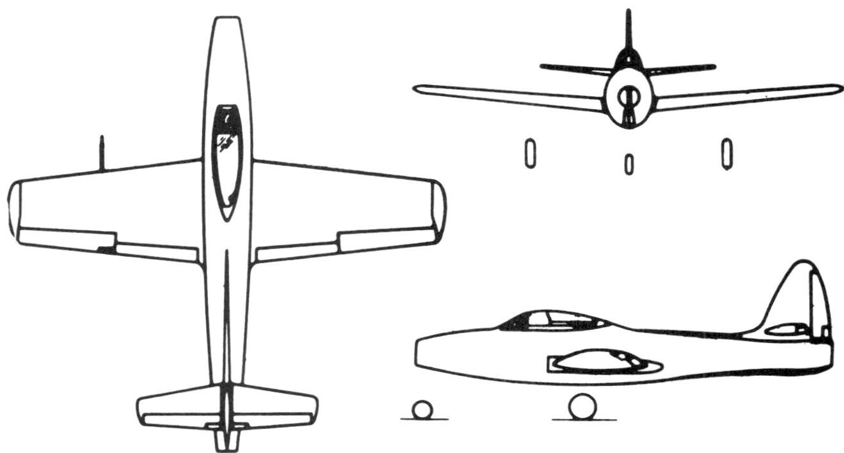

REPUBLIC F–84 THUNDERJET

F–84Bs/Cs/Ds:	Almost alike.
F–84Es:	Slightly longer fuselage; fuel tanks carried on bomb-schackles, located beneath the wings and inboard of the landing gear.
F–84G:	First fighter built with the capability of refueling in flight. The F–84G was also the first single-seat fighter-bomber with atomic capability.
F–84F:	Republic development of its straight wing Thunderjet into a swept-wing, single-seat fighter-bomber. Originally labeled F–96, the "Thunderstreak" was redesignated F–84F in September 1950. Yet, it was largely a new aircraft.
RF–84F Thunderflash:	Elongated and enclosed nose, containing 15 cameras; engine air intake ducts located in the wing roots (rather than in the nose section).
RF–84K:	A recon F–84F, modified for use with the B–36. It featured a reconfigured tail and a retractable hook in the nose section. The RF–84K could be stored half-way within the bomb-bay of the B–36.

REPUBLIC F-84 THUNDERJET

Manufacturer's Model AP-23F (F-84C)

Basic Development **1944**

Republic F–84, like the subsequent F–105 Thunderchief, was a descendant of the first bearer of the "Thunder" name, the company's P–47 Thunderbolt, famed "jug" of World War II.[1] Conceived as a jet successor to the Thunderbolt and first designated the P–84, the F–84 was designed around the General Electric TG–180 (J–35) turbojet and was of straightforward design and construction.

General Operational Requirements **11 September 1944**

This GOR called for development of a mid-wing day fighter having top speed of 600 miles per hour (521 kn), combat radius of action of 850 miles (738 nm), and an armament installation of eight .50-caliber machineguns or six .60-caliber guns. It was soon recognized, however, that military requirements were penalizing the plane too severely. In the final version of the basic airplane, armament was reduced to six .50-caliber guns, or an alternate installation of four .60-caliber machineguns, and radius of action was decreased to 705 miles (612 nm). The object of these deviations was to reduce weight, which, together with low thrust, constituted the aircraft's most serious problem.

Other Requirements **11 September 1944**

The purpose of procuring the new aircraft was also to secure a suitable airframe for the GE TG–180 axial flow gas turbine engine, that the Air Technical Service Command of the Army Air Forces was committed to develop—production of this engine was later taken over by the Allison Division of General Motors.

Contractor Proposal **November 1944**

This was a revised proposal for three fighter airplanes, static test article, mockup, models, and engineering data. It included AAF Engineering Division comments on an informal proposal submitted 2 months before.

Go-Ahead Decision **11 November 1944**

The decision was made and a letter contract was issued without resorting to the commonly used competitive-bid contract method. Two factors accounted for this unusual procedure. The proposed

---

[1] The Thunderbolt first took shape in a sketch made by Alexander Karveli, Republic vice-president and renowned designer, on the back of an envelope. That was at an Army fighter-plane requirements meeting in 1940. Kartveli, who was born in Russia and educated in Czarist military schools and leading French engineering institutions, joined Republic's predecessor company, Seversky Aviation Corporation, in 1931 after serving with several other outstanding aviation enterprises in Europe and the United States.

airplane promised higher maximum speed and greater combat radius than were provided by the P–80, and the Republic Aviation Corporation had had experience in single-place fighter design and development.

Initial Letter Contract **4 January 1945**

The AAF order covered 100 service test and production P–84 airplanes—25 of the former and 75 of the latter. This was subsequently decreased to 15 service test articles, which were redesignated YP–84As. The production articles were correspondingly increased from 75 to 85 and redesignated P–84Bs.

Mockup Inspection **5-11 February 1945**

The inspection, conducted at the contractor's plant, revealed a satisfactory mockup. However, certain design changes would have to be made to improve the safety and tactical suitability of the aircraft.

First Definitive Contract **12 March 1945**

This was a formal cost-plus-a-fixed-fee (CPFF) contract (W33–038 ac–11052) for three XP–84 airplanes, static test model, small models, spare parts, and data at estimated cost of $2.5 million, plus a 4 percent fixed fee of some $99,000.00. This contract was first amended on 17 May 1945 to include a blanket bailment agreement providing for governmental loan to Republic of aircraft, aircraft engines, and aircraft equipment or materiel for use in experimental research, testing, or development work. With Republic's concurrence, it was further amended on 25 June 1945 to comprise the January LC, which was nullified. In the process, the amount of expenditure originally authorized by the nullified LC was raised from $17.5 million to almost $24 million.

Development Problems **May-July 1945**

Development tests at the Langley Field Laboratory of the National Advisory Committee for Aeronautics were disappointing. Bulging of the stabilizer skin became evident and undesirable longitudinal stability characteristics showed up in high-speed tunnel tests of the semispan horizontal model. The armament installation, even then, posed a major problem. Weight was increasing at such an alarming rate that in July a revised version of the P–84 was agreed upon. Design gross weight was set at 13,400 pounds. Necessary changes would be incorporated in the third experimental plane, which was designated XP–84A.

Testing Slippages **December 1945**

The lack of satisfactory engines delayed flight testing of the No. 1 and No. 2 XP–84 airplanes at Muroc Flight Test Base. Republic wanted to know when additional engines would be available.

First Flight (XP-84) **28 February 1946**

The first test flight from Muroc was successful and performance of the experimental planes soon proved spectacular. The second XP–84 flew in August 1946 and, a month later, established a US national speed record of 611 mph (530 kn). Both these aircraft had a 3,750 lb. s.t. J35–GE–7 turbojet. The 4,000 lb. s.t. Allison-built J35–A–15 engine was fitted in the XP–84A, in the 15 YP–84A prototypes reserved for special evaluation, and in all the initial P–84B productions.

New Procurement **1946**

In that year, Republic was awarded two letter contracts for 141 and 271 aircraft, respectively. A definitive contract for the lot of 141 airplanes was to have followed the first of the two new LCs by 1 August 1946, but the many problems encountered at that time and during the later part of the year postponed its approval until June 1947. This delay, in turn, partly accounted for the deeper problems that overtook Republic late in 1946, when advance payments on the XP–84 contract had to be made in order to preserve production.[2] The second batch of new aircraft was also ratified by contract in June 1947 (after Republic's financial status had improved sensibly), but was reduced from 271 to 191 airplanes to allow immediate reinstatement of Lockheed's P–80s. With the new fiscal year, another contract for 154 additional P–84s was issued and approved in October 1947.

Other Problems **1946–1947**

Problems of sizeable proportions began to manifest themselves. Republic expressed its concern that production quantities of P–84 aircraft were in "final stages of completion with little knowledge of certain stability and control characteristics." This situation arose partly from the lack of Government-furnished TG–180 engines during the Muroc test program. Also, because attempts to make an official world speed record had prevented comprehensive flight testing of the No. 2 XP–84 airplane. Nevertheless, a major contributing factor was the contractor's slow delivery of the third XP–84 (XP–84A) and static test article in 1946. Important design changes that were being made on the XP–84A would go into later production planes. The AAF had warned Republic that if untried designs were put in production models (as had happened in the B–29 and

---

[2] Republic's financial status was investigated and approved in 1945. Nevertheless, in October 1946 the corporation was so hard pressed for funds that it had only enough cash to carry it for 3 weeks. By May 1947, tax refunds in the amount of approximately $6,000,000.00 had alleviated the crisis, but the AAF was awaiting further evidence of Republic's financial improvement before considering additional P–84 procurement.

P–80 programs), the costly modifications that would inevitably follow might "eliminate" the P–84 program.

Prototype Acceptances **1947**

The AAF took delivery of its 15 YP–84As in February. Aside from a more powerful engine, the prototype aircraft also differed from the first two experimental planes by having provisions for wing-tip fuel tanks, and by mounting six .50-inch M2 machineguns—four in the upper front fuselage and two in the wings.

F-84B

First Production Deliveries **1947**

The P–84Bs began reaching the AAF in the summer of 1947. The first P–84B productions were virtually the same as the YP–84A prototypes, but M3 machineguns were used instead of M2s.

Enters Operational Service **December 1947**

With the 14th Fighter Group at Dow Field in Bangor, Maine. The initial operational capability (IOC) of December 1947 was accompanied by stringent flying restrictions, pending correction of new deficiencies discovered 3 months before. Speed was limited to a Mach number of .80 because of a slight reversal of trim. Wrinkling of the fuselage skin restricted the first P–84Bs to a maximum acceleration of 5.5 "G's."[3]

Operational Problems **December 1947**

Operational deficiencies were immediately compounded by critical shortages of parts and by innumerable maintenance difficulties that were to earn for several of the aircraft model series the nickname "Mechanic's Nightmare." The maintenance problems were particularly acute at first, because Republic's early delivery slippages had delayed training of jet maintenance personnel deployed to Muroc for this very purpose.

Production Modifications **December 1947**

Beginning with the 86th production late in 1947, the P–84B's armament was supplemented by eight retractable rocket launchers beneath the wing.

Grounding **24 May 1948**

Because of structural failure and almost concurrent with the end of its production, the entire P–84B fleet was grounded for inspection. The inspected aircraft returned to flying status were limited to specific maximum speeds until necessary fairing modifications could be accomplished by Republic.

[3] One G is the measure or value of the gravitational pull of the earth or of a force required to accelerate or decelerate at the rate of 32.16 feet per second per second any free moving body.

New Designation **11 June 1948**

The newly formed US Air Force stopped using US Army's aircraft terminology. The AAF pursuit aircraft, formerly identified by the letter P, acquired the F prefix for fighter, their new classification. In the process, the P–84 Thunderjet officially became the F–84. The name "Thunderjet," suggested by Republic, had been approved late in 1946.

Subsequent Model Series

F–84C

Other Configurations

None

End of Production **June 1948**

With delivery of one last aircraft.

Total F–84Bs Accepted

The Air Force accepted 226. This was less than half of the total ordered. The other F–84Bs under contract underwent production changes sufficiently important to warrant new designations.

Acceptance Rates

Three F–84Bs were accepted in FY 47, all the others in FY 48—14 in July 1947, 3 in August, 11 in September, 25 in October, 17 in November, 18 in December, 13 in January 1948, 50 in February, 35 in March, 30 in April, 6 in May, and one in June 1948, when production was ended.

Flyaway Cost Per Production Aircraft

The cost of the first 100 P–84s (15 prototypes and 85 F–84Bs), authorized for procurement in FY 45, was set at $286,407.00 per aircraft. The next 141 aircraft, authorized for procurement in FY 46, also came off the production line as F–84Bs. Their unit cost was lower and decreased to $163,994.00. Neither of the two figures reflected subsequent modification costs.

Postproduction Modifications **1949-1950**

The F–84Bs were covered by the $8 million modification program approved in May 1949—a few months after the entire F–84 program was nearly disolved. This "mandatory" program included reinforcement of the aircraft's wings and over 100 other structural and engineering modifications.

Phaseout **1952**

Although the directed modifications substantially improved the F–84B's operational capability, the aircraft left the Air Force inventory before the end of 1952.

F-84C

Previous Model Series

F-84B

New Features

There was an engine change from the J-35-A-15 to the A-13 engine in the F-84C, and a new electrical system. Otherwise, few features distinguished the new model from its predecessor.

First Acceptance **May 1948**

Eleven aircraft were delivered.

Enters Operational Service **1948**

The 20th Fighter Group, Shaw AFB, Sumter, S.C., was first to receive the F-84B. The second unit to be equipped with the aircraft was the 33rd Fighter Group, relocated in 1949 from Roswell, N. Mex., to Otis AFB, Mass. Both the F-84B and C aircraft became operational equipment for the 31st Fighter Group at Albany, Ga., and the 78th Fighter Group, Hamilton AFB, Calif.

Total F-84Cs Accepted

191

Acceptance Rates

All the aircraft were delivered over a 6-month period. The last 23 joined the Air Force inventory in November 1948.

Operational Problems

Being almost similar, the Cs shared most of the F-84B problems. The F-84Cs also had trouble with their new engine.

Modifications

While in production, the F-84C underwent numerous engineering changes in its prototype engine installation and other equipment.[4] Like the Bs, the F-84Cs later received the extensive structural modifications, approved in the spring of 1949.

Subsequent Model Series

F-84D

Other Configurations

None

Flyaway Cost Per Production Aircraft

Unit cost of $147,699.00 was set for the 191 aircraft authorized for procurement in FY 47—a $16,000.00 decrease from the previous

---

[4] The only jet craft in service when the F-84 production began was the Lockheed F-80, powered by a totally different J-33 turbojet engine from the one installed in the F-84C. In addition, the F-84's jet tailpipe with a cooling shroud was a Republic innovation and a radical departure from the F-80.

lot's unit cost. As in the F–84B, these figures did not reflect subsequent modification costs.

Attrition **1950**

The F–84B and C inventories registered heavy losses. Shortly before the start of the Korean conflict, overall fighter accident rates reached new post-WW II high levels. Although materiel failures accounted for many of the accidents, pilot errors were a major factor.

Revised Training **1950**

To curb the accident trend, Headquarters USAF directed that more thorough indoctrination be given pilots in planes new to them, and that better training be given to new pilot trainees in jet aircraft. In addition, in collaboration with factory representatives, presentations were made on the flight characteristics and limitations of the F–84 Thunderjets. The success of these presentations was so great with the several groups to which they were given that they were distributed in printed form to all F–84 units. Similar presentations were given to various summer encampments of the Air National Guard.

Phaseout **1952**

Like the F–84Bs, the Cs disappeared from USAF inventory within a few years. The last F–84C was phased out in 1952.

F-84D

Previous Model Series

F–84C

New Features

As a development of the F–84B, the F–84D introduced a number of new features. These included a thicker skin gauge on wings and ailerons, winterized fuel system suitable for JP4, and mechanical linkages instead of hydraulic in the landing gear to shorten the shock strut during retraction. The F–84D was fitted with the J–35–A–13 engine, first used on the F–84C.

Procurement **October 1947**

This contract was negotiated as a supplement to the $19 million fixed-price contract of 30 June 1947, which covered the 191 F–84Cs. The $16 million October supplement called for delivery of 154 additional aircraft—F–84Ds.

First Acceptance **November 1948**

The Air Force accepted one aircraft in November, and 36 others in December. The first 4 months of 1949 saw the delivery of 117 additional F–84Ds.

Production Modifications

Since the early F–84s were less than satisfactory maintenance-wise, development changes, geared toward some kind of improvement, accompanied each production group of F–84D airplanes.

Program Appraisal **September 1948**

Two months before taking delivery of the first F–84D and 2 months after procurement of the aircraft's subsequent model series had been tentatively approved, the Air Force undertook a complete review of the entire F–84 program. Results of the study that ensued were baffling. The F–84 of the B and C series did not satisfactorily meet "any phase of the missions of the major commands," and only a major retrofit program could make the aircraft operational. Although 571 F–84s of the B, C, and D series had been purchased on four previous procurement programs, amounting to a total of some $80 million, production was a year behind schedule. Theorically, cancellation of the F–84D production would save the government close to $20 million, but in actuality, production of the D had progressed to the point that if cancelled, "more than half the cost of the 154 F–84D aircraft would be spent without anything in return." Too, the resultant adverse effect upon Republic's financial status might jeopardize the F–84E production, should it be finally approved.

Special Testing **2 February-6 March 1949**

To solve its dilemma, the Air Force directed special tests. Specific purposes were to determine if discrepancies in the F–84 prototypes had been corrected on the D type, and which of the F–84 or F–80 aircraft was the more suitable for fighter operation. Results of the tests conducted early in 1949 at both Wright-Patterson AFB, Ohio, and Eglin AFB in Florida, were encouraging. They indicated that many of the deficiencies of previous types of F–84 aircraft had been eliminated in the D model. The Air Proving Ground (APG) tests also concluded that "the F–84 range, acceleration, versatility, load carrying ability, high altitude climb, and level flight speed exceeded that of the F–80. Not all comments were favorable, however. The F–84 was inferior to the F–80 in shortness of takeoff roll, low altitude climb, and maneuverability. Furthermore, it was the opinion of maintenance personnel at both air bases that the maintenance improvements made in the F–84D airplanes were partially offset by the additional time required to change accessories on the front end of the engine.

Program Re-endorsement **1949**

Despite other minor discrepancies uncovered during the APG tests, the Air Force reached a final decision in favor of the F–84 program. Specifically, the F–84Ds would be accepted for standard use, but no further procurement beyond the current contract would be made. Additional funds in the amount of $3.3 million would be secured for design improvements of the programmed F–84E, and $8 million would be spent to modernize the 382 F–84B and C aircraft remaining in the operational inventory. In May 1949, implementation of the $8 million modernization program received Presidential approval.

Enters Operational Service **1949**

The F–84D was the first version of the Thunderjet to arrive in Korea (December 1950).

Total F-84Ds Accepted

154

Acceptance Rates

One F–84D was accepted in November 1948, 36 in December of the same year. Thirty were delivered during each of the first 3 months of 1949, and the last 27 aircraft were delivered to the Air Force in April.

Subsequent Model Series

F–84E

Other Configurations

None

Flyaway Cost Per Production Aircraft

$212,241.00—airframe, $139,863; engine (installed), $41,654; electronics, $7,165; armament, $23,559.

Postproduction Modifications

Republic, at a cost of about $2.9 million, modified the leading edge of all F–84D wings and made other engineering changes. Attempts also were made to correct some of the additional discrepancies uncovered during the APG tests. Efforts centered on improvement of the A–1B gunsight, and reduction of the tailpipe's excessive temperature caused by the aircraft's high thrust J–35–A–13 engine.

Oversea Deployments **1951-1952**

The F–84B and C aircraft were not assigned to oversea units because early versions of the J–35 engine allowed only 40 hours of operation between overhauls. Although also not earmarked for oversea use, modified F–84Ds were deployed to the Korean war theater where they began serving with the 27th Fighter Escort Wing. In the spring of 1952, as the Fifth Air Force's fighter-bomber strength had been seriously depleted by logistical causes and excessive losses during the railway interdiction campaign, additional F–84Ds were sent overseas. Headquarters USAF decided that the Fifth Air Force would for 5 months receive a total of 102 F–84Ds as attrition replacements. Most of these aircraft were assigned to the 136th Wing, a former Air National Guard organization whose period of authorized service was running out.

Phaseout **1952-1957**

Receipt of new F–84 models during August and September 1952 accelerated phaseout of the F–84Ds, which had created many combat logistical and operational problems. In mid-1957 the Guard[5] likewise phased out the last of its Ds.

F-84E

Previous Model Series

F–84D

New Features

Allison J–35A–17 engine, rated at 5,000 lb. s.t. Strengthened wing structure to increase permissible G loads, and a longer fuselage to give more room in the cockpit. The F–84E had a radar gunsight and improved wing-tip tanks for combat use. Also, a modified fuel system allowing use of two 230-US gallon tanks to increase combat radius from 850 to over 1,000 miles (739 to 869.5 nm).[6] These tanks were carried on bomb-shackles, located beneath the wings and inboard of the landing gear.

Basic Development **1948**

Republic proposed a new version of the existing F–84 type—then referred to as P–84—early in 1948, a few months before the entire F–84B fleet was grounded. Notwithstanding the fact that the new version did not "compare favorably with the [North American] P–86 airplane," procurement was tentatively approved in July 1948. Several factors contributed to the Air Force decision. It would cost little more to buy the new F–84 version than to improve existing models. Republic was overcoming earlier production difficulties and future delivery schedules appeared realistic. Finally, it seemed advisable to maintain two sources of fighter production—North American and Republic.

Procurement **29 December 1948**

The Air Force approved the first contract for the "E" model and then re-endorsed the entire F–84 program. This first "E" contract provided for the production of 409 aircraft at a cost of $44 million.

---

[5] While on active duty, the 116th Fighter Group had flown F–84Ds as early as 1950.

[6] Up to the early 1950's, aircraft speed and range were generally defined in statute miles. Later, the Air Force calculated speed in knots and range in nautical miles, even though speed records remained in miles per hour and kilometers showed distances. A knot (nautical mile per hour) is 1.1516 times faster than a statute mile per hour; a nautical mile equals about 6,080 feet, i.e., 800 feet longer than the statute mile.

In mid-1949, following completion of the APG tests connected with the entire F–84 program's reappraisal, $3.3 million were added to the $44 million procurement contract to ensure further preproduction improvements of the new model. The Air Force subsequently issued three other F–84E production contracts, including one for 100 articles earmarked for the Mutual Defense Assistance Program (MDAP).[7]

First Flight (Production Aircraft) **18 May 1949**

First Acceptance **26 May 1949**

Two aircraft were delivered.

Testing **August 1949**

Accelerated service tests at Wright-Patterson AFB demonstrated that the F–84E met serviceability standards and was "comparatively easy to maintain." General flight handling characteristics also were satisfactory, but the complex A–1B sighting system was still unreliable. Despite renewed efforts, modified sights (A–1Cs) did not become available until the beginning of 1950. Pending their availability the F–84E deliveries were suspended.

Enters Operational Service **1949**

They went to Korea 1 year later (December 1950) with SAC's 27th Fighter-Escort Wing.

Total F-84Es Accepted

843—743 for the Air Force and 100 for MDAP.

Acceptance Rates

Two F–84Es were accepted in FY 49, 348 in FY 50, and 393 in FY 51. The MDAP deliveries were made toward the end of production—97 in FY 51 and three during the first month of FY 52.

End of Production **July 1951**

Production ended with delivery of the last three MDAP F–84Es.

Subsequent Model Series

F–84G. The normally intervening F–84F—largely a different aircraft—was preceded by F–84G productions by almost 2 years.

Other Configurations

None. As an answer to USAF need for an interceptor, Republic early in 1949 offered to produce still another F–84 version at a unit cost of $190,000.00. The contractor also offered to substitute future productions of its new proposal for the F–84E fighter-bombers already under contract. The Air Force turned down both offers.

---

[7] The Mutual Defense Assistance Program was created by the Mutual Defense Assistance Act of 6 October 1949—6 months after the North Atlantic Treaty was signed. The MDAP became the Military Assistance Program 5 years later. The new program reflected changes in the basic legislation of the MDA Act, effective 26 August 1954. (The MDAP designation lingered a while longer).

Flyaway Cost Per Production Aircraft

$212,241.00—airframe, $139.863; engine (installed), $41,654; electronics, $7,165; armament, $23,559.

Operational Problems **1950–1951**

More than 50 percent of the F–84s in USAF operational inventory were out of commission in April 1950. One year later, despite determined efforts in the intervening months, in-commission rates were still below par and only 549 of the Air Force's 829 F–84B, C, D, and E aircraft were operational. The main problem was the critical shortages of spare parts and supporting equipment, especially in the engine field. In the F–84E's case, the J–35–A–17 engines had been procured on the assumption that units would operate each plane for 25 hours per month and for 100 hours between overhauls. But the worldwide dispersal of F–84Es and the required low number of hours between overhauls made it doubtful in April 1951 that enough engines could be produced in a short period to meet the flying time planned for this plane even if the manufacturer were allocated funds. By May, the engine shortage endangered future oversea deployments of F–84Es. Although US commanders in Korea were asking for the accelerated conversion of all fighter-bomber squadrons to F–84E aircraft, Fifth Air Force received no immediate relief. The US Air Force allocated $26 million to expand GM's Allison Division J–35 productions, but the scheduled augmentation of North Atlantic Treaty Organization (NATO) air forces retained its higher priority and prevented any accelerated buildup of F–84E aircraft in the Far East.

Combat Appraisal **1951–1953**

Only 27 of the first 60 F–84Es deployed to the Far East in December 1950 were operationally ready, but this situation was quickly improved. Nevertheless, the aircraft were much too slow to cope on even terms with the swept-wing MIG–15s. They, therefore, never did perform outstandingly as escort for the B–29 bombers. On the other hand, the F–84E by the end of 1951 had acquired the reputation of being "the best ground-support jet in the theater."

Phaseout **1951**

The inventory of war-committed F–84D and F–84E aircraft shrank through attrition, especially during the winter of 1952–1953. Other significant losses occurred because of materiel failures and pilot errors, continuing problems that led the Tactical Air Command (TAC) to use a number of F–84Es for training until 1956, when these aircraft finally ended their active service. Other F–84Es had begun to reach the ANG in 1951, totaling 115 in 1957. The Guard phased out their last two F–84Es in mid-1959—2 years after the Air Force Reserve (first assigned a few F–84Es in mid-1954) gave up all its fighters.

Special Achievements **22 September 1950**

Two F-84Es (redesignated EF-84Es), fitted with probe equipment and using air refueling, made an experimental nonstop flight across the North Atlantic. Both aircraft left England on 22 September, piloted by Col. David C. Schilling and Lt. Col. William Ritchie, respectively. Schilling touched down in the United States 10 hours and 2 minutes later, after three inflight refuelings.[8] Ritchie had to bail out over Newfoundland. The flights explored the feasibility of rapidly moving large numbers of jet fighters across the Atlantic. They also tested new air-to-air refueling techniques, using the British-developed "probe and drogue" refueling system. TAC later adopted this system as standard on its fighters and converted B-29 and B-50 tankers.[9]

Other Uses **1951**

Korean experience pointed up the urgent need of a powerful air-launched projectile that could penetrate armor and knock out enemy tanks. Four F-84Es were modified to carry 24 Oerlikon[10] 8-cm. aerial rockets. The aircraft sent to the Far East for evaluation incurred minimum performance degradation as a result of their new armament. The high velocity of the Swiss rocket also resulted in much greater accuracy of fire. This armament project, however, never went beyond testing.[11]

Other Countries **1951-1952**

Before 1950, the foreign aid program had been primarily in the planning stage. By contrast, the regular FY 51 congressional appropriation for the MDAP amounted to more than $1.2 billion, with an Air Force allocation for materiel aid of some $181 million. This included 307 new F-84Es to be distributed to France, Belgium, the Netherlands, and Turkey. Soon afterward, a supplemental appropriation gave the Air Force another $800 million to hasten the supply of USAF weapons to NATO nations. The Air Force subsequently reduced to 100 the MDAP quota of F-84Es and made-up the difference with newer F-84G and F aircraft.

---

[8] This first nonstop jet flight across the Atlantic was not Colonel Schilling's first brush with fame. The 30-year-old pilot had in World War II shot down 24 German planes and destroyed another 10 on the ground. Schilling died in an auto accident 6 years later, and Smokey Hill AFB, Kansas, was renamed in his memory.

[9] Use of an in-flight refueling system to stretch aircraft range had long been held feasible. In 1923, two US Army Air Service Lieutenants (Ritcher and Smith) flew a bomber (DH-4B-Liberty 400) nonstop between Canadian and Mexican borders, by means of two in-flight refuelings.

[10] Oerlikon Machine Tool Works, Hispano-Suiza Company, Switzerland.

[11] A later USAF test program of a costly Oerlikon surface-to-air missile was cancelled before completion.

F-84G

Previous Model Series

F–84E

New Features

Incorporating in-flight refueling equipment with wing receptacle in port wing for use with the Boeing-developed and SAC-endorsed "flying boom" system, the F–84G was the first fighter built with the capability of refueling in-flight and at a single point. Allison J-35-A–29 engine, autopilot, A–4 gunsight, new instrument landing system, and a revised armament, with up to 4,000 lb. of external stores—the F–84G was also the first single-seat fighter-bomber with atomic capability.

Production Modifications **1951**

The F–84G was progressively developed from the F–84E. Production variances, therefore, occurred. The new A–4 gunsight first appeared on the 86th article, the new instrument landing system on the 301st. Similarly, an atomic capability was only introduced in the F–84Gs late in 1951, after a number of the new aircraft had already left the production line.

First Delivery **July 1951**

Eighty aircraft were accepted. This was a delivery slippage of several months, caused by difficulties with the new J–35–A–29 engine.

Enters Operational Service **1951**

The 31st Fighter-Escort Wing at Turner AFB, Ga., was the first SAC wing to receive the new aircraft, beginning in August 1951. By the end of the year, the 31st, like the 27th Fighter-Escort Wing at Bergstrom AFB, Tex., possessed about half of their complement of F–84Gs—35 and 36, respectively. However, F–84G aircraft, equipped to refuel with the flying boom system, did not enter the SAC inventory until 1952.

Total F-84Gs Accepted

3,025—789 for the USAF and 2,236 for the MDAP.

Acceptance Rates

The Air Force accepted 447 F–84Gs in FY 52, 342 in FY 53. The Air Force also took delivery of the aircraft earmarked for the MDAP during the same period—710 in FY 52, 1,505 in FY 53, and 21 during the first month of FY 54.

End of Production **July 1953**

It ended with delivery of the last 21 F–84Gs purchased for the MDAP.

Subsequent Model Series

F–84F. Although this F–84 aircraft carried the F suffix, it was preceded in the USAF operational inventory by more than 700 F-84Gs.

Other Configurations

None

Flyaway Cost Per Production Aircraft

$237,247.00—airframe, $150,846; engine (installed), $41,488; electronics, $4,761; ordnance, $2,719; armament, $37,433.

Oversea Deployments **1952-1953**

F-84Gs began reaching the Far East in the summer of 1952. Even though some of the new planes arrived without various items of needed supporting equipment, the F-84Gs were available in sufficient numbers by September 1952 to permit Fifth Air Force to bring its war depleted Thunderjet wings up to unit-equipment strength for the first time in more than a year. In December, Fifth Air Force moved the 49th Wing's 9th Fighter-Bomber Squadron of F-84Gs from Korea to Japan to train its aircrews in the delivery of tactical atomic weapons. In mid-1953, concurrent with development of the low-altitude bombing system (LABS) to allow safe delivery of nuclear bombs from low altitudes, the 49th Air Division, based in the continental United States (CONUS), converted to a nuclear force and with the F-84G-equipped 81st Fighter Bomber Wing deployed to Bentwaters in the United Kingdom (U.K.). The following month, on 20 August 1953, 17 USAF F-84Gs, refueling from KC-97s, flew nonstop 4,485 miles from Albany, Ga., to Lakenheath, also in the U.K. This was the longest nonstop mass movement of fighter-bomber aircraft in history and the greatest distance ever flown nonstop by single-engine jet fighters.

Special Achievements **1952**

The success of the in-flight refueling capabilities developed by SAC was first confirmed in mid-1952 with the staged deployment of the 31st Fighter-Escort Wing from Turner to Misawa Air Base in Japan. Dubbed Operation Fox Peter I, this July oversea deployment counted 58 F-84Gs, configured to refuel with the flying boom system.

1953

In March 1953, a few months before the end of hostilities on 27 July, F-84Gs of the Fifth Air Force completed the longest mission to that date in the Korean war. These fighter-bombers made an 800-mile round trip to strike at the industrial center of Chonjin on the east coast of North Korea, approximately 40 miles south of the Manchurian border.

War Attrition **December 1950-July 1953**

A total of 335 F-84D, E, and G aircraft were lost in Korea, where the F-84s earned such appellations as "workhorse" and "champ of all low-level bombers." More than 50 percent of these losses were due to ground fire.

Other Uses **1953**

The Air Force Air Demonstration Squadron, Thunderbirds, was organized in May 1953 to promote a better understanding and appreciation of air power. One of the most important decisions of the newly-formed Thunderbirds was the selection of their first aircraft. Primarily, the aircraft had to be stable for maneuvers in formation; reliable to meet show schedules; rugged for demonstration aerobatics; and combat proven. The choice was the F-84G Thunderjet. In 1955, the Thunderbirds transitioned into the faster and more maneuverable F-84F Thunderstreak. The team was re-equipped with the supersonic F-100C Super Sabre in mid-1956.

1954

F-84G aircraft were being employed in conjunction with Project ZELMAL (Zero Length Launch and Mat Landing), one of the Air Force's several projects in the area of reducing required takeoff and landing distances. The ZELMAL program was conducted by The Glen L. Martin Company to study rocket boost takeoff and arrested landing on a pneumatic landing mat. The first pneumatic mat landing with a ZELMAL-modified F-84G airplane was attempted on 2 June 1954.

Phaseout **1955-1960**

The F-84G had been retired from SAC by August 1955, but the aircraft continued to serve TAC for a few more years and did not completely disappear from USAF inventory until mid-1960.

F-84F Thunderstreak

Previous Model Series

The F-84G, not the F-84E—from which that aircraft was progressively developed—was produced before the F-84F. Actually, the swept-wing, single-seat F-84F was largely a new aircraft.

New Features

Wings and tail with sweepback of 40° at 25 percent of the chord; use of many press forgings in wing structure instead of built-up components; wings fitted with leading-edge auto slats; Wright J65-W-3 turbojet engine, rated at 7,220 lb. s.t.; irreversible power-boost control system; upward-hinged canopy; perforated air-brakes hinged to the fuselage sides aft of the wing trailing edge; F-84G's in-flight refueling equipment, with inlet nozzle relocated in the upper surface of the port wing; F-84G's standard armament, but capable of carrying heavier loads of offensive stores, including atomic weapons; and two adaptable 450-gal (US) external tanks for long-range escort fighter missions.

General Operational Requirements **December 1948**

The Air Force issued a revision of the GOR published by the AAF in September 1944. The revision called for significant increases of the operational performances required by the original document.

Basic Development **November 1949**

The F–84F aircraft was officially conceived in November 1949 in a letter proposal through which Republic offered to satisfy the USAF-revised GOR by changing its straight wing F–84 to a model incorporating a swept back wing and swept back tail. In a further proposal, the contractor offered to build an increased ordnance capability into the aircraft. Although its drawings were labeled F–96, Republic also stated that the proposed low-cost aircraft would be a modification of the F–84E that was entering USAF inventory and that 55 percent of the F–84E tooling would be utilized for the new production. The Air Force tentatively endorsed Republic proposal in December 1949. During the same month, Republic was allocated one F–84E to build a prototype of its swept-wing aircraft. At the insistence of the Air Force, the paper F–96 was redesignated, officially becoming the F–84F on 8 September 1950. The aircraft's "Thunderstreak" nickname, result of a "new name" contest among Republic employees, was retained.

Prototype Testing **June-November 1950**

Republic delivered the YF–84F prototype at Edwards AFB, Calif., in May 1950. Phase I tests were started in June and completed in approximately 1 month by a Republic test pilot. Air Force pilots conducted Phase II tests, which ended in November, after 64 flights totaling 70 hours of flying time. The tests demonstrated conclusively that the 5,300 pounds of engine thrust generated by the YF–84F's Allison J–35–A–25 engine was not sufficient for the proper performance of the mission assigned the aircraft under the revised GOR of December 1948.

Initial Shortcomings **1950**

Almost as soon as the YF–84F flight tests had begun, both Republic and the Air Force realized the extent of the J–35–A–25 engine deficiencies and both agreed to rework an F–84E fuselage to fit the more powerful Sapphire jet engine, selected in mid-1950 as the best possible replacement. The Sapphire was a hand-tooled production of the British firm Armstrong-Siddeley for which the Curtiss-Wright Corporation at Wood-Ridge, New Jersey, had acquired a manufacturing license. However, production of the Wright YJ–65 (as the Sapphire engine was redesignated) was not expected to begin before September 1951. This forecast was the first indication that, if produced, the F–84F would be off Republic initial production schedule by at least 3 months. In any case, while the Air Force in December 1949 had practically bought the

Republic-proposed F–84F, the engine deficiencies of the first F–84F prototype created a new situation and procurement, which had been expected to be finalized in August 1950, was postponed. In November of the same year, the Air Materiel Command (AMC) recommended that two additional prototypes be built to evaluate the F–84F and Sapphire combination before to entertain further production consideration.

Production Decision **December 1950**

Before the additional prototypes could be obtained and prior to the testing of the Republic prototype with the Sapphire engine, Headquarters USAF ordered full production of the new combination. Because of the urgent need for improved fighter-bombers since the outbreak of the Korean war, the Air Force also directed the opening of second sources of production for both the airframe and engine. The Buick, Oldsmobile, Pontiac Assembly Division of the General Motors Corporation at Kansas City, Kans., was selected as the second producer of the F–84F airframe in January 1951, 1 month after the production decision. The Buick Division of the General Motors Corporation was also selected as the second source for the Sapphire engine.

First Flight (Revised Prototype) **February 1951**

The new F–84F prototype, powered by an "imported" Sapphire engine, was first flown from the Air Force Flight Center at Edwards AFB on 14 February 1951. While the performances were impressive, the airplane proved unsafe and flying was restricted to Edwards AFB.

First Definitive Contract **9 April 1951**

This contract, AF 33(038)–1438, covered production of 274 F–84Fs at a unit target cost of $215,035.27—about one-third of the aircraft's eventual unit price, all modification costs excluded. This first contract was amended in less than a year by nine supplementary agreements, which raised the F–84F procurement to the FY 51 approved total of 719 aircraft and endorsed substantial price increases. Two other definitive contracts, AF 33(600)–6704 and AF 33(600)-22316, were issued in FY 52 and FY 53, respectively, but the number of aircraft they covered was drastically reduced in later years. Believing the F–84F to be a production modification of the F–84E, no development contract preceded any of these contracts. However, notwithstanding nonavailability of the Wright YJ–65 engines until at least September 1951, Republic had optimistically signed on 22 March an Air Force fighter-bomber configuration contract, calling for delivery of the first F–84F productions in December 1951.

Unexpected Setback **1951-1952**

Despite Republic's belief at the outset that 55 percent of the tooling used in the production of the F–84E would be adapted to the manufacture of the F–84F, experience proved that only 15 percent could be reusable. This problem was quickly compounded by a shortage of aluminum alloy and the fact that once available, the aluminum alloy could not be processed. Only three presses in the United States could produce the aluminum wing spar and rib forgings for the F–84F, and these presses were almost fully occupied with satisfying concurrent forging requirements for the B–47, which enjoyed the Brickbat[12] Scheme's priority precedence. Unexpected difficulties also were encountered during the Americanization of the Sapphire engine. Again, contrary to the contractor's expectations, the scarcity of machine tools (diverted to higher priority programs) was a major problem until April 1952, when the Wright engine and the F–84F airframe finally were also assigned to the Brickbat Scheme. Other engine problems remained, however. Foremost in these problems was the engine's weight increase, which degraded its performance. By January 1952, the YJ–65–W–1 engine was considered obsolescent and further modifications had to be made to keep it in operation.

First Flight (Production Aircraft) **November 1952**

First Production Deliveries **November 1952**

On 3 December, the Air Force officially accepted the first two F–84F productions that had been delivered in November 1952. The delivery date was an 11-month slippage from the contractor's schedule. Moreover, the Air Force approved a revised schedule authorizing further slippage at both the Republic and General Motors plants.

Propulsion Problems **1952-1954**

The YJ–65 engine was not interchangeable in successive models. Hence, an airplane built for the YJ–65–W–1 was bound to use the engine. Yet, while Wright replaced the obsolescent YJ–65–W–1 with the improved YJ–64–W–1A and developed their successor, the more powerful J–65 engine. Republic had begun producing F–84F airframes at the rate of three per day and merely put them into storage pending delivery of a satisfactory engine. In mid-1953, while investigating the possibility of equipping the F–84F with a General Electric engine, the Air Force of necessity decided that the first 275 F–84Fs would retain the YJ–65–W–1 engine. But for some 100 other F–84Fs that were fitted with the YJ–65–W–1A, all F–84Fs were eventually equipped with the J–65–W–3 engine.

---

[12] A high priority list of critical items designated for specific Air Force procurement programs.

Other Major Difficulties **1952-1954**

Major difficulties were also encountered because of design deficiencies in the F–84F airframe and airframe components. Development of the F–84F's subsystems also proved more difficult than first anticipated. In mid-1953, after more than a year of corrective effort, the tail of the F–84F was still considered unacceptable for any kind of tactical operations; both the aircraft's longitudinal and lateral controls remained inadequate at high speeds; a redesign of the landing gear up-lock was necessary; the basic hydraulic system was still over-sensitive; the extremely sensitive electrical emergency system still caused concern; the aircraft's dive brakes were susceptible to damage from ejected spent cartridges; and none of the aircraft's weight problems had been solved.

Production Modifications **1952-1954**

By mid-1954, correction of most of the F–84F design deficiencies was assured, but unavoidable delays occurred that created further difficulties. Incorporation of a stabilator in production F–84F aircraft, although approved in 1953, had to be postponed because of the long lead time required for the manufacture of the stabilator. In the meantime, in order to continue production, an interim measure was taken. A number of F–84Fs were equipped with the two-piece "poor man's flying tail," which consisted of an interconnected horizontal stabilizer and elevator. Although successfully flight tested by Republic, this expedient did not work. In December 1953 the Air Force directed that the installation be stopped and that the "poor man's flying tail" be removed from the aircraft already so equipped. By the end of 1954, numerous other expensive or time consuming modifications had been made or were scheduled for the near future. More than 785 F–84Fs had been modified through the installation of aileron spoilers at a cost of $4.7 million; 506 by receiving true air speed indicators for a $1.3 million outlay; and 258 F–84F airplanes were to be modified by installing the F–5 auto-pilot at an estimated cost of $3 million.

Enters Operational Service **January 1954**

SAC's 506th Strategic Fighter Wing,[13] at Dow AFB, Maine, received the first F–84Fs. However, these aircraft, 14 of which were in the hands of SAC by mid-January, were of limited use because of their unsatisfactory engines and other deficiencies. They required special inspections and maintenance and were part of some 400 early F–84F productions, conditionally accepted by the Air Force. By May 1954, SAC had received 125 of the 400 F–84Fs having obsolescent YJ–65–W–1 engines, still deficient YJ–65–W–

[13] SAC's fighter-escort wings were redesignated strategic fighter wings on 20 January 1953.

1As or other shortcomings. Twelve similar aircraft were undergoing additional testing, 20 had been delivered to the Air Training Command (ATC) at Luke AFB, Ariz., and the remainder would be modified and also released to training.

Operational Capability **May 1954**

Initial operational capability with J–65-equipped F–84Fs did not come until 12 May 1954, when a few of them finally reached TAC's 405th Fighter Bomber Wing at Langley AFB, Va. Although first on the priority list, the 405th had less than half its quota of new aircraft—36 against 75—by the end of June. On 18 June, SAC's first J–65-equipped F–84Fs had joined the 27th Strategic Fighter Wing at Bergstrom AFB. This was another 6-month slippage of the latest delivery date which SAC had anticipated.

Program Reappraisal **July-December 1954**

Deficiencies found in the J–65-equipped F–84Fs, accepted since May 1954, compelled the Air Force to ground several of the aircraft and to suspend Republic deliveries. Other stringent measures ensued. In August the contractor was directed to reduce its daily output from five to three aircraft—two F–84Fs and one RF–84F—and in September a hold order was placed on 400 of the last 500 articles scheduled for production. The Air Force concurrently initiated a series of new operational suitability tests. Referred to as Project Run In, these tests upon completion in November 1954 "proved the F–84F a satisfactory figher-bomber, capable of the mission role for which it had been planned" as well as a "considerably better aircraft than the [F–84]G." The results of Project Run In, together with Republic reorganization of its quality control group and increases in plant personnel, induced the Air Force to approve an accelerated delivery schedule that would make up for some of the time lost. This year-end schedule called for all Republic-stored aircraft to be readied for delivery late in March 1955.

New Operational Problems **1955**

Early in 1955 TAC F–84F units experienced difficulties in the aircraft's braking system. Meanwhile, the new J–65-equipped F–84Fs continued to present problems.

Fleet Grounding **1955**

Engine failures in late 1954 led to the grounding of all F–84Fs in early 1955. Because of the latest grounding, the Air Force once again stopped accepting F–84F deliveries. Although a number of engines had to be overhauled, most grounded aircraft returned to flying status after inspection. The production hold-order of September 1954 was rescinded in February 1955, after which F–84F deliveries were resumed. The idea of making F–84Js out of some F/

RF–84Fs—by exchanging the J–65 engine for the General Electric J–73[14]—was reconsidered but rejected for the last time in March. Soon afterward, however, SAC and TAC F–84Fs again experienced a number of engine flame outs when flying in heavy precipitation. Several accidents occurred in severe weather because of engine failures that were attributed to faulty compressor shrouds. Pending correction, flying restrictions were imposed.

Final Slippage **1956**

F–84F production slipped another 6 months in 1956. This time the slippage stemmed from a 4-month labor strike at Republic early in the year.

End of Production **August 1957**

With Republic delivery of the last MAP F–84F. Republic production of USAF F–84Fs ended in February 1957, that of General Motors in February 1955.

Total F–84Fs Accepted

2,348—852 for MAP and 1,496 for the Air Force. Air Force's total represented a reduction of 756 articles from the contingent originally funded. The Air Force also accepted three YF–84Fs from Republic.

Acceptance Rates

Forty-eight F–84Fs were accepted in FY 53 from the Republic plant in Farmingdale, N.Y., 510 in FY 54, 597 in FY 55, 103 in FY 56, and one in FY 57. One F–84F, built in Kansas City by the General Motors Corporation, was accepted in FY 53, 56 in FY 54, and 180 in FY 55. The F–84Fs earmarked for MAP were accepted by the Air Force between FY 55 and FY 58—77 in FY 55, 326 in FY 56, 400 in FY 57, and 49 in FY 58. All MAP F–84Fs were manufactured at the Republic plant.

Flyaway Cost Per Production Aircraft

$769,330.00—airframe, $562,715; engine (installed), $146,027; electronics, $9,623; ordnance, $9,252; armament, $41,713.

Average Cost Per Flying Hour

$390.00

Average Maintenance Cost Per Flying Hour

$185.00

Subsequent Model Series

None—the F–84G, progressively developed from the F–84E, entered USAF inventory ahead of the F–84F.

---

[14] The J–73, used by North American F–86H, was in short supply. Furthermore, it also had more than its share of problems.

Other Configurations **1953-1954**

RF-84F. Reconnaissance version of the Thunderstreak and only other F-84F configuration that went into full production.

XF-84H. First aircraft powered solely by a supersonic propeller driven by a gas turbine. The XF-84H, first flown in 1953, was designed for possible tactical use after completing its research role. Two F-84F airframes were modified for this purpose.

YF-84J. An F-84F airframe, modified by Republic to incorporate a General Electric J-73 engine with 2,000 pounds more thrust than the J-65-W-3 Sapphire. This prototype, delivered to Edwards AFB on 24 April 1954, on 7 May reached a speed of Mach 1.09 during a 52-minute flight that encountered no major difficulties. Nevertheless, the Air Force rejected a new engine as the solution to the F-84F's problem because it would cost more than $70 million just to retrofit the 295 aircraft under consideration. Republic's second YF-84J was cancelled on 16 June 1954; the entire conversion program on 31 August. The F-84J project, first conceived in mid-1953, was re-entertained in early 1955, but again did not materialize.

Initial Phaseout **1954-1958**

Soon after the F-84Fs arrived in SAC and TAC, they were turned over to the ANG. SAC transferred its first lot in August 1954. The remainder were cleared from the regular combat inventory by 10 January 1958, when TAC released its last aircraft. TAC received some F-84Fs in July 1958, when it assumed former ATC responsibilities at Luke and at Nellis AFB, Nev., but these aircraft were used only for training.

Reactivation **October 1961**

The Berlin crisis of 1961-1962 brought four ANG wings of F-84Fs to active duty. A number of these units were deployed to Europe, the other trained under TAC for possible contingency deployment. In late 1961 the Air Force decided to retain the ANG F-84Fs after the wings returned to state control. These F-84Fs would equip USAF tactical fighter units to be activated. Then, as the new units received later-model aircraft, the F-84Fs would be returned to the Guard. The Air Force would loan the F-84Fs to the ANG until required by the newly activated units. This would avoid downgrading ANG capability until absolutely necessary.

Reactivation Problems **1962**

Despite all efforts, operationally ready F-84Fs decreased early in the year. Recall of the ANG units made spare parts more critical. Age of the F-84F imposed heavier maintenance requirements. In March, all F-84Fs were grounded for replacement of corroded control rods. Modifications were also necessary to increase the aircraft's conventional ordnance capability. In effect, some 1,800 manhours were expended on each of the 222 F–84Fs that temporarily equipped TAC's new 12th and 15th Tactical Fighter Wings and the new 366th TFW of the United States Air Forces in Europe (USAFE).

Final Phaseout **1963–1964**

USAF. As more modern fighters became available, F–84Fs were returned to the ANG. In June 1964, 13 years of MAP F–84B/C/F training at Luke AFB, ended in favor of the F–104G program. In July 1964 TAC returned the last USAF F–84Fs to the ANG.

1971–1972

ANG. The Guard still had 56 F–84Fs in November 1971 when a serious accident occurred due to structural corrosion. The 183rd Tactical Fighter Group, Springfield, Ill., the only ANG unit still equipped with F–84Fs, was programmed for F–4C aircraft, and over 90 percent of the grounded F–84Fs showed signs of stress corrosion. Hence no repairs were made. In February 1972, however, the Air Force used two ANG F–84Fs in developing repair procedures that would be offered to the many allied nations using the elderly aircraft.

Other Countries

The F–84F aircraft saw long service with some of the United States's most sophisticated allies. Beginning in 1955, the French Air Force flew F–84Fs for over 10 years. In 1972 the aircraft was still flown by air forces in such countries as Denmark, Italy, Belgium, the Netherlands, Greece, and Turkey.

RF-84F Thunderflash

Previous Model Series

F–84F, which shared the same basic characteristics as the RF-84F.

New Features

Engine air intake ducts were located in the wing roots of the RF–84F rather than in the nose section. The elongated and enclosed nose contained 15 cameras: six standard forward-facing, one Tri-Metrogen horizon-to-horizon, and eight in oblique and vertical positions for target closeups. The RF–84F featured many firsts: the Tri-Metrogen camera, a computerized control system based on light, speed, and altitude, it adjusted camera settings to produce pictures with greater delineation and a vertical view finder with a periscopic presentation on the cockpit panel to enhance visual reconnaissance. Talking into a wire recorder, the pilot could describe ground movements that might not appear in still pictures.

Production Decision **1951**

Production of the RF–84F was linked to that of the F–84F. In both cases, the Korean War prompted the decision.[15] Nonetheless, the first RF–84F order was not formalized until 12 June 1951—2 weeks after satisfactory inspection of the mockup and 6 months past official endorsement of the F–84F full-scale production. The initial RF–84F contract only called for two prototypes (later reduced to one), but the Air Force was already convinced the new aircraft would be the best in terms of endurance, speed, and sensors. The RF–84F would also be able to fly night missions by using magnesium flares carried under its wings in flash-ejector cartridges. Hence, the first 130 RF–84Fs were ordered before the new fiscal year (July 1951).

First Flight (YFR-84F) **February 1952**

Before this flight, an F–84F prototype had already tested the RF–84F's new air intake configuration. The test disclosed no serious impairment of overall aircraft performance.

First Production Delivery **August 1953**

Almost 1 year after delivery of the first F–84F. The Air Force accepted a second RF–84F in September.

First Flight (Production Aircraft) **9 September 1953**

The flight lasted 40 minutes.

Production Slippages **1953-1955**

Being almost identical to the F–84F, the RF–84F did not escape some of its predecessor's problems. Republic's shortage of forgings prevented further deliveries of the RF–84Fs until January 1954. In April, after only 24 of the reconnaissance aircraft (counting the 2 released in 1953) had been accepted, engine troubles brought another delay. Eighteen months passed before RF–84F deliveries finally resumed in November 1955.

Enters Operational Service **March 1954**

First with TAC, but in December 1955, SAC began equipping a Strategic Reconnaissance Wing, Fighter, with a mix of RF–84Fs and RF–84Ks. (The latter were specially configured RF–84Fs, developed during the Fighter Conveyor (FICON) B–36 project.)

Production Modifications **1953-1957**

The RF–84F underwent most of the F–84F's production modifications. Likewise, while the first RF–84F lot was equipped with the 7,200-lb static thrust Wright J–65–W–3 engine, later ones received the –W–7 (a 7,800-lb static thrust version of the same Wright engine).

---

[15] The Tactical Air Command had to withdraw tactical aircraft from storage and modify active F–80s to meet the war's reconnaissance requirements. The RF–80 actually became the Air Force's recon workhorse in Korea, but this plane could not fly at low altitude long enough to perform suitable visual reconnaissance.

End of Production **December 1957**

With delivery of 28 RF–84Fs—the last of 327 RF–84Fs ordered into production for the Military Assistance Program.

Total RF-84Fs Accepted

There were 715 accepted—327 for MAP and 388 for the Air Force. Included in USAF total were 25 reconfigured RF–84Fs, subsequently identified as RF–84Ks.

Acceptance Rates

The Air Force accepted 24 RF–84Fs for its own use in FY 54, 163 (counting 6 future RF–84Ks) in FY 55, 137 (19 RF–84Ks included) in FY 56, and 64 in FY 57. All MAP RF–84Fs were accepted within 3 years—47 in FY 55, 174 in FY 56, and 106 in FY 57.

Flyaway Cost Per Production Aircraft

$667,608.00—airframe, $482,821; engine (installed), $95,320; electronics, $21,576; ordnance, $4,529; armament, $63,632.

Average Maintenance Cost Per Flying Hour

$185.00

Postproduction Modifications **1957**

Originally fitted for the boom type of aerial refueling, the RF–84F was later modified for the probe and drogue method.

Subsequent Model Series

None

Other Configurations

RF–84K. This was a modified RF–84F, developed for the Fighter-Conveyor B–36 program of 1953. The FICON program would stretch the RF–84F's effective operating radius, which was relatively short (700 nautical miles at high altitude, but only half this distance when flying low). It would also extend the usefulness of the B–36 (growing vulnerable as more modern jet fighters were being produced by the Soviet Union to protect its vital installations). The Air Force decided to go ahead with the program after successful tests of an ordinary F–84F prototype during April-July 1953. In the fall of 1955, Republic delivered 25 RF–84Fs, modified for use with the B–36. Soon known as the RF–84K, the modified plane featured a reconfigured tail and retractable hook in the nose section. Meanwhile, Convair had attached a trapeze-yoke system to the B–36's underside. This let the B–36 hook and store the RF-84K (half-way within the bomb bay), fly close to the target, and release the K to perform reconnaissance. After retrieving and storing the RF–84K, the bomber returned to a friendly base.

Initial Phaseout **1957**

SAC's 71st Strategic Reconnaissance Wing flew the last RF–84F/K mission on 22 May 1957. Within the next 12 months, TAC turned over the remainder of its RF–84Fs to the ANG.

Reactivation **1961**

The Berlin crisis brought the recall of the ANG's 117th Tactical Reconnaissance Wing, equipped with about 60 RF–84Fs. The 117th returned to state control after the crisis.

Final Phaseout **1972**

The drain of TAC units to Southeast Asia in the late 1960's rendered TAC dependent upon ANG units for support of other contingency plans. Hence, by 1967 six of seven RF–84F ANG squadrons had attained either C–1 or C–2 readiness status.[16] USAF plans called for the ANG to keep at least three RF–84F squadrons through fiscal year 1976. However, more advanced aircraft became available, and the ANG disposed of its RF–84Fs more rapidly. On 26 January 1972, the last RF–84Fs were flown to a storage depot. They had belonged to the 155th Tactical Reconnaissance Group, which traded them for RF–4Cs.

Other Countries

RF–84Fs were flown by the Chinese Nationalist Air Force as well as by air forces of eight other countries: Germany, France, Greece, Turkey, Italy, Belgium, Denmark, and Norway. In the late 1950's the Italian Air Force put into practice President Eisenhower's "Open Skies" aerial inspection proposal for enforcing arms limitation agreements. While crisscrossing Italy at 550 mph (477.5 kn), RF–84Fs were able to photograph small vehicles and people as well.

PROGRAM RECAP

Counting 3,515 aircraft accepted by the Air Force for MDAP, the program attained a grand total of 7,524 F–84s of all sorts. The 4,009 tagged for the Air Force embraced 2 XP–84s (accepted by the AAF in 1946), 15 YF–84As, 226 F–84Bs, 191 F–84Cs, 154 F–84Ds, 743 F–84Es, 789 F–84Gs, 3 YF–84Fs, 1,496 F–84Fs, 1 YF–84J, 1 YRF–84F, 25 RF–84s (FICON), and 363 RF–84Fs. MDAP acceptances consisted of 100 F–84Es, 2,236 F–84Gs, 852 F–84Fs, and 327 RF–84Fs.

[16] The same rating system still applied in mid-1973. The Air Force gave C–1 ratings to units that were fully combat ready and C–2 ratings to those substantially combat ready. Units marginally combat ready received a C–3 rating; the ones not combat ready, a C–4—the lowest rating.

TECHNICAL DATA

F–84B, F–84C/D, F–84E, and F–84G

Manufacturer	(Airframe)	Republic Aviation Corporation, Farmingdale, N. Y.
	(Engine)	Allison Division of General Motors Corporation, Kansas City, Mo.
Nomenclature		Fighter, Fighter-bomber.
Popular Name		Thunderjet

Characteristics	*F–84B*	*F–84C/D*	*F–84E*	*F–84G*
Engine, Number & Designation	1 J–35–A–15	1 J–35–A–13	1 J–35–A–17	1 J–35–A–29
Length/Span	37.5 ft/36.5 ft	37.5 ft/36.5 ft	38 ft/36 ft	38.1 ft/36.5 ft
Weight (empty)	9,538 lb		11,000 lb	11,095 lb
Max. Gross Weight	19,689 lb		18,000 lb	23,525 lb
Max. Speed	509.7 nm		521 nm	540 nm
Cruise Speed	378.6 nm			418.4 nm
Service Ceiling	40,750 ft		45,000 ft	40,500 ft
Range	1,114.7 nm			1,739 nm
Combat Radius			739 nm (869.5 nm w/4 external fuel tanks)	
Armament	4 .50-cal machine guns	6 .50-cal machine guns	6 .50-cal machine guns	6 .50-cal machine guns
Ordnance Max.			up to 4,500 lb	6,000 lb
Crew	1	1	1	1

TECHNICAL DATA

F–84F and RF–84F

Manufacturer	(Airframe)	Republic Aviation Corporation, Farmingdale, N. Y.
	(Engine)	General Motors Corporation, Kansas City, Mo.
Nomenclature	(F–84F)	Fighter, Fighter-bomber.
	(RF–84F)	Reconnaissance.
Popular Name	(F–84–F)	Thunderstreak
	(RF–84F)	Thunderflash

Characteristics	*F–84F*	*RF–84F*
Engine, Number & Designation	1 7,200 lb s.t. J–65–W–3	1 7,200 lb s.t. J–65–W–3 or 1 7,800 lb s.t. J–65–W–7.
Length/Span	43 ft/33 ft	47 ft/33 ft
Max. Takeoff Weight	24,200 lb	25,400 lb
Takeoff Ground Run	4,500 ft	5,000 ft
Cruise Speed	.82 Mach	480 kn
Max. Speed	600 kn (35,000 ft)	536 kn
Service Ceiling	44,300 ft	45,600 ft
Rate of Climb (sea level)	6,300 fpm	
Radius	375 nm	
Ferry Range		1,570 nm
Endurance		3.4 hr
Armament	6 0.5-in Colt-Browning M–3 machine guns	4 0.5-in Colt-Browning M–3 machine guns
Crew	1	1
Ordnance—Max. Tons	.81	NA

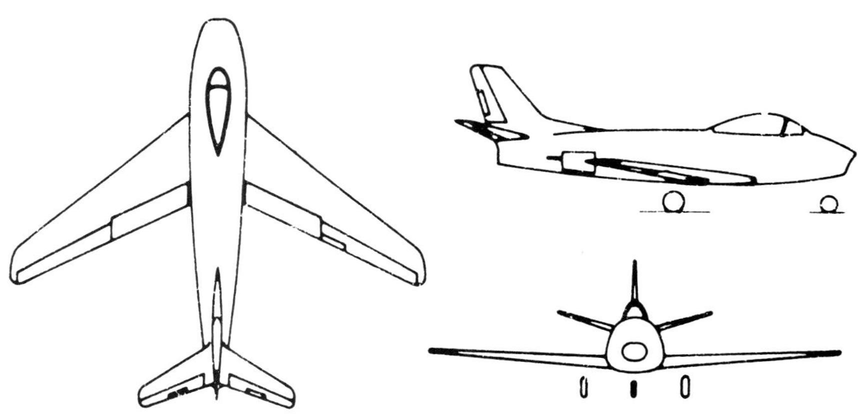

NORTH AMERICAN F–86 SABRE

F–86A: The Air Force's first swept-wing fighter. Rushed to Korea, the F–86As quickly captured the air superiority gained at the onset of the Korean conflict by the inferior F–51s, and a few F–80 jets, skillfully piloted against a not-too-determined enemy.

F–86E: Flying a Canadian-built F–86E at Edwards AFB on 18 May 1953, Jacqueline Cochran became the first woman to fly faster than sound.

F–86F: With its new engine and built-in improvements, the F–86F eventually supplanted the F–86E in Korea. Nonetheless the overall F–86 combat performance was remarkable. The final boxscore showed 14 MIGs downed for every F–86 lost.

F–86D: The F–86D fighter interceptor was virtually a new machine, retaining only the wing common to other F–86s. It was also the first single-seat fighter in which the classic gun armament gave way to missiles.

F–86K: Developed from the F–86D for supply to the NATO forces. The F–86K featured an extended fuselage, cannon ports in the walls of the nose intake, and simplified electronic equipment.

F–86L: A converted F–86D, with slightly longer wings, and data-link components for operation in the semi-automatic ground environment system, deployed in the late fifties.

NORTH AMERICAN F-86 SABRE

Manufacturer's Model NA-151

Basic Development **1944-1945**

The F-86 grew out of North American's several straight-wing configurations of the XFJ-1 Fury (a projected Navy jet fighter) and engineering (including wind-tunnel data) on swept-wings obtained in Germany after V-E Day. The Army Air Forces accepted a variant of the straight-wing XFJ-1 design in May 1945, ordered two prototypes, and applied the designation XP-86. Soon afterward, North American engineers found that adapting the Messerschmitt 262 swept-wing design would give the XP-86 about 70 mph (60.7 knots) greater speed.

General Operational Requirements **May 1945**

The GOR called for a day fighter of medium range that could work as an escort fighter and dive bomber. Speed was one of the primary military characteristics on which the AAF was most insistent. The straight-wing XP-86 under letter contract, with an estimated top speed of 582 mph, fell short of the minimum 600 mph required.

Design Change **1 November 1945**

The AAF endorsed North American proposal to scrap the straight-wing design in favor of the swept-wing, even though this would probably mean a year's delay in delivery.

Definitive Contract **20 June 1946**

The LC of May 1945 was superseded by a definitive research and development (R&D) contract that raised to three the number of prototypes ordered.

Production Go-Ahead **20 December 1946**

Although the prototypes were still under construction, a production order was released. Unit cost of the first 33 P-86s authorized for procurement was set at $438,999.00—more than twice the aircraft's eventual price.

First Flight (Prototype) **1 October 1947**

The aircraft, powered by a Chevrolet-built General Electric J35-C-3 turbo-jet, delivering 3,750 lb. s.t., was later re-equipped with the more powerful J47-GE-3 engine. A re-engined prototype (YP-86A) first exceeded Mach 1 on 25 April 1948.

Flight Testing **1947-1949**

Category II flight tests were started in December 1947; Category III, in January 1949—1 month before the first F-86As entered operational service.

F-86A

Additional Procurement **28 December 1947**

North American received a second production order for 188 P–86s, but these aircraft, as ordered at the time never materialized. They actually came off the production lines as early F–86As, after also receiving a 5,200 lb. s.t. J–47–GE–3 engine. Subsequent F–86A productions were successively fitted with the J47–GE–7, –9, and –13.

First Flight (Production Aircraft) **20 May 1948**

The Air Force accepted two other initial productions of its first swept-wing fighter on 28 May and changed their P–86A designation to F–86A the following month. In June also an order for another 333 F–86As was awarded.

Enters Operational Service **February 1949**

The 94th Fighter Squadron[1] of the 1st Fighter Group received the first F–86As at March Field, Calif. The Group was completely equipped by the end of May.

Oversea Deployments **1 December 1950**

The 4th FI Group of the 4th Fighter Interceptor Wing (urgently deployed to Japan in November 1950) was the first F–86 unit to reach the Korean war theater.

War Commitments **16 December 1950**

Despite a shortage of aircraft (only 15 of the 19 F–86As initially deployed to Korea were combat ready), the 4th FI Group began combat operations in support of the Far East Air Force on 16 December. The following day, the first recorded combat between swept-wing fighters ended in favor of the F–86A. Four other Russian-built MIG–15s were claimed during the week without any F–86 losses. The retreat of United Nations (UN) ground forces in the last days of 1950 forced redeployment of the F–86As to Japan. Despite the availability of the long-range F–84Es, B–29 raids over North Korea could not be resumed until late in February 1951, when the F–86As returned to Korea.

Combat Achievements **1951**

Following their first successes, the F–86As quickly captured the air superiority gained at the onset of the Korean conflict by the inferior F–51s, F–82 Twin Mustangs, and a few F–80 jets, skillfully piloted against indecisive opposition. Chinese Communist MIG–15s later threatened this supremacy. F–86As of the 4th FI Group, although designed to escort the B–29s and fighter-bombers of the Fifth Air Force operating deep in North Korea, at first were used primarily as an air superiority force. They were pitted against

[1] Redesignated 94th Fighter-Interceptor Squadron (FIS) on 16 April 1950.

large numbers of MIG–15s that could take refuge on the Manchurian side of the Yalu River where they enjoyed the immunity of UN aircraft. Of the Group's 4,885 sorties between 16 December 1950 and 28 June 1951, only 336 resulted in combat. Yet, the Group destroyed 40 MIG–15s, probably destroyed 6, and damaged 71. In contrast, it lost 7 F–86As—one due to operational accident.

Overall Appraisal

The F–86A's initial performances balanced those of its Russian counterpart. In light of later model improvements, the Air Force eventually judged the two aircraft roughly equal. Meanwhile, the F–86A success over the MIG–15 rested chiefly in the ability and aggressiveness of its pilots. Paradoxically, the F–86's lopsided victory score in 6 months of operation also pinpointed a serious deficiency. Inadequate armament (the M–3 .50-caliber machinegun in particular) explained the high number of MIGs "damaged and probably destroyed" against those positively "destroyed" (77 to 44). Despite all efforts, this armament problem persisted in the F–86E that followed the F–86A into production and combat. The F–86A's gross weight was also criticized—16,000 lbs against the MIG's 12,000. Some of this excess derived from such "gadgets" as emergency fuel pumps, self-sealing fuel tanks (that did not hold against the MIG–15's 23- and 37-mm cannons), and an unreliable, electronic gunsight that was hard to maintain.[2] Fuel pump and fuel tank improvements in subsequent F–86 models, and another gunsight introduced in the last F–86A off the production line took care of difficulties in an otherwise sound aircraft.

Modifications **1951**

In the last 24 F–86As produced, the Mk 18 gunsight was supplanted by the A–1CM sight, which was coupled with an AN/APC–30 radar installed in the upper lip of the aircraft's nose intake. Earlier F–86As were retrofitted with the A–1CM sight, which was linked either to an AN/APG–5C radar or, more commonly, to the AN/APG–30.

[2] The Air Force concurrent concern over the increasing complexity and size of fighter aircraft was acknowledged in a December 1951 GOR that called for a compact, lightweight supersonic day fighter. In the following months, as no American aircraft company appeared capable of satisfying these requirements in their entirety, the Air Force investigated the British "Annihilation," a proposed lightweight fighter, capable of being "zero-launched and landed on unprepared surfaces." While awaiting the results of a Navy lightweight fighter design competition, the Air Force also studied two Lockheed proposals for construction of two development aircraft in the lightweight fighter class. Late in 1952 a Republic design, the future F–105 with certain modifications and much lighter than the eventual production configuration, finally set the stage for satisfying the day fighter weapon system requirement, although one of the Lockheed projects, the subsequent F–104, for a while seemed to be a surer contender.

Subsequent Model Series

F–86E. The production of several intervening models in the series either did not materialize or was delayed.

Other Configurations

F–86B. An F–86A with deeper fuselage and larger tires. The 188 aircraft on order were cancelled in favor of an equivalent number of additional F–86As.

F–86C (YF–93A). This variant had a completely redesigned fuselage with flush side air-intakes (replacing one intake in the nose). They were to lead to a Pratt and Whitney J48–P–6 engine which, fitted with an afterburner, would have delivered 8,750 lb thrust. Because of such extensive changes, the F–86C designation was changed to F–93. Although the first of two prototypes (YF–93A, powered by a J48–P–3 engine) flew on 25 January 1950, production of the 118 aircraft on order since 9 June 1948 was cancelled.

F–86D (YF–95A). This major F–86 variant should have followed the F–86A, but it was preceded in production by the F–86E.

RF–86A. Some F–86As, mostly from the early lot of aircraft powered by the J47–GE–3 engine, were fitted with reconnaissance equipment. The modification, referred to as Project Ashtray, followed combat experience in Korea where, in areas dominated by MIG interceptors, the speed-limited RF–80s were virtually useless. The photographic capability of the faster RF–86A, although below RF–80 standard, was still superior to that of the RF–51. Moreover, the small number of cameras installed in the modified F–86A allowed retention of the aircraft armament. As in the RF–51 and in contrast to that of the RF–80, this gave reconnaissance pilots a means of defense. Although considered at the time as a temporary expedient, the few RF–86As available in mid-1952 in effect weathered the Korean conflict without the help of the production-delayed RF–84, which had been chosen as the RF–80's successor.

End of Production **December 1950**

The last two F–86As manufactured were accepted by the Air Force in February 1951.

Total F-86As Accepted

554—the Air Force also accepted three YF–86As, first ordered as experimental aircraft.

Acceptance Rates

Three F–86As were accepted in FY 48, 148 in FY 49, 304 in FY 50, and 99 in FY 51. The three YF–86As were accepted in FY 49—the first two in December 1948, the third in March 1949.

Flyaway Cost Per Production Aircraft

$178,408.00—airframe, $101,528; engine (installed), $52,971; electronics, $7,576; armament, $16,333.

Total RDT&E Costs

$4,707,802.00—this amount (not included in the compilation of the F–86A's unit cost) also covered the cost of carrying the three experimental aircraft (YF–86As) through their Category II flight tests.

Phaseout **1954**

The F–86A, which comprised the bulk of the F–86 day fighters in early combat, was almost completely replaced by the F–86E and F models by the fall of 1952. Withdrawal from Korea did not spell the end of the F–86A service and the aircraft remained in the regular Air Force several more years. The first ANG units to receive F–86As early in 1952 were the 123d FIS (giving up its WW II F–51s) and the 126th (formerly equipped with F–80 jets), but these units had been recalled to active duty early in 1951 and, when released from federal service late in 1952, their aircraft were retained by the Air Defense Command. In effect, the F–86A only began reaching the Guard in 1954. There it remained active until the late fifties, when it was replaced by the F–86D.

Milestones **15 September 1948**

The Air Force established a new world's speed record of 670.981 mph over a measured course at Muroc, with a standard F–86A complete with armament and normal combat equipment.

F-86E

Previous Model Series

F–86A—the normally intervening F–86D was actually preceded in production by the E.

New Features

As a progressive development of the F–86A, the F–86E featured a new tail with both tailplane and elevators controllable and linked for coordinated movement. All controls were power-operated. The F–86E retained the F–86A's M–3 guns and the J47–GE–13 engine of the latest F–86As.

First Flight (Production Aircraft) **23 September 1950**

The Air Force accepted its first two F–86Es in February 1951—just a few months after the aircraft's first flight.

Enters Operational Service **May 1951**

The first aircraft were assigned to ADC's 33d Fighter Interceptor Wing.

Oversea Deployments **July 1951**

The Air Force furnished FEAF whatever F–86s it could spare from air defense. Almost as soon as operational, F–86Es joined the F–86As in the Korean war.

Logistical Problems **1951-1952**

Initial provisioning for the F–86 was based on peacetime consumption rates. Hence, the 51st Wing's unprogrammed conversion to F–86Es severely strained logistical support. By January 1952, 45 percent of the war-committed F–86A and E fighters were out of commission for want of parts or maintenance. Theater supplies of external fuel tanks, without which the range-limited F–86s were badly handicapped, also were nearly exhausted. "Peter Rabbit," a crash project for buying a 1-year supply of all urgently needed items, solved most of these problems, but it took several months.

Other Difficulties **1951-1952**

The F–86As, first deployed to the Far East, were flown by highly qualified, regular and reservist, career pilots. Most of these men were being rotated as 100-mission veterans by mid-1951, when the F–86Es arrived, and supplying qualified replacement pilots for service in Korea became a challenge. During the winter of 1951–1952 the 4th FI Wing (still flying a mixture of F–86As and Es) and the F–86E-equipped 51st received pilots whose previous experience had been attained in multi-engine transports and bombers. This problem persisted until March 1952, when large numbers of jet fighter pilots began to arrive from replacement training centers in the United States.

Combat Achievements **1952**

Largely outnumbered by an enemy favored by the odds of combat,[3] F–86Es of the 51st FI Wing destroyed 25 MIGs during January 1952. Most of the kills were achieved by patrols that entered the combat area at 45,000 feet and made astern attacks on the elusive enemy aircraft, sighted at lower altitudes. Held to reduced flying rates because of logistical deficiencies, the 4th and 51st Wings could only claim the destruction of 17 MIGs during February, but impressive victories were recorded soon afterward. Although some MIG pilots continued to avoid action, enemy tactics changed and MIG formations were met at lower altitudes in March and April. In these months, at the cost of only 6 F–86s, 83 MIGs were destroyed.

Modifications **1952-1953**

The operational suitability tests that ended in July 1952, after the F–86E had already acquired some 12 months of combat experi-

[3] As already noted, the MIGs were provided with an inviolable sanctuary where they could take refuge when damaged or unwilling to fight. By contrast the combat area was at the outer range of the F–86E's combat radius and over enemy territory at all times. While visual acuity was a problem that affected both sides equally at high altitudes, the MIG pilots had the advantage of GCI direction. In essence, the F–86E, a relatively general purpose aircraft, faced the specialized MIG–15 under conditions which favored the specialized type.

ence, called for improvement of the aircraft's overall performance. This was particularly urgent because of the enemy's increasing capability. Yet, none of the several courses of action available to the Air Force appeared too promising. The F–86E could be retrofitted with the more powerful J–47–GE–27 engine, for this possibility had been taken into consideration before production, but this engine was in short supply. As recommended by North American, the thrust of the F–86E's J–47–GE–13 engine could be boosted. This would alleviate the aircraft's most serious shortcoming by increasing its rate of climb.[4] However, neither General Electric nor the Air Force favored this second solution. The former, because it would severely reduce the engine life; the latter, because it would pose a difficult, "if not impossible," supply and maintenance problem. After combat testing proved its effectiveness, a kind of expedient was adopted that later became a standard feature of subsequent F–86 models. Referred to as the "6–3 wing," the modification, credited with speed increases of several knots, gave the F–86E wing a slightly increased sweepback. This was achieved by extending the wing inboard and outboard edges by 6 and 3 inches, respectively, and by eliminating the slats of the wing's original leading edges. The "6–3 wing" modification kits were inexpensive, $4,000 each, but only 50 had been sent to Korea by the end of 1952, and they were not plentiful until mid-1953.

End of Production **April 1952**

The Air Force took delivery of its last six F–86Es in October.

Total F-86Es Accepted

456—396 for the Air Force[5] and 60 for the Mutual Defense Assistance Program. Because of the Korean War demands on American production, 60 of the Air Force's 396 F–86Es were built by Canadair, a Canadian aircraft company. Like other F–86Es, they were powered by the J47–GE–13 engine. The 60 MDAP F–86Es were also produced by Canadair, but they were fitted with the Avro Canada Orenda engine and the designation F–86J was applicable to this version.

Acceptance Rates

Eighty F–86Es were accepted in FY 51, 218 in FY 52, and 98 in FY 53. Fifty-five of the 60 USAF F–86Es bought from Canadair were received in FY 52, the remaining five in FY 53. The 60 MDAP F–86Es were accepted in 1953, 26 each in June and July, and 8 in August.

---

[4] The F–89A Scorpion, with afterburner, could outclimb the unmodified F–86E.

[5] Of the 396, 225 were ordered as F–86Fs but completed as F–86Es, owing to a shortage of the F's powerful J47–GE–27 engine.

Flyaway Cost Per Production Aircraft

$219,457.00—airframe, $145,326; engine (installed), $39,990; electronics, $6,358; ordnance, $4,138; armament, $23,645.

Other Configurations

F–86G. Similar to F–86E but fitted with J47–GE–29 engine which required a longer fuselage by about 6 inches. The prototype on order was cancelled.

F–86J. Canadair-built F–86E, fitted with the Avro Canada Orenda engine and delivered to the Air Force for the MDAP.

Phaseout **April 1954**

Like the F–86As, the F–86Es began leaving the Air Force operational inventory soon after the end of the Korean war. The ANG owned 140 F–86Es by mid-1956 and still flew a few of them in 1960. Also, several foreign countries received badly needed F–86Es through the Military Assistance Program—using them until the end of 1958.

Milestones **17 August 1951**

The Air Force set world record of 635.685 mph for a 100-kilometer closed course at Romulus, Mich.

18 May 1953

Flying a Canadian-built F–86E at Edwards AFB, Jacqueline Cochran became the first woman to fly faster than sound. She broke the international speed record for a 100-kilometer closed course by averaging 652.337 mph, also breaking the women's jet speed record.

Other Countries

The Canadian government decided to manufacture the F–86 under license in 1949 and in August of that year placed an order for 100 of them with Canadian Limited. Initially, it was planned to manufacture the F–86A but only one example, designated Sabre Mk.1, was completed, subsequent productions being built to F–86E standards as Sabre Mk.2s. A number of modifications, introduced by Canadair after the 353rd Mk.2 production, changed the aircraft's designation to Mk.4, of which 438 examples were built. The United Kingdom and West Germany, with the assistance of MDAP funds, acquired many Mk.2 and Mk.4 aircraft that were flown by the Royal Air Force (RAF) until mid-1956, when they were transferred to the Italian Air Force. A further 120 ex-RAF Sabre Mk.4s were also transferred to the Yugoslav Air Force. Former Royal Canadian Air Force Mk.2 and Mk.4 aircraft, after being retrofitted with extended-wing leading edges, were redesignated F–86E (M)s and allocated to the Royal Hellenic and Turkish air forces.

F-86F

Previous Model Series

F–86E, although a few F–86Ds came off the assembly line ahead of the F–86F.

New Features

The F–86F incorporated the J–47–GE–27 turbojet engine, which had a military rating of 5,910-lb thrust (a 700-lb thrust increase over the –13 engine of the F–86E), and 200-gallon, droppable fuel tanks (replacing the 120-gallon tanks of the F–86A and E models). The F–86F also featured the so-called "6–3" solid-wing leading-edge (later modified to reintroduce deleted slats), with small boundary layer fences fitted for the first time.

Production Decision **1951**

The Korean War precipitated a kind of blanket decision. The F–86A and E day fighters (called for by the May 1945 GOR) could double as escort fighters or dive bombers, but the Air Force now wanted mainly a fighter-bomber. Overriding efforts were then underway to enhance the performance of all F–86s—war-committed or earmarked for combat in Korea. Hence, it was mid-1952 before final configuration changes were established, after production of the urgently needed aircraft had already begun. Nonetheless, the F–86F eventually satisfied the USAF fighter-bomber requirements. Equipped with four underwing pylons, it could carry bombs and external stores at the same time. Other configuration changes added 5″ High Velocity Aircraft Rockets (HVARs) and various tactical nuclear stores.

First Flight (Production Aircraft) **19 March 1952**

This F–86F and 77 other first productions barely differed from the F–86E. They were equipped with the J–47–GE–27 engine which, if available, would also have powered the F–86E.

First Acceptance (Production Aircraft) **27 March 1952**

With the delivery of 6 aircraft. Under the impetus of the war, North American opened a second F–86 plant in Columbus, Ohio, where the F–86F was the first model built. Beginning in April 1952, after completion of the 396th and last F–86E, F–86F were also manufactured in Los Angeles.

Oversea Deployments **Mid-1952**

The new F–86F began serving with the 51st Fighter Interceptor Wing in Korea within 3 months of being first accepted by the Air Force.

Production Modifications **1952-1953**

A second production batch of F–86Fs featured for the first time larger fuel tanks that increased combat radius to 402.6 nautical miles—115.6 nautical miles farther than the F–86A and E fighters. The F–86F's external fuel tanks could also be dropped. Extra care helped eliminate tank hangups that too often had kept F–86s from air-to-air combat. In effect, each F–86F variance included additional improvements, the nature of which had been determined through combat experience in Korea. Replacement of the A–1 gunsight by the simpler A–4 was followed by a revised cockpit arrangement, a modified radio system, and better armor protection for the tail-plane control system. Another group of F–86Fs introduced dual-store provision and even more fuel tanks that stretched combat radius another 100 miles (87 nm). The last F–86Fs produced for the Air Force carried a LABS computer, a 1,200-lb tactical nuclear store, more conventional bombs, and two 750-lb Napalm tanks (or eight 5″ HVARs). After combat-testing the 20-mm cannon, the F–86Fs again retained the deficient M–3 machine-guns of early F–86s.[6]

Other Modifications **1952-1955**

More than half of the Air Force F–86Fs were retrofitted with the extended, solid-wing leading edges, first tested on the F–86E. Other F–86Fs were produced under this new configuration. In both cases, the results were gratifying. Operating altitude jumped to 52,000 feet (a 4,000-ft gain); maximum Mach went to 1.05; climb exceeded earlier rates by almost 300 fpm; and tighter turns could be made at high altitudes. These reduced the advantages of the highly maneuverable MIG–15—still, the Air Force sought improvement. After extensive tests, it found it in a reversion to slats, plus a leading edge and wing tip extension. This raised the F–86F's combat capability over the two original configurations—the first slat-equipped, short-wing leading-edge F–86Fs (subsequently retrofitted), and the extended wing leading-edge F–86F productions in which all slats had been eliminated. The combination slat-extension improved the aircraft handling at low speeds, extended combat radius, increased maneuverability at high altitudes, and reduced landing and take-off speeds. The slats also added 200 pounds to the 17,000-lb F–86F, but it was well worth it.[7] In March 1955 the Air Force directed retrofit of all F–86Fs with the new, slated leading edge.

---

[6] The 20-mm cannon, tested in Korea during the spring of 1953 as part of Project "Gun Val," showed promise, but was not yet combat-ready.

[7] Reduction of the F–86's weight and the performance improvements to be gained from such a reduction received particular attention in 1952, during the F–86E modification. North American several proposals came to no avail, however, for the Air Force could not chance decreasing the aircraft capability by stripping it from any of its components.

Combat Appraisal **1952-1953**

Despite the higher thrust of the F-86F's new engine, early F-86Fs demonstrated no marked combat superiority over modified F-86Es. Yet, they outperformed their predecessors in acceleration and rate of climb below 30,000 feet. Ensuing F-86F variances with their built-in improvements increased the gap and, by March 1953, F-86Es were being withdrawn from combat in favor of the new model. In the fighter-bomber role, F-86Fs also proved their effectiveness quickly. In mid-1953, after but a few months in combat, the Fifth Air Force described the aircraft as "the most suitable fighter-bomber employed in Korea." The F-86F "displayed a superior ability to survive, was a stable gun and bomb platform, had no airfield or operating problems not peculiar to other jets, and possessed satisfactory stability when carrying external ordnance at high altitudes."

Combat Achievements **27 July 1973**

By the end of the war, the F-86s—and the F-86Fs in particular—had achieved and held air superiority in Korea. The final boxscore showed 14 MIGs downed for every F-86 lost (818 versus 58).

End of Production **October 1955**

Fifteen months after delivery of the Air Force's last 40 F-86Fs. All productions accepted by the Air Force after June 1954 were allocated to MAP, the last such lot of 13 aircraft being delivered in December 1956.

Total F-86Fs Accepted

1,959—700 from Columbus, the remainder from Inglewood, Calif. The Air Force accepted also from Inglewood an additional 280 F-86Fs, earmarked for the MAP.

Acceptance Rates

The Air Force accepted for its own use 111 F-86Fs in FY 52, 971 in FY 53, and 877 in FY 54. The MAP F-86Fs were accepted after a 2-year lapse—142 in FY 56 and 138 in FY 57.

Flyaway Cost Per Production Aircraft

$211,111.00—airframe, $140,082; engine (installed), $44,664; electronics, $5,649; ordnance, $3,047; armament, $17,669.

Average Maintenance Cost Per Flying Hour

$135.00

Subsequent Model Series

F-86H

Other Configurations

RF-86F. As in the F-86A's case, a few F-86Fs were fitted with reconnaissance equipment. The RF-86Fs served in Korea with the 67th Tactical Reconnaissance Wing.

TF–86F. Two-place version of the basic F–86F, requested by TAC as a replacement for the T–33 trainer. The first TF–86F flew for the first time on 14 December 1953 and was destroyed in an accident soon after. A second TF–86F was completed and flown in the summer of 1954, but the Air Force cancelled the program a few months later.

Phaseout **1954–1956**

The F–86F, like the F–86E, left the Air Force inventory after the Korean war. By early 1955, the Air Defense Command had no F–86F interceptors. By the end of the year, the remaining 53 F–86F fighter-bombers of TAC's 323d Fighter Bomber Wing and 83d Fighter Day Wing were being replaced by F–86Hs (the F–86F's subsequent model). The Guard inventory, which counted four F–86Fs in mid-1957, reached a peak of 25 F–86Fs 2 years later, but these ANG aircraft were also quickly supplanted by F–86Hs. Export of surplus F–86Fs to MAP recipient nations began in 1954. Within 4 years, the F–86Fs had become the Free World's most widely-used jet combat aircraft. TAC used some F–86Fs for training of allied foreign pilots through the early sixties.

Other Uses **1954**

F–86Fs of TAC's 612th Fighter Bomber Squadron participated in Night Owl, an Air Proving Ground Command project to determine the feasibility of using fighter bombers at night. The F–86Fs convinced the Night Owl observers of their effectiveness. Moreover, necessary modifications would not affect the aircraft daytime capabilities. Pilot training, if closely monitored, also should present no problem. TAC considered the positive results of Night Owl the greatest single development in night operations since the end of WW II. The F–86F was also used in 1954 to test future computer equipment (the M–1 toss-bomber computer was under development and the "A Box" computer, due in mid-1957). Four F–86Fs were therefore equipped with the basic BT–9 computer—Swedish made, production-limited, and not yet installed in any other aircraft. The tests uncovered technical malfunctions which could also impair the improved M–1 toss-bomber computer.

Other Countries **1954**

One of the first recipients of F–86Fs (either surplus or specifically purchased for the Mutual Defense Assistance Program) was Nationalist China, who also received several RF–86Fs equipped with one K–17 and two K–22 cameras. Most of these aircraft, totaling eventually more than 325 aircraft, were still in operation at the end of 1964. The Spanish Air Force also received a significant number of F–86Fs (some 250). The Republic of Korea gained no fewer than 112 F–86Fs and 10 RF–86Fs; Pakistan received 120 F–86Fs; Norway, 90; Portugal, 50; Thailand and the Philippines, 40 each. Twenty-eight F–86Fs were allocated to Argentina, 22 to Venezuela, and 10 to Peru. A joint production agreement between North American and Japanese Mitsubishi manufacturers provided Japan with numerous F–86Fs—180 completed aircraft were delivered by North American and Mitsubishi assembled a total of 300 F–86Fs from imported components. Before North American deliveries of the F–86F to Japan began, the Japanese Air Self-Defense Force received 28 MAP F–86Fs for training operations, the first of these arriving in December 1955.

F-86H

Manufacturer's Models NA-187 and -203

Previous Model Series

F–86F

New Features

General Electric J73 turbojet (substantially more powerful than the F–86F's J47–GE–27 engine), deeper fuselage, larger intake duct, greater fuel capacity, larger tail-plane without dihedral, electrically-operated flaps, hydraulically-operated speed brakes and controls, heavier landing gear, improved suspension and release mechanism for carrying droppable wing tanks in conjunction with bombs and rockets. Clamshell-type canopy (similar to that of the F–86D), superior armament (four 20–mm. M–39 cannons, beginning with the 116th production) and improved ejection seat.

Go-Ahead Decision **16 March 1951**

The Air Force ordered the F–86H fighter-bomber at about the same time the F–86F entered production. Installation of the new J73 engine in the future F–86H was slated from the outset. Since this would entail a departure from previous F–86 airframes, two prototypes were included in the production contract, officially approved in May 1951.

New Requirements **1952**

Late in 1952 the Air Force reclassified the F–86H as a primary day fighter—coincident with finalization of the fighter-bomber configuration for the F–86F and the emergence of development problems on the urgently needed F–100 day fighter. The F–86H mission change did not affect the production order issued 18 months earlier or the aircraft's planned configuration. No appreciable performance increase was expected from the deletions to be made as a result of this reclassification, since the F–86H would still retain a secondary fighter-bomber capability.

First Flight (Prototype) **9 May 1953**

The Air Force had taken delivery of the first YF–86H in January

1953, and of the second one 2 months later. Early flight tests did not uncover any problems serious enough to warrant a major redesign of the new aircraft. However, completion of the Phase II tests in December of the same year confirmed that "numerous deficiencies" existed in both the airframe and power plant. The latter had yet to complete the usual 150-hour qualification test and this alone was a sure indication that F–86H allocations to the tactical forces would be delayed.

First Flight (Production Aircraft) **4 September 1953**

The F–86H production at the North American Columbus plant began in September 1953 at a very slow rate and, as a result of the YF–86H's aerodynamic and propulsion problems, the Air Force earmarked for testing all 20 aircraft produced through January 1954. Notwithstanding, additional testing time would probably still be needed to test the bombing equipment required by the F–86H day fighter's secondary mission.

Reclassification **14 May 1954**

The F–86H's high-wing loading and power deficiencies at high altitudes demoted its role. The J–73 engine generated almost 50 percent more thrust (with only 18 percent more gross weight) but gained little in top speed due to the airframe's Mach limitations.[8] Hence, the F–86H, ordered in 1951 as a fighter bomber, reclassified in 1952 as a primary day fighter, ended up in 1954 as a tactical support fighter-bomber. This did not mark the F–86H—last of the F–86 series—as a complete failure. It eventually became a better air-to-ground gunnery platform than the F–86F, with faster climb and acceleration rates. Meanwhile, problems of all kinds plagued the aircraft.

---

[8] The "Loose Shoe" concept (the practice of providing for a certain growth potential in a given aircraft by designing the airframe so as to permit installation of newly developed engines) was not new. The F–86H could not exactly qualify as a case in point, however. It might look like previous F–86s, but its fuselage had been split longitudinally and an additional 6-in. portion spliced in to increase its depth. Nonetheless, despite the extra 3,000-lb thrust of the J–73 engine, early F–86Hs performed little better than the J47–GE–13-equipped F–86A. This matter received particular attention in late 1953, as a result of a Northrop proposal which significantly differed from the older theory of growth potential. In its second design of the "Fang" (a light-weight day fighter in competition with the North American design of the "Rapier"), Northrop suggested an airframe that could accommodate future engines and allow use of present power plants. While the suggestion appeared cost-effective, the Air Force did not endorse either Northrop's "Fang" or its long-term growth concept. Mainly, it doubted anyone could technically anticipate the kind of airframe needed 10 years hence. The Air Force also detected two basic fallacies in the Northrop's new "Loose Shoe" concept. In the first place, the immediate maximum performance of the aircraft would be below par because the airframe would not be the best for the interim engine. Secondly, the long-term performance of the plane would be poor for the airframe would be obsolete when the engines of the rather distant future arrived.

Delivery Slippages **Mid-1954**

A series of engineering problems delayed the F–86H deliveries. In September a production pool of 58 F–86Hs awaited modifications of one kind or another because of defective gun blast panels, repeated gun jamming, misalignment of the wing spar attaching bolts, defective fire detectors, and a number of other deficiencies of lesser importance.

Enters Operational Service **Fall of 1954**

With the delivery of 68 aircraft to TAC's 312th Fighter Bomber Wing at Clovis AFB, N. Mex.

Engine Shortages **1954–1955**

The new J–73 engines were in short supply and this problem was soon compounded by a lack of spare parts. Logistical support of the J–73 became even more difficult following modification of all J–73s to the –3A configuration and the subsequent upgrading of all –3As to the –3D final version. In May 1955 General Electric was 224 production engines behind schedule, the Air Force was unable to satisfy projected engine changes, and logistical support of the engines in use remained critical. In the meantime, to make matters worse, F–86H airframes had to be modified before any of the earlier J–73 engines could be replaced by the new J–73D.

Operational Problems **1955–1956**

The January discovery that firing the guns dented and cracked various parts of the F–86H structure called for tight flying restrictions that remained in effect through most of the first half of 1955. Engine failures, due to faulty second stage compressor discs made of titanium with an abnormally high hydrogen content, were next. This problem accounted for the loss of two aircraft and the grounding of all F–86Hs equipped with J–73 engines incorporating the faulty titanium items. The F–86Hs were also temporarily grounded on several other occasions either because of their disconcerting ability to shed nose landing gear doors in flight, or because of deficient ejection seats. Nonetheless, although still slated for modification, the F–86H in mid-1956 already encountered fewer operational problems than the F–84F.

Modifications **1955–1956**

Except for the last 10 F–86Hs that were modified before leaving the production lines, all F–86Hs were retrofitted with slat-equipped, extended-wing leading edges, similar to those of the F–86F. The F–86H's tail pipe also was modified, but the resulting improvement was considered modest for its cost ($13,000 per aircraft). Hence, although there might be future promise in an improved version of tail augmentation, the Air Force cancelled the requirement for further consideration of augmentation—for the F–86H at least. In any case, the F–86H with wing slats and a longer tail pipe proved to have a considerably better performance than the F–86F. The tail pipe augmentation, alone, gave the F–86H as much as 10 percent more thrust at sea level.

End of Production **August 1955**

The Air Force took delivery of its last seven F–86Hs in October 1955.

Total F-86Hs Accepted

473

Acceptance Rates

The Air Force accepted 18 F–86Hs in FY 54, 378 in FY 55, and 77 in FY 56 (from July through October 1955). The two YF–86Hs were accepted in early 1953.

Flyaway Cost Per Production Aircraft

$582,493.00—airframe, $316,360; engine (installed), $214,612; electronics, $6,831; ordnance, $17,117; armament, $27,573. The cost of the two YF–86Hs totaled $3 million.

Average Cost Per Flying Hour

$451.00

Subsequent Model Series

None

Other Configurations

None

Initial Phaseout **1956-1958**

The Air Force quickly disposed of its F–86Hs in favor of the F–100C—TAC's first level flight, supersonic day fighter. In late 1957 the only F–86Hs still possessed by TAC were assigned to a fighter-day unit at Seymour Johnson AFB, N.C., and their transfer to the Air National Guard was completed in June 1958.[9]

Reactivation **October 1961**

The Berlin crisis of 1961–62 brought one ANG wing of F–86Hs to temporary active duty. The F–86Hs, deployed to Europe shortly after the 102d Tactical Fighter Wing was recalled, were armed with conventional weapons. They featured four 20-mm. M–39 guns, six .50 caliber M3s, and four MA–3 launchers. They could carry two M–117 general purpose bombs and two M–116 Napalm bombs.

Final Phaseout **1970**

The Guard operational inventory reached a peak of 168 F–86Hs in 1961 and that aircraft remained an ANG asset for more than a decade. Conversion of the 174th Tactical Fighter Group to the A–

[9] Some F–86Hs briefly served with the Air Force Reserve in 1957, then went to the Guard.

37B-type aircraft marked the end of the last F–86Hs in the fall of 1970. The ANG had first received early F–86 models in 1954.

F-86D Interceptor

Weapon System 206A

Previous Model Series

F–86A— the F–86B and C were cancelled. In terms of time, a few F–86Ds came out of production between the F–86Es and F–86Fs. In actuality, the F–86D was virtually a new machine, retaining only the wing common to other F–86s. Its concept was unprecedented—an all-weather interceptor in which the second crew member (standard in all aircraft of this category) was supplanted by highly sophisticated electronic systems. The F–86D was also the first single-seat fighter in which the classic gun armament gave way to missiles.

New Features

Air intake repositioned under nose, which enclosed radar scanner; stronger wing (the wing slats of earlier F–86s were retained) and enlarged vertical tail surfaces to compensate for the additional fuselage area. Vortex generators (small tabs) fitted around the fuselage and tail-plane to ruffle the air flow around these areas and prevent air on the airframe surface from separating and causing drag. Hughes Aircraft Company's interception radar and associated fire-control system.[10] These electronic devices could compute an air target's position, guide the fighter on to a beam-attack converting to a collision course, lower a retractable tray of 24 rockets (2.75-inch Mighty Mouse,[11] each with the power of a 75-mm shell) and within 500 yards of the targets fire these automatically in salvos. More than half of the F–86Ds were powered by either the J47–GE–17 turbojet or by the –17B. Later productions received the higher-thrust J47–GE–33. All had afterburners. Engine control was an added feature of every F–86D. An electronic device to control fuel flow, it relieved the lone pilot of another responsibility.

Basic Development 1949

Slippage of the F–89 program which prompted the decision to procure the F–94 also led to conversion of the F–86 to interceptor configuration.[12] Other proposals were considered, but selection of

[10] This equipment was not confined to the North American F–86D; Lockheed had dispensed with machineguns in their two-seater F–94C.

[11] Test-firing of the Navy's Mighty Mouse, the first successful air-to-air rocket, was announced by the Department of Defense on 6 February 1950.

[12] An intelligence warning of 1948—when the F–102 program began to take shape as the so-called "1954 Interceptor"—underlined the urgent need to bridge the gap between the F–89 and F–102 interceptors.

the F–86 as the basic airframe for elaboration was almost automatic. It was the best of the current jet fighters. Moreover, it would require little structural modification to accommodate the necessary nose radar and afterburner. Doubts of a single-seat interceptor's feasibility caused a slight delay, but production availability and tooling clinched the January selection. The F–95, as the one-man interceptor was then designated, went on the drawing boards in March 1949—at about the same time the F–86A entered operational service. In May North American began to modify two F–86A aircraft in line with the tentative interceptor specifications drawn during the intervening months.

Go-Ahead Decision **19 July 1949**

The Secretary of the Air Force formally endorsed the Board of Senior Officers' recommendations 3 weeks after the Hughes Aircraft Company had been issued a contract for developing the new interceptor's fire-control system. The Secretary's approval was accompanied by the authorization to spend $7 million for conversion of the F–86 to the interceptor configuration.

First Flight (XF-95) **September 1949**

An engineering inspection of the experimental aircraft in August 1949 and the ensuing flight of September favorably impressed the Air Force. In the latter month, $79 million were made available for the purchase of 124 aircraft. The new interceptor, designated as the F–95 during the early stage of development, reverted to the F–86D designation soon afterwards.

Initial Procurement **7 October 1949**

This order covered two prototypes and 122 production articles. Two months later, concurrent with the December decision that Soviet possession of the atomic bomb dictated prompt creation of a modern interceptor force, the F–86D was chosen to be the backbone of that force until the advanced "1954 Interceptor" became available. Another procurement order for 31 F–86Ds was issued in June 1950.

First Flight (Prototype) **22 December 1949**

The YF–86D was powered by a J47–GE–17 turbojet. Its afterburner boosted its 5,000-lb static thrust to 6,650 pounds. The second prototype, fitted with a similar engine, was completed in March 1950.

Development Problems **1950-1951**

North American used the second YF–86D to test a prototype of the Hughes 50–kw E-3 fire-control system (developed in advance of the more sophisticated 250-kw E–4). In October 1950, after numerous engineering changes, the E–3-equipped YF–86D moved to Hughes for further testing. The number and extent of the changes that ensued delayed until July 1951 delivery of the E–3 productions that eventually equipped some 35 F–86Ds. Meanwhile, fabrication of the E–4 prototype proceeded. When completed in November 1950, however, no F–86Ds were available to flight test it and a B–25 had to be used. E–4 production systems reached North American in December 1951, after a 3-month delay. Still, the new E–4s did not properly perform. In addition, deficiencies in components shared by both the E–3 and E–4 fire-control systems continued uncorrected.

First Production Deliveries **March 1951**

The Air Force earmarked for testing the first F–86D deliveries because the F–86D had been committed to production before receipt (or even development) of its fire-control system and of the first electronic engine fuel control.[13] Too, the Air Force could expect a number of problems simply due to the aircraft's overall complexity.[14] Nonetheless, there was still hope in mid-1951 that the F–86D would reach the operational units by the spring of 1952.

Additional Procurement **1951-1953**

In March 1951, 341 F–86Ds were on order. Two months later this total jumped to 979 aircraft. The growth to 2,500 planes by January 1953 underlined the F–86D program's urgency and scope. Yet, by that time, the Air Force had accepted less than 90 F–86Ds.

Program Slippages **1951-1953**

Delay of the F–86D program stemmed from two principal problems. First, the E–4 fire-control system had deficiencies not detected until service tests were run, and the development period was unusually long (in 1952 alone, Hughes had to make 150 changes to the system). Second, the General Electric J47–GE–17 turbojet engine—chiefly its electronic fuel control system—was far from ready. By early 1952, GE had fallen 18 months behind in engine deliveries and the J47–GE–17 did not pass its 150-hour qualification test until the latter part of 1952. Meanwhile, after an initial production slippage, airframes had begun piling up around the North American plant for lack of engines.

Other Initial Deliveries **March 1952**

The Air Force received more F–86Ds in March 1952. Although no

---

[13] Several years later, the Air Materiel Command still stressed that it took much more time to design, develop, and produce new equipment such as guns, engines, and fire-control systems than it did to produce new fighter airframes.

[14] A chief source of the F–86D's complexity stemmed from placing the intercept responsibility with a pilot-radar operator. Yet it had offsetting advantages. It saved the weight of the radar operator and his gear (350 pounds); his training costs; and the cost of designing/fabricating his share of the aircraft. It also lowered the entire operation's overhead costs. The pilot had only to stretch his training slightly to understand radar equipment.

longer considered test aircraft, they (and a few more delivered during the summer) did not fully satisfy the Air Force requirements. They lacked the Lear F–5 autopilot and the E–4 fire-control system. The former had failed its qualifying environment tests and the latter was not reliable enough for inclusion in production aircraft until August 1952. The Air Force allocated these early F-86Ds to the Air Training Command.

Enters Operational Service **April 1953**

Nearly 2 years behind schedule and 6 months past the revised date of November 1952. However, several ADC squadrons were quickly equipped and later buildup was rapid. The Air Defense Command had 600 F–86Ds by the end of 1953. In June 1955, 1,026 (or 73 percent) of the command's 1,405 tactical aircraft were F-86Ds—the remainder were F–94Cs and F–89Ds.

Operational Problems **1953–1954**

Engine malfunctions dogged the F–86Ds almost as soon as they became operational. When engine fires and explosions destroyed 13 aircraft, the entire F–86D fleet was grounded in December 1953. Most of the aircraft were back flying by the end of February 1954, after hastily formed teams of North American and General Electric technicians corrected the faulty fuel system. This was merely a stop-gap measure, however. Soon afterward, 19 more accidents occurred in 1 month, this time because of poor maintenance of the complex weapon system (a situation which had been predicted in early service tests of the F–86D' single-man concept). Meanwhile, despite other deficiencies, production rates increased significantly.

Program Appraisal **1953–1954**

The Air Force knew the F–86D needed improvement. Back in January 1953, 40 mandatory engineering fixes had been identified along with required changes to bring the aircraft to peak capability. Nevertheless, the F–86D was still a better interceptor than the other two in service and its immediate availability was crucial. The Air Force deemed the F–86D "almost as important as the B-47" and the rash of operational troubles in 1953 only hastened the aircraft improvement. Project Pullout would embody in all F–86Ds the fixes accumulated piecemeal thus far, as well as the more important modifications previously intended for the future.

Oversea Deployments **1953–1959**

Cold War pressure forced the Air Force to ship 52 F–86Ds to the Far East Air Force in the fall of 1953. These aircraft were known to be deficient. Of those sent to Korea (where only short landing strips were available), few ever flew. The contingent soon returned to the United States and went through the Pullout modifications as part of FEAF's retrofit program. FEAF received in exchange modified or new F–86D productions. In 1959, 6 years after the first F–86D oversea deployment, two squadrons of F–86D interceptors (the 431st and 437th FIS), recently placed under the Strategic Air Command's control, stood on alert at Torrejon and Zaragoza Air Bases in Spain.

Modifications **1954–1955**

The Pullout modifications, started in March 1954, were completed at a cost of some $100 million after a purposeful year-and-a-half schedule. It was important that the 1,128 aircraft involved (plus 53 spare aft fuselages) be modified as rapidly as possible. Still the Air Force could not chance endangering the nation's air defenses by pulling too many F–86Ds out of service at once. Each aircraft underwent close to 300 modifications, some involving major changes. These included: correction of the autopilot and fire-control systems (accomplished by Lear and Hughes, respectively); installation of a radar tape system to record radar-scope data during flight; modification of the stabilizer control system; installation of a 16-foot, ring-slot type drag chute in the aircraft tail (expected to reduce landing roll as much as 40 percent); and replacement of the J47–GE–17 engine by the much improved –17B (predecessor of the J47–GE–33 which powered the last 987 F–86D productions). The Sacramento Air Materiel Area (SMAMA) at McClellan AFB, Calif., was charged with the entire Pullout program. A large part of the work, however, was done under contract by the North American plants at Inglewood and at Fresno, Calif. Upon completion, the Air Force had a modern, all-weather interceptor, but problems still loomed ahead.

Special Tests **1954–1955**

An F–86D squadron operational suitability test (OST), Project Lock-On, was conducted at George AFB, Calif., during February 1954—1 month before the beginning of Pullout. As anticipated Lock-On concluded that an ADC F–86D squadron could not perform its assigned mission until elimination of the aircraft malfunctions by the forthcoming Pullout modifications. The Lock-On findings also confirmed ineffectiveness of the F–86D squadron's air-ground control team and known requirements for additional ground-support equipment, better maintenance personnel, and increased pilot training. Other tests disclosed that the F–86D's 2.75-inch folding-fin aerial rockets were marginal in accuracy and effectiveness. Use of the Falcon missile (given up in 1952) was reconsidered, but again discarded because it would require refitting the aircraft with the E–9 fire-control system. In early 1955 the Air Force also decided not to arm the F–86D with Ding Dong rockets, since the Air Defense Command's two-missile load requirement would drastically reduce the aircraft's radius of action.

Continued Engine Problems **1955–1956**

The new J47–GE–33 fitted in the last 987 F–86Ds was much more powerful than the –17 engine of the earlier productions. The –33's static thrust with afterburner reached 7,650 pounds, a 1,000-lb increase over the –17, under similar conditions. The –33 had better cooling and afterburner ignition. It also featured several detail changes which eliminated the flaws that had led to replacement of the original –17 by the improved –17B. Yet, 65 of 209 accidents in the 15 months preceding mid-1956 were attributed to the aircraft's –17B or –33 engine. Of these 65 accidents, 22 were caused by engine fuel control malfunctions, 17 by defective engine parts, and the remaining 26 (most occurring in early 1955) by turbine wheel failures in the –17B power plants.[15] In mid-1955 the Air Force thought of retrofitting all –17B engines (as well as the –17 which still powered several F–86Ds) with a redesigned "locking-strip" model. This project's $20 million price tag shaped the ultimate decision of installing the redesigned turbine wheels only upon attrition. Insistence on accurate records of turbine wheel use would assure adequate protection.

Other Operational Deficiencies **1956–1957**

In addition to engine problems and despite the remarkable overall achievement of Pullout, the F–86D needed further improvement. Its E–4 fire-control system remained unreliable and difficult to maintain. Various engineering changes could still be made to increase reliability, ease maintenance and, perhaps, raise the F–86D's kill capability. However, the gain would not justify the cost. The Air Force, therefore, reconsidered providing the aircraft with additional armament. Two F–86Ds were prototyped, one with GAR–1B Falcons, the other with infrared homing Sidewinder missiles. Budgetary limitations, nevertheless, ended the two projects in September 1957. The Air Force concurrently altered several plans. It decided to phaseout the F–86D as soon as possible and its converted version, the F–86L, tentatively by mid-1960.[16]

End of Production **September 1953**

With delivery of the last 26 F–86Ds.

Total F-86Ds Accepted

The Air Force accepted 2,504, in addition to two F–86D prototypes.

---

[15] This problem immediately concerned only the F–86D. However, B–47s powered with J47–GE–23 and –25 engines had the same type turbine wheel. The cost of replacing these would be $100,000,000.

[16] Two former ADC squadrons of F–86Ds received a temporary lease of service life. They were transferred to SAC and sent overseas.

Acceptance Rates

The Air Force accepted 3 F–86Ds in FY 51, 26 in FY 52, 448 in FY 53, 1,014 in FY 54, 860 in FY 55, and 153 in FY 56 (from July through September 1955). The two YF–86Ds were accepted in FY 52.

Flyaway Cost Per Production Aircraft

$343,839.00—airframe, $191,313; engine (installed), $75,036; electronics, $7,085; ordnance, $419; armament, $69,986.

Subsequent Model Series

F–86K

Other Configurations

F–86G. As an F–86E prototype with a different engine, the F–86G never materialized. The designation was also provisionally applied to an F–86D development with the new J–47–GE–33 engine and a few other changes. However, the 406 aircraft ordered under the latter configuration as well as other –33-equipped productions were completed as F–86Ds.

F–86L. A converted F–86D with slightly longer wings and data-link components for operation in the semi-automatic ground environment (SAGE) system which was deployed in the late fifties.

Phaseout **1958-1961**

The F–86D was phased out of the Air Defense Command in April 1958. By mid-1959 two ANG squadrons (the 122 and 182 FIS) were fully equipped. However, the Guard's F–86Ds were also quickly supplanted by F–86Ls (converted F–86Ds). By June 1961 the F–86D no longer appeared on either the USAF or ANG rolls. Yet, the interceptor's operational life was not over. Of 300 F–86Ds reaching MAP countries, Japan received 106.

Milestones **19 November 1952**

The Air Force set world speed record of 699.92 mph over a 3-kilometer course at Salton Sea, Calif. This record was to stand unbeaten until raised by another F–86D.

16 July 1953

New world speed record of 715.74 mph established with F–86D over the Salton Sea 3-kilometer course.

2 September 1953

The Air Force set world speed record of 690.185 mph over 100-kilometer closed course at Vandalia, Ohio. On the same day, with another F–86D, the Air Force also set speed record of 707.876 mph over the Vandalia 15-kilometer straight course.

F-86K

Previous Model Series

F–86D

New Features

Extended fuselage (8 inches longer than that of the F–86D) and cannon ports in the walls of the nose intake. Reduced electronic equipment and modified armament.

Go-Ahead Decision **18 December 1952**

The Air Force decided that the F–86K, a future development of the F–86D, would be the all-weather interceptor for supply to NATO forces under the MDAP. The Air Force reached its decision in December 1952, when less than 90 F–86Ds had been accepted, because it was already convinced of the aircraft' superiority. Moreover, a great deal of the F–86D's initial problems stemmed from the E–4 fire-control system, which would be excluded from the F–86K.

Basic Development **14 May 1953**

The Air Force provided North American with two F–86Ds. These aircraft were modified as F–86K prototypes.

Initial Procurement **1 June 1953**

The Air Force called for North American production of 120 F–86Ks. An additional lot of 221 aircraft, produced by North American, was assembled in Italy under a special agreement reached with the Fiat Company on 18 May 1953.

First Flight (Prototype) **15 July 1954**

This prototype and the second YF–86K were powered by the J47–GE–17B engine and this engine could be installed in all the F–86K airframes subsequently built. The F–86Ks could also be equipped without significant modifications with either one of the F–86D's successive engines (J47–GE–17, –17B, or –33). However, to simplify logistical support the Air Force decided in mid-1954 that all F–86K productions would receive the same type of engine. The latest and more powerful –33 was chosen.

Testing **1954–1955**

Major operational suitability tests were conducted to devise tactics for the NATO-committed F–86Ks. Qualification tests (10,000-round firing) of the North American-developed MG–4 fire-control system, earmarked to replace the E–4 which equipped the F–86D, were completed and the new aircraft's modified armament was selected. Instead of the F–86D's retractable tray of folding fin rockets, the Air Force decided to arm the F–86K with four 20-mm M–24A–cannons and two AIM–9B Sidewinders. The F–86K retained the AN/APG–37 radar of the F–86D.

First Flight (Production Aircraft) **23 May 1955**

This was the first of the 221 Fiat-assembled F–86Ks. This flight followed by 1 month the Air Force acceptance of the first five F–86Ks completed by the North American's Inglewood plant.

Enters Operational Service **Mid-1955**

First to fly the F–86K was the Italian Air Force's 1st Aerobrigata. Other initial F–86K recipients were the French Armée de l'Air and the Federal German Luftwaffe.

Total F-86Ks Accepted

The Air Force accepted 120 F–86Ks assembled by North American for MAP (MDAP until mid-1954).

Acceptance Rates

21 F–86Ks were accepted in FY 55 and 99 in FY 56—all during 1955, from April through December.

Flyaway Cost Per Production Aircraft

$441,357.00—airframe, $334,633; engine (installed), $71,474; electronics, $10,354; ordnance, $4,761; armament, $20,135.

Subsequent Model Series

None—the F–86L was a converted F–86D.

Other Configurations

None

Phaseout **1964**

The Italian Air Force started to replace its F–86Ks by more modern F–104Gs during 1964. Still, the aircraft's service life was far from concluded. Overhauled F–86Ks, formerly flown by the Royal Netherland Air Force, just began reaching the Turkish Air Force in 1964.

Other Uses **1959**

The Air Force flew an F–86K to test the so-called Thunderstick fire-control system. It also planned to use the aircraft for testing of a blind-dive toss bombing system, still under development in the fall of 1959.

F-86L

Previous Model Series

F–86D, from which the F–86L was converted.

New Features

Electronic equipment (AN/ARR–39 Data Link receiver, AN/ARC–34 command radio, AN/APX–25 identification radar, and new glide slope receiver) that permitted the aircraft to operate in conjunction with the SAGE ground environment and with the GPA–37, electronic heart of an advanced system of ground control interception which immediately preceded SAGE. Also, slat-equipped, extended-wing leading edges (similar to those of the F–86F and F–86H), which brought the aircraft's empty weight to 13,822 pounds (a 1,352-lb increase), but improved maneuverability at high altitudes.

Preconversion Problems **1955**

Conversion of the F–86D to the F–86L was more a matter of modification than development, but delays arose. In January 1955 deficiencies were noted in the control surface tie-in (CSTI) equipment, the signal data recorder (NADAR) slipped, a coupler for the data link (AN/ARR–39) was needed, and modification of the E–4 fire-control system to accept inputs from the coupler remained to be done. Despite such uncertainties, the Air Force hoped to have a completed electronic prototype by December 1955.

Mockup Inspection **16 May 1955**

The Air Force conducted a development engineering inspection of the F–86D cockpit mockup readied for the new electronic configuration. The inspection, held at the North American Fresno plant on 16 May 1955, was a success. The Air Force found the new cockpit satisfactory and only minor changes were forecast. The ensuing lack of installation data, lack of flight test data, and nonavailability of the equipment to be installed, torpedoed North American's optimism that the electronic modification program might well start earlier than planned.

Program Change **1955–1957**

In the fall of 1955 when the modification program was officially announced, the Air Force intended to modify 1,240 ADC F–86D aircraft, but the number actually converted amounted to about half that number.

Modifications **May 1956**

Conversion of the F–86D to the L configuration was accomplished by the Sacramento Air Materiel Area and North American's Inglewood and Fresno plants. Known as Project Follow-On, the modification program did not begin until May 1956. Once started, however, the Follow-On outputs accelerated rapidly.

Enters Operational Service **October 1956**

The first to receive the new aircraft was the 49th Fighter Interceptor Squadron at Hanscom Field, Mass. By the end of 1957, only 18 months after the beginning of Follow-On, ADC had received 576 F–86L aircraft.

Flyaway Cost Per Production Aircraft

The F–86L, being a converted F–86D, carried that aircraft's price tag of $343,839.00. This amount did not reflect the significant cost of the Follow-On modifications.

Average Maintenance Cost Per Flying Hour

$187.00

Phaseout **1960–1965**

With the advent of more modern interceptors of the F–101B and F–106 types, the need for the F–86L declined. Two ANG squadrons (the 111th and 159th) already had flown the F–86L by mid-1959, and by the end of that year the ADC inventory of F–86Ls was down to 133. The last F–86L left the Air Defense Command in June 1960, but the interceptor remained a valuable Guard asset until mid-1965.

Other Countries

A small number of F–86Ls went to the Royal Thai Air Force.

PROGRAM RECAP

The Air Force accepted 6,353 F–86s (all models included), 5,893 of them for its own use and 460 ordered into production for MDAP. A breakdown of the USAF F–86 total showed 3 experimental and prototype F–86As, 554 F–86As, 393 F–86Es, 1,959 F–86Fs, 2 YF-86Hs, 473 F–86Hs, 2 YF–86Ds, and 2,504 F–86Ds (all F–86Ls being converted F–86Ds). The MDAP count was 60 F–86Es, 280 F–86Fs, and 120 F–86Ks.

TECHNICAL DATA

F–86, F–86F, and F–86H

Manufacturer	(Airframe)	North American Aviation Inc., Inglewood, Calif. and Columbus, Ohio.
	(Engine)	Aircraft Gas Turbine Division, General Electric Company, Cincinnati, Ohio.
Nomenclature		Fighter, Fighter-bomber.
Popular Name		Sabre

Characteristics	*F–86A*	*F–86F*	*F–86H*
Engine, Number & Designation	1 5,200 lb s.t. J47–GE–13	1 5,910 lb s.t. J47–GE–27	1 8,920 lb s.t. J73–GE–3D
Length/Span	36.6 ft/37.1 ft	36.6 ft/39 ft	38.8 ft/39.1 ft
Weight (empty)	10,495 lb	10,950 lb	13,836 lb
Max. Gross Weight (Takeoff)	16,357 lb	20,650 lb	21,800 lb
Takeoff Ground Run		4,100 ft	4,500 ft
Cruise Speed		.83 Mach	.84 Mach
Max. Speed (35,000 ft)		600 kn	650 kn
Service Ceiling		45,000 ft	47,200 ft
Rate of Climb (sea level)		6,000 fpm	6,300 fpm
Radius		250 nm	365 nm
Crew	1	1	1
Armament	6 0.5-in Colt-Browning M–3 machine guns	6 0.5-in Colt-Browning M–3 machine guns	4 20-mm M–39 cannons
Ordnance Max.		2,000 lb*	1.36 ton (8/5" HVAR)

*2 M–64 or M–65 or M–117 or Napalm Bomb, or 4 GAR–8

TECHNICAL DATA

F-86D—F-86L

Manufacturer	(Airframe)	North American Aviation Inc., Inglewood, Calif.
	(Engine)	Aircraft Gas Turbine Division, General Electric Company, Cincinnati, Ohio.
Nomenclature		Fighter Interceptor.
Popular Name		Sabre

Characteristics	*F-86D*	*F-86L (Point)*[17]	*F-86L (Area)*[18]
Engine, Number & Designation	1 5,550 lb s.t. J47-GE-33	1 5,550 lb s.t. J47-GE-33	1 5,550 lb s.t. J47-GE-33
Length/Span	40.3 ft/37.1 ft	40.3 ft/39 ft	40.3 ft/39 ft
Weight (empty)	13,498 lb		
Max. Gross Weight (Takeoff)	18,160 lb (Point) 19,952 lb (Area)	18,480 lb	20,275 lb
Takeoff Ground Run		2,450 ft	3,000 ft
Max. speed (sea level)	601.7 kn (0.9 Mach) 534.9 kn (at 40,000 ft)	464.5 kn (at 35,000 ft)	464.5 kn (at 35,000 ft)
Service Ceiling	49,600 ft	49,600 ft	48,250 ft
Rate of Climb (sea level)		11,100 fpm	10,600 fpm
Radius/Loiter Time	234.7 nm (combat radius) at 477.6 kn		227 nm/15.3 min
Crew	1	1	1
Armament/Ordnance	24 2.75-in FFAR	24 2.75-in FFAR	24 2.75-in FFAR

[17] Point Defense—defense of specified geographical areas, cities, and vital installations.
[18] Area Defense—locating defense units to intercept enemy attacks remote from and without reference to individual vital installations, industrial complexes, or population centers.

NORTHROP F–89 SCORPION

Northrop engineers chose to place the horizontal stabilizer well above the turbulent exhaust from the two jet engines. This gave the F–89 the appearance of an angry Scorpion—its tail raised to strike.

F–89A/B/C: Almost alike.

F–89D: The 20mm. nose-mounted cannons of earlier F–89s were replaced by 104 2.75 in. folding-fin aerial rockets, carried in permanently mounted wing-tip pods.

F–89H: Redesigned wing-tip pods each carrying three of the new Falcon air-to-air missiles.

F–89J: An F–89D modified to carry two Douglas-built, unguided, air-to-air Genie rockets. The F–89J was the Air Force's first nuclear-armed interceptor.

NORTHROP F-89 SCORPION

Manufacturer's Model N-35

Basic Development **1945**

The basic development started with the Northrop design of an all-weather ground attack fighter incorporating General Electric TG-180 axial-flow gas-turbine engines and many of the desired features of penetration and interceptor fighters. Engineers chose to place the horizontal stabilizer well above the turbulent exhaust from the two jet engines. This gave the proposed aircraft the appearance of an angry scorpion, its tail raised to strike. It influenced the selection of a nickname.

Military Characteristics **1945**

The Army Air Forces set general requirements—known in later years as Advanced Development Objective—in the spring of 1945 and on 28 August asked aircraft manufacturers to submit design proposals conforming to the tentative military characteristics listed in these general requirements. The specifications confronting the competitors called for a conventional (propeller-driven) aircraft that could fly at 525 mph (455.8 kn) at 35,000 feet, 550 mph (477.6 kn) at sea level, climb to 35,000 feet in 12 minutes, and have a 600-mile (521.7 nm) combat radius. A capability for launching air-to-air rockets would also be included.

Competitors and Selection **March 1946**

Six aircraft manufacturers entered the competition (Bell, Consolidated, Curtiss, Douglas, Goodyear, and Northrop), and most submitted designs for a jet-propelled model instead of the propeller-driven type originally sought by the AAF. Although Curtiss had already been given a contract to develop its entry (a jet-propelled development of the A-43, subsequently known as the XP-87), one of the four designs actually submitted by Northrop was selected.[1] This design also called for the use of jet-propelled engines.

---

[1] Included in the three Northrop proposals that were rejected was the design of a radical tailless "flying wing" jet, first conceived in the fall of 1942. Northrop, manufacturer of the P-61 Black Widows, had been so busy with standard types of aircraft during World War II that development of the P-79, as the "flying wing" jet was called, had been turned over to a small subcontractor that proved unable to do what Northrop wanted done. The project had been resumed in Northrop's own shops in 1944 and the only P-79 ever built was completed in 1945. Aside from its distinctive appearance, the P-79 was also unique in that the pilot was placed in a prone position. It was powered by a single Westinghouse jet engine and was designed to reach a speed of 630 miles an hour and an altitude of 45,000 feet. The P-79—which, Northrop believed, could easily be adapted to all-weather use—crashed and was destroyed during its first flight on 12 September 1945.

Initial Procurement **13 June 1946**

Northrop received a $4 million letter contract for two experimental, two-place, twin-engine, turbojet propelled P–89 fighters. After several change orders requesting modifications of the aircraft's basic design, the LC of June 1946 was superseded. Procurement negotiations for the two XP–89s finally ended on 21 May 1947, with the execution of the first definitive contract. This $5.6 million contract—an increase of $1.6 million from the LC's amount—called for delivery of the first XP–89 within the next 14 months, i.e., not later than mid-1948.

Mockup Inspections **1946**

The Air Materiel Command was not favorably impressed with the mockup presented by Northrop in September 1946. The AMC inspection team wanted the radar operator moved closer to the pilot, the canopy redesigned, aluminum substituted for magnesium in the wings and something done about unsatisfactory fuel and oil systems. After another mockup session in December, Northrop was authorized to proceed with construction of the first XP–89 on the basis that certain other changes would also be made in order to improve the safety of the aircraft.

Development Problems **1948**

Despite the contractor's efforts, following the mockup inspections of 1946, an engineering acceptance inspection in June 1948 revealed that many discrepancies remained in the first XP–89.[2] Foremost was the aircraft's instability (caused by tail flutter) and buffeting, the latter generally attributed to the airframe's basic design. Structural integrity also was still questioned. Further modifications and development changes would have to be incorporated in the second XF–89 in order to produce a satisfactory aircraft.

First Flight (XF-89) **16 August 1948**

The flight took place 9 months later than planned, but the ensuing flight tests conducted by the contractor's pilots at Edwards AFB divulged no special problems. The first XF–89 finally appeared airworthy and functionally dependable.

Go-Ahead Decision **14 October 1948**

Comparisons with three possible all-weather interceptors—the Curtiss XF–87, the Lockheed XF–90, and the Navy's Douglas F3D—showed none to be really satisfactory, with the F–89 perhaps the least unsatisfactory. The successful flight of the Northrop experimental aircraft clinched the Air Force decision. In November 1948, concurrent with Secretary of Defense James Forrestal's

[2] Like other pursuit aircraft of the former AAF, the experimental P–89 in mid-1948 became the XF–89 fighter.

endorsement of the Air Force decision, Curtiss' 4-month old contract for 88 F-87 Blackhawks was cancelled.

F-89A

First Production Order 1949

Funds released by President Harry S. Truman in January 1949 enabled the Air Force to execute, during May of that year, a cost-plus-a-fixed-fee contract amounting to some $48 million, excluding a fixed-fee of almost $3 million. The estimated costs stipulated in the contract covered modification of the second XF-89 (YF-89) and fabrication of the first 48 production aircraft (F-89As). Spare parts, ground-handling equipment, special tools, and one static test article were included. Northrop received an additional order for 27 F-89As on 19 September 1949.[3]

First Acceptance (XF-89) July 1949

Although damaged on 27 June 1949, because of the failure of its main landing gear, the experimental aircraft was repaired in time for Air Force acceptance in July 1949—1 year behind schedule. This aircraft, involved in a new series of trials since February, had been re-equipped with "decelerons," a split surface operating in one piece as a conventional aileron but which could be opened out to serve as dive brake and auxiliary landing flap. The decelerons, developed by Northrop, eventually became a standard feature of all F-89 productions.

Unexpected Setback 1950

On 22 February, during the second Phase II flight test of its ability to meet all-weather interceptor requirements, the XF-89 crashed and was damaged beyond repair. By that time, the second experimental F-89 (YF-89) was already in flight test, having been first flown on 15 November 1949 and accepted by the Air Force in January 1950.

Program Reappraisal 1950

Review of the XF-89's last flight test report aroused great concern. Despite substitution of the J-35-A-9 for the TG-180[4] (J35-GE-3) engine (initially proposed by Northrop), the aircraft still lacked power; it also had poor takeoff characteristics and a slow rate of climb. In addition, the tests confirmed the existence of suspected deficiencies and disclosed that known failings had not been corrected. Shortly before the February crash, the aircraft had demonstrated little endurance, disappointing altitude per-

[3] The number of F-89As on order became meaningless because production-line modifications resulted in many being delivered as new model series.

[4] First tested by Republic during the F-84 development, and also subsequently replaced by increasingly more powerful engines.

formance, signs of instability, and questionable structural integrity. Moreover, although major changes had already been introduced in the second experimental aircraft (YF–89), the latter undoubtedly still carried many of the deficiencies recently identified in the lost aircraft.

Prototype Modification **1950**

Loss of the XF–89 prompted the modification of the YF–89 and addition of an "A" suffix. Among the changes made to improve performance was the substitution of even more powerful engines—J–35–A–21s with afterburners in place of the J–35–A–9s that had powered the first experimental aircraft. The YF–89A also had a more pointed nose which lengthened its fuselage to 53 feet (3 feet longer than that of the F–89). The newly designated YF–89A first flew on 27 June 1950.

First Acceptance (Production Aircraft) **28 September 1950**

As pointed out by Northrop in mid-1950—immediately following the YF–89A's successful June flight—the F–89 was probably as good as "the state of the art at the moment would permit" and most likely surpassed any other aircraft currently in production. Although skeptical, the Air Force decided to reserve judgement until further testing of the Northrop second F–89 configuration could be made. For this purpose, one of the F–89As already manufactured was accepted on 28 September 1950, and two more before the end of the year. Meanwhile, production, which had been halted after the February crash, remained suspended.

Program Re-endorsement **November 1950**

With the understanding that unless solutions were forthcoming, other interceptor sources would be investigated, the Air Force re-endorsed the F–89 program. The decision was accompanied by stringent conditions. Testing of the new YF–89A would be accelerated; early F–89A productions (particularly, the three aircraft already accepted) would be subjected to a series of special tests to determine if recently introduced modifications had eliminated earlier flutter problems; no other unproven F–89As would be accepted, and production would not resume until January 1951—Northrop's deadline for correcting all known deficiencies.

Additional Procurement **1951**

Satisfied with Northrop's progress, the Air Force finalized long-pending negotiations for the purchase of additional F–89As. Procurement of the F–89As ordered in September 1949 was re-approved and a July 1950 letter contract was reactivated. Overall, though, the number of additional aircraft purchased was decreased because of the extra costs generated by recent configuration changes. In fact, the aircraft finally bought in 1951 differed sufficiently from early F–89As to acquire new model designations. They entered the Air Force inventory either as F–89Bs or F–89Cs and carried higher price tags than first anticipated.

Total F-89As Accepted

Eleven were accepted—37 less than ordered under the first production contract of May 1949.

Acceptance Rates

All F–89As were accepted in FY 51—between September 1950 and March 1951.

Enters Operational Service **1952**

Because of their limited number, the F–89As contributed little to the Air Force operational capability. Most of them were used for extensive operational suitability tests that did not end until mid-1952. Nonetheless, some F–89As joined subsequent model series in the operational inventory of the Air Defense Command.

Subsequent Model Series

F–89B

Other Configurations

None

Phaseout **1954**

F-89B

Previous Model Series

F–89A

New Features

Internal changes and additional equipment, including Lear F–5 autopilot, a Zero-Reader,[5] and an instrument landing system (ILS).

First Acceptance (Production Aircraft) **February 1951**

The F–89B was first accepted more than 5 years from the date Northrop had been authorized to proceed with development of the F–89.

Enters Operational Service **June 1951**

ADC's 84th Fighter Interceptor Squadron, at Hamilton AFB, was the first to acquire the new aircraft.

Initial Problems

Engine failures marred the beginning of the operational life of both the F–89A and F–89B aircraft and seriously affected the Air Proving Ground concurrent operational suitability tests of the two

[5] Trade name of a gyroscopic instrument that combined the functions of gyro horizon, direction gyro, magnetic compass, sensitive altimeter, and cross-pointer indicator.

model series. This problem led to the use of modified engines (J–35–A–21A) that eventually replaced the J–35–A–21s, originally installed in the first 48 F–89s to emerge from the assembly line.

Modifications

All F–89As and Bs had externally mass-balanced elevators, adopted to overcome a severe high-frequency, low-amplitude flutter induced by the jet exhaust, but elevators with internal mass balance were fitted to earlier models after being developed for the F–89C, which followed the B series from the production line. Most of the first 48 F–89s were included in the F–89C's postproduction modification program.

End of Production **September 1951**

Production terminated with the delivery of the final four aircraft.

Total F–89Bs Accepted

37—remainder of the first production order of May 1949.

Acceptance Rates

Nineteen F–89Bs were accepted in FY 51, and 18 during the first 3 months of FY 52.

Flyaway Cost Per Production Aircraft

$1,085,882.00—airframe, $950,298; engines (installed), $90,364; electronics, $4,870; armament, $40,350.

Phaseout **1954**

Like the As, the F–89Bs left the Air Defense Command early in 1954. They first equipped the ANG's 176th FIS, replacing the squadron's elderly F–51s.

F–89C

Previous Model Series

F–89B

New Features

As a progressive development of the F–89B, the C presented few new features. However, elevators with internal mass balances replaced external mass-balanced elevators of previous model series.

First Acceptance (Operational Aircraft) **September 1951**

The aircraft was first accepted with the delivery of four aircraft.

Enters Operational Service **January 1952**

ADC's 74th FIS at Presque Isle AFB, Maine, had received only 19 F–89Cs by March, when the Air Force stopped further allocations because of the aircraft's lack of structural reliability.

Engine Problems **1952**

The F–89's J–35 engine continued to cause a great deal of difficulty. In addition, the low-slung engine of the F–89 earned a reputation as the "world's largest vacuum cleaner" by picking up litter from the runway. A vagrant piece of metal, on several occasions, was sucked into engine inlets, causing disintegration of the compressor blades. Pieces of the compressor then destroyed the remainder of the engine. Inlet screens were an answer of sorts, although it was discovered that at extremely high altitudes the inlet screen could become completely clogged with ice. Grounding orders, engine changes, inlet screen modifications, and similar actions seemed to have partially resolved the problem by mid-year.

Other Operational Problems **1952**

While the F–89's propulsion problems were being tended, a far more serious crisis developed. Starting with a crash on 25 February, a whole series of almost identical accidents occurred. Despite increasingly severe speed restrictions, six F–89s—mostly F–89Cs—had disintegrated in mid-air by 15 September. Accident investigations and study of the F–89 structure made it appear that the failures resulted from the stresses imposed by maneuvers, poor stability, and possible structural fatigue.

Grounding **1952**

On 22 September, except for 13 aircraft that would be flight tested to identify needed structural and stability corrections, all F–89 aircraft—including five new model series already accepted by the Air Force—were grounded. At year-end, the grounding was still in effect.

Modifications **1953**

The structural failures of the early F–89 productions were finally attributed to a faulty design of the wing structure—a mistake, however, that most "aerodynamicists and structures designers" would not have recognized at the time it was made. All that could be done at that point was to redesign the F–89s already produced (at a cost of approximately $17 million) and apply the new knowledge to aircraft to be produced. Modification of the F–89C received the highest priority, but by the middle of 1953 ADC still had only 31 of the modified F–89Cs available. Moreover, the modified aircraft could be used at only 80 percent of performance potential. This was true of the 194 early F–89s reworked by January 1954, when the modification program ended.

End of Production **November 1952**

Production ended with the delivery of six aircraft. The design improvements directed in late 1952 did not find their way into the Northrop production line until April 1953 and all F–89Cs were modified after production.

Total F-89Cs Accepted

163

Acceptance Rates

Except for 48 aircraft delivered during the last 4 months of 1951, all F-89Cs were accepted during 1952—128 in FY 52 and 35 in FY 53.

Flyaway Cost Per Production Aircraft

$797,202.00—airframe, $612,533; engines (installed), $95,110; electronics, $10,557; ordnance, $4,519; armament, $74,483.

Subsequent Model Series

F-89D

Other Configurations **1954**

YF-89E—an F-89C re-equipped with two Allison YJ71-A-3 engines. This experimental project, under contract since 5 November 1951, reached a cost of $5.7 million but never went past the prototype stage. The YF-89E, accepted by the Air Force on 27 August 1954, was used as an engine test bed until 1955.

Phaseout **1954**

The F-89C, in development for so many years, almost reached obsolescence before to become operational to a significant degree. Like the F-89As and Bs, the aircraft left the active inventory in 1954. The three model series were still being flown by the ANG in early 1960.

F-89D

Previous Model Series

F-89C

New Features

Different Allison J-35 engines and high-altitude afterburners; additional 262-gallon nose fuel tank; and improved fire control and armament—the 20-mm nose-mounted cannons of earlier F-89 model series were replaced by 104 2.75 in. folding-fin aerial rockets, carried in permanently mounted wing-tip pods.

Military Characteristics **1945**

The tentative military characteristics of early 1945, as revised in November of that year, were nearly satisfied in 1954 (after almost 10 years), when the F-89D became operational.

First Acceptance (Production Aircraft) **1952**

Northrop met its latest target date of June 1952 by delivering two of the interceptor aircraft, but the Air Force grounded the entire

F–89 force 2 months later. Full production of the F–89D was not resumed until November 1953 and that aircraft did not reach the Air Defense Command until 1954—a new setback of more than a year.

Production Modifications **1953**

The initial F–89Ds were almost of the same configuration as the earlier, structurally deficient F–89 aircraft. Major changes, therefore, were phased into production in order to correct the faulty wing design that had been principally responsible for the series of F–89C mid-air disintegrations.

Necessary Retrofit **1953-1954**

Only five F–89Ds had been accepted by the Air Force by November 1952, when the structural failings of the basic F–89 were finally ascertained, but another 120 F–89Ds had already left the production lines. Moreover, although Northrop daily programmed output of 17 aircraft came practically to a halt, several other F–89Ds were manufactured before the appropriate modifications could be merged into production. Hence, approximately 170 F–89Ds required some postproduction modifications similar to those made on the 194 earlier model series.

Enters Operational Service **7 January 1954**

ADC's 18th Fighter Interceptor Squadron at Minneapolis, St. Paul, Minn., was the first to receive F–89Ds. At year-end, 118 F–89Ds were in the command's inventory, but these urgently needed aircraft lacked the E–6 fire control system and E–11 autopilot of subsequent D productions.

Subsystem Integration **1953-1954**

The F–89D, the most produced of the F–89 model series, actually epitomized the transition from WW II gun-armed interceptors to ADC's guided missile carriers of the late fifties. The transitional nature of the F–89 meant that engineering problems were all but certain to arise. The crash on 20 October 1953 of a structurally modified F–89B, that had been adapted to the D configuration and specially fitted for the testing of rocket firing equipment, offered an example of the complexity of the pioneering problems encountered. Examination of the YF–89D wreckage, while uncovering no evidence of structural failure, failed to reveal what part had been played by the rocket malfunctions, reported by the pilot prior to the accident. Ensuing testing of the E–6, Hughes' new fire control system, was further hampered by its scarcity—the E–6 was also being tested with North American F–86D and Lockheed F–94C—and by the manufacturer's deficient spare part support. Similarly, the integration of new autopilot systems proved to be more difficult than anticipated. Beginning in July 1954, F–89Ds in production were equipped with E–11 autopilots (replacing the F–5 retrofitted in the F–89D and C aircraft and long considered a candidate for the first 193 F–89Ds, which like earlier F–89 productions had been delivered without autopilots), but use of the E–11 at speed in excess of Mach .75 had to be temporarily prohibited.

Structural Limitations **1954**

The F–89D also continued to suffer from the fact that the Northrop designers of the ground-attack F–89, in fashioning the aircraft as the high-altitude interceptor that the Air Force needed, had seemingly sacrificed the necessary structural features that would have enabled the plane to withstand low-level, high-speed flight maneuvers. Hence, despite the successive structural changes made between 1948 and 1953, all F–89Ds early in 1954 were still restricted from exceeding a speed of 425 knots at altitude of less than 20,000 feet—a restriction which essentially limited the F–89D's effectiveness to B–29 type targets. Subsequent improvements to the rudder and automatic pilot improved the maneuver capability of the aircraft but only to a degree.

New Propulsion Problems **1954–1955**

Although the modified J–35–A–21A engines of the F–89B and C model series had already been replaced in the F–89D by the more powerful J–35–A–33s, engine troubles continued to plague the F–89. More specifically, "power droop" under certain conditions, particularly at altitudes in excess of 30,000 feet, induced a significant loss of thrust in both the –21A and –33. Substitution of yet another model in the J–35 series did not cure the problem immediately for "power droop" also began to affect the operation of the new –35 engine. Because of the basic difficulty in finding the precise cause of the improper engine operation, the problem was not resolved until early 1955. Shielding of the temperature-sensing element of the J–35–A–35 engine power control proved to be the answer. Yet, the use of another engine was considered for a time.

Other Difficulties **1954**

One of the new features of the F–89D aircraft was the addition of permanently mounted wing-tip pods. This configuration, first flown in 1951 (on the modified F–89B, lost in October 1953), still proved troublesome 3 years later. The pods became excessively corroded after a few rocket firing missions and operational squadrons were sometimes required to dissemble and rebuild them. Moreover, corrosion and the damage it caused accounted on several occasions for minor explosions which collapsed the rocket tubes. The problem seemed to solve itself, however, with the introduction of new "thick wall" rocket launcher pods, successfully tested by mid-1954.

Program Change and Final Procurement **1954**

The fate of the F–89 as prospective carrier of the Falcon[6] was still uncertain early in 1954—2 years after the F–86D and F–94 had been dropped as potential Falcon carriers in favor of the Northrop interceptor. Adaptation of the early F–89 productions to the Falcon-carrying mission was no longer considered, and although provisions for the E–9 fire control system and Falcon missiles were included in all F–89Ds (605 of which were in the production program by 1954), the original 1 January 1954 IOC for the F–89-Falcon combination had already slipped. In March 1954, after a 6-month review of the entire F–89 program, the Air Force decided to dispense entirely with plans for fitting the E–9 system and Falcon pods into the F–89Ds. The decision was accompanied by a new and final procurement order for 233 additional F–89s. The first 77 aircraft in this group would be identical to the F–89Ds then being produced, but the other 156 future productions would incorporate the E–9 fire control system and pods for 42 standard folding-fin rockets and six Falcon missiles. The combination was officially dubbed F–89H in April 1954, to distinguish it from the earlier F–89D, which had provisions for the installation of this equipment but lacked the equipment itself.

Total F-89Ds Accepted

Of 682 accepted, 350 were identified as F–89Js after delivery, leaving a remainder of 332 F–89Ds.

Acceptance Rates

Two F–89Ds were accepted in FY 52, 10 in FY 53, 191 in FY 54, 300 in FY 55, and 179 during the first 9 months of FY 56. Delivery rates were almost constant between February 1954 and December 1955, with a monthly average of 25 aircraft.

Flyaway Cost Per Production Aircraft

$801,602.00—airframe, $598,439; engines (installed), $101,954; electronics, $11,392; ordnance, $1,857; armament, $87,960.

End of Production **March 1956**

Production ended with delivery of the last seven aircraft.

Subsequent Model Series

F–89H

---

[6] Originally known as the XF–98, redesignated GAR–1, and first in the family of Falcon homing missiles developed by Hughes in the early fifties. The XF–98 Falcons were supersonic, fighter-launched, air-to-air missiles, propelled by solid-fuel rocket engines and equipped with semi-active radar-seekers to guide them on a collision course to their targets. They had a maximum range of 4.5 nautical miles, a maximum speed of Mach 3, and were to be used against subsonic targets operating at altitudes between 5,000 and 40,000 feet.

Other Configurations **1952-1954**

F–89F—this aircraft, which would have featured the armament of the F–89D and the Allison YJ71–A–3 engines of the YF–89E, never flew. The Air Force inspected the F–89F mockup at the Northrop plant in Hawthorne, Calif., on 26 May 1952, but cancelled the project 3 months later.

F–89G—patterned on the F–89F and programmed to include revised armament and a new fire control system, the expensive F–89G also did not materialize.

F–89J—a reconfigured F–89D, modified after production, but which acquired the status of a new model series.

F–89X—an F–89D that had traded its Allison J–35 engines for the Wright J–65 Sapphires, utilized by Republic F–84F. The new combination raised the combat ceiling of the aircraft and improved its rate of climb. Maximum speed, however, was barely affected. Mach .85 was reached, but this was essentially the top speed of the J–35-equipped F–89D. In July 1954 Northrop reported a new technique to reduce induced drag by setting the wing flaps and speed brakes at specific and unconventional angles. This would further increase the F–89X's ceiling to 57,000 feet or more, thereby enabling the proposed aircraft to compete better with modern high-speed, high-altitude bombers. Although ensuing tests substantiated Northrop's estimates, the Air Force toward the end of November notified the contractor that it had no further interest in the F–89X proposal for it would eventually result in development of an entirely new aircraft.

Phaseout **1958**

ADC used the two-place F–89D until late 1958, then began to equip the ANG's 178th FIS.

Milestones **21 October 1953**

Actually, the F–89D was the initial carrier of Hughes' Falcon air-to-air missiles. The first firing (October 1953) was not entirely successful for the missile pod collapsed after firing. Necessary redesign postponed the operational date of Falcon-equipped F–89s (F–89Hs) from January 1954 to late 1955.

27 January 1955

An armed Falcon, also fired from a modified F–89D, downed a QB–17 drone—the first GAR–1 armed with a warhead to strike an airborne aircraft. This time the operation was a complete success.

F-89H

Previous Model Series

F–89D

New Features

E–9[7] fire control system; redesigned wing tip pods each carrying three Falcons (Hughes GAR–1, –2, –3 or –4 air-to-air missiles) and 21 folding fin aerial rockets (FFAR); up to six more FFARs carried under the wings.

Production Problems **1954–1956**

Technical difficulties slowed Northrop development of F–89H wing tip pods that preceded integration of the Falcon missile. By mid-1955 these pods—the third F–89 pod model, but the first specifically designed to house GAR–1 Falcons—had been successfully tested, but corrosion of the missile cavities again occurred. The need to modify the E–9 fire control system for improved missile performance also delayed deliveries of the F–89H. Because these changes would apply to similar fire control systems, the Air Force in June 1956 postponed acceptance of the last 25 F–89Hs until completion and testing of the E–9-required modifications.

First Acceptance (Production Aircraft) **September 1955**

One aircraft was delivered.

Enters Operational Service **March 1956**

The first recipient was ADC's 445th FIS at Wurtsmith AFB, Mich. This was more than 2 years after the date originally set for operational employment of the Falcon-equipped F–89.

Subsequent Model Series

None, for the F–89J was a modified F–89D. The F–89H was the final production version of the Scorpion.

Other Configurations

None

End of Production **August 1956**

The Air Force took delivery of Northrop's last seven F–89Hs 2 months later.

Total F-89Hs Accepted

156

Acceptance Rates

Except for one aircraft delivery in September 1955, and another 2 months later, all F–89Hs were accepted during 1956—109 in FY 56 and 47 during the first 4 months of FY 57.

---

[7] The E–9 fire control system differed from the E–6 (used in early F–89s) by the inclusion of a universal computer. Essentially, this computer made it possible for the pilot to select either a lead collision or a lead pursuit course for rocketry, with the option of a lead collision course for missile launching.

Flyaway Cost Per Production Aircraft

$988,884.00—airframe, $536,748; engines (installed), $105,697; electronics, $10,094; ordnance, $998; armament, $335,347.

Phaseout **1959**

The delay in converting the F–89 to missile armament doomed the F–89H to short operational life, because the F–102A, which also mounted Falcon missiles and offered performance superior to that of the F–89H, was nearly ready by the time the F–89H became available. The F–89Hs began reaching the ANG in November 1957–first replacing F–89Ds of the Guard's 123d FIS at Portland, Oreg. Only 21 F–89Hs remained in the ADC inventory by the middle of 1959 and these had disappeared by the following September.

F-89J

Weapon System 205G

Previous Model Series

None—the F–89J was a modified F–89D. The modification, accomplished after production at Northrop's Palmdale plant in California, gave the aircraft a new armament—a change sufficiently important in this case to warrant a new designation.

New Features

Hughes MG–12 fire control system;[8] two Douglas-built, unguided, air-to-air MB–1 Genie rockets—subsequently redesignated AIR–2As. The F–89J was the first nuclear-armed interceptor.

First Acceptance (Modified Aircraft) **November 1956**

Initial deliveries of Genie-equipped F–89Ds began in November and December 1956. The aircraft were identified as F–89Js soon afterward.

Enters Operational Service **January 1957**

With ADC's 84th FIS at Hamilton AFB, thereby meeting the deadline established in March of 1955.

End of Modification **21 February 1958**

While the F–89Js were accounted for as F–89Ds, the production of which ended at the contractor's Hawthorne plant in March 1956, their modification did not end until 2 years later. This was still 2 weeks ahead of schedule.

Modification Costs

The new armament, and airframe modification for its installation, raised the price of the aircraft, but Northrop completed the

[8] A modified E–9, including the "snap-up" attack mode—a somewhat misleading description of a technique involving rocket launch while the interceptor was in a nose-high, climbing altitude. Its purpose was to permit the fighter to "kill" a bomber which was cruising at a higher altitude.

modification with a cost underrun. The first modified F–89Ds cost $1,008,884.00 apiece, or $207,282.00 more than each original F–89D. Despite unchanged armament costs, the overall unit price of the modified F–89Ds was later cut by $20,000.00. The reduction lowered the aircraft unit price to that of the F–89H.

Total F-89Ds Modified

350

Flyaway Cost Per Modified Aircraft (F-89J)

$988,884.00—airframe, $536,748; engines (installed), $105,697; electronics, $10,094; ordnance, $998; armament, $335,347.

Average Maintenance Cost Per Flying Hour

$223.00

Phaseout **1960**

Although several ANG units began to convert to the F–89J in July 1959, the aircraft remained much in evidence at the end of the year. Two hundred and seven of a peak ADC inventory of 286 (30 June 1958) were on hand at that time. However, the increasing availability of F–101Bs and F–106As (ADC's subsequent atomic carriers) in 1960 marked the end of the F–89J as a most important member of the regular forces. But the aircraft's operational life was not over. Eight ANG squadrons flew F–89J aircraft that were to be equipped with nuclear Genies in mid-1961. In 1962, a ninth ANG squadron, the 124th at Des Moines, Iowa, received F–89Js. This squadron, together with the 132d, located at Dow AFB, still flew nuclear armed F–89Js in 1968.

Milestones **19 July 1957**

Firing of the first air-to-air rocket (modified MB–1 Genie) with nuclear warhead. The rocket, launched from an ADC F–89J, was detonated at a point in space more than 15,000 feet above the northern portion of Yucca Flat, Nev. The warhead was of a weapon design by Los Alamos Scientific Laboratory.

1964

148th Fighter Group of the Minnesota Air National Guard became the first ANG unit to win the US Air Force Missile Safety Award. Equipped with F–89Js, armed with AIR–2A Genies, the 148th based at Williamson-Johnson Municipal Airport in Duluth, Minn., flew active air defense missions on a 24-hour-a-day alert basis with the Air Defense Command.

PROGRAM RECAP

The Air Force ordered and accepted for its own use a grand total of 1,052 F–89s—2 XP–89s, 11 F–89As, 37 F–89Bs, 163 F–89Cs, 682 F–89Ds (350 of them, redesignated F–89Js after modification), and 156 F–89Hs.

TECHNICAL DATA

F–89J

Manufacturer	Northrop Aircraft Incorporated, Hawthorne, Calif.
Nomenclature	Subsonic Fighter Interceptor (all-weather, day/night)
Popular Name	Scorpion

Characteristics	*Point Intcp*	*Area Intcp*
Takeoff Weight	45,575 lb	45,575 lb
Length Fuselage/Wing	53′.7″/59′.8″	53′.7″/59′.8″
Max. Speed at 35,000 ft	450 kn	450 kn
Radius		435 nm
Engine, Number & Designation	2J35–A–35	2J35–A–35
Takeoff Ground Run	3,950 ft	3,950 ft
Rate of Climb (sea level)	5,160 fpm	5,160 fpm
Combat Ceiling	42,100 ft	43,500 ft
Crew	2	2
Ordnance	2 AIR–2A	2 AIR–2A

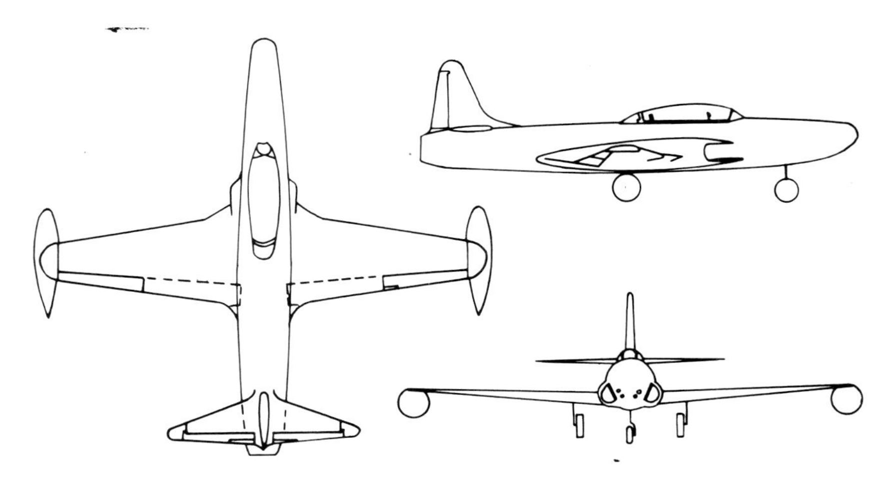

LOCKHEED F–94 STARFIRE

First jet-powered all-weather fighter to enter service with the U.S. Air Force and first to feature a speed-boosting afterburner.

F–94A and B: Both closely resembled Lockheed's two-seater TF–80C, first of the famous T–33 trainers.

F–94B: Differed from the F–94A by using larger, better-shaped, drop fuel tanks, and improved electronics and hydraulic systems.

F–94C: Initially known as the F–97A, the redesignated F–94C was the third, biggest, and last of the Starfires as well as the final upshot of the basic Shooting Star design. It was also the first rocket-bearing interceptor.

Pilots generally like the F–94C, commenting that the J48–P–5 engine "wheezed, coughed, spurted, and blurped at altitude; but it never quit running."

LOCKHEED F-94 STARFIRE

Manufacturer's Model 780-76-08 (F-94B)

Basic Development **June 1943**

The roots of development for the F–94 lay in the WW II P–80 Shooting Star, USAF's first truly operational jet fighter. Specifically, however, the F–94 interceptor stemmed from Lockheed's successful conversion of the basic P–80 into a two-seat trainer. This TF–80C, first flown in March 1948, became the T–33 in mid-1949. The F–94 was born the same year.

General Operational Requirements **8 October 1948**

The GOR called for the extra punch of an all-weather jet interceptor. Early availability took precedence over its capability to counter any threat beyond that of the TU–4 (Russian equivalent to the B–29).

Go-Ahead Decision **14 October 1948**

One week after re-endorsing continued development of the Northrop F–89,[1] the Air Force directed production of the two-place, radar-equipped F–80 (christened F–94 in 1949). Two major factors prompted the decision. The North American F–82 (the only "all-weather interceptor" available) was highly unsatisfactory.[2] Moreover, operational integration of its replacement would probably be delayed, since the F–89 was an entirely new design.

Initial Procurement **January 1949**

Secretary of Defense Forrestal's approval of the future interim F–94 in November 1948, followed by President Truman's release of funds, led to a January letter contract with Lockheed. This LC was replaced a few months later by a definitive contract (AF–1849) covering 150 F–94 productions (later reduced to 109).

First Flight (XTF-80C) **16 April 1949**

By a radar-equipped TF–80C.

F-94A

First Flight (YF-94) **1 July 1949**

By one of two T–33A trainers (improved, redesignated TF–80Cs),

---

[1] The Air Force considered the F–89 "the best of a poor lot." It reluctantly voted to uphold the project on 8 October 1948. General operational requirements for an interim interceptor were issued on the same date.

[2] North American never built any interceptor-type F–82s. But the two-engine, twin-fuselage, low-wing, long-range escort fighter could be converted into a single-place interceptor by removing the controls and canopy from the right-hand cockpit. The F–82Fs, –Gs, and –Hs, officially classified as fighter-interceptors, were two-seaters with a radar operator in place of the copilot. These F–82s actually could not cope with bad weather. Even as night fighters, their performance was becoming obsolete.

modified for the interceptor role by adding radar noses and rear-fuselage afterburners. Lockheed used the converted T–33s as F–94 prototypes to speed development, but both were little more than TF–80Cs. In effect, production aircraft flight-tested before the end of 1949 comprised 75 percent standard F–80C parts.[3] Like the F–80/T–33 Shooting Stars, the Starfire's first model (F–94A) had wing tip drop tanks.

Program Changes **1949**

The F–94 program changed twice in less than a year. Despite reduction of the Air Force's size, procurement quickly rose to 288—almost double the quantity sought in January 1949. The August detonation of an atom bomb in Russia forced another evaluation of Air Force planning. The F–94 procurement was raised again in December (to 368 aircraft) because "foreign possession of the atomic bomb necessitates acceleration of the USAF program to modernize its interceptor and all-weather force at the earliest possible time." Growing F–94 importance brought renewed, concerted efforts to improve the aircraft's overall performance. Lockheed proposed and the Air Force bought the F–97A, a drastically redesigned F–94. When technical hindrances immediately arose, the Air Force had to endorse still another, but far less ambitious, F–94 configuration. This became the F–94B, while the F–97A ended up as the F–94C.

Enters Operational Service **May 1950**

F–94As began reaching air defense units about 6 months behind schedule. These makeshift interceptors were received at McChord and Moses Lake, Wash., by the 325th Fighter Wing of the Continental Air Command.[4]

Initial Operational Capability **August 1950**

By the end of the year, CONAC's operational inventory counted 60 of the new F–94A.

Operational Problems

The F–94A's Allison J–33 engine, slated for the F–94B, did not work well. Despite improvement, it still suffered from turbine blade failures 2 years after the first F–94A had become opera-

---

[3] Advertising the Starfire's last model (F–94C) in later years, Lockheed praised it as "an engineering achievement of creating a more advanced model out of an existing airplane." By then, however, the Air Force generally believed this was the aircraft's foremost shortcoming.

[4] CONAC, formed on 1 December 1948, included the Air Defense Command, the Tactical Air Command, and nine fighter squadrons formerly assigned to the Strategic Air Command. The rationale for CONAC (under economy programs of the pre-Korean years) was to train all fighter units for both tactical and air defense action. This would make many more aircraft available for all missions.

tional. Also, the F–94's fuel system was far from perfect; the aircraft was unstable and hard to maneuver at high altitude. Moreover, the cockpits were too small. The pilot and radar operator found it impossible to get in and out quickly during alerts and scrambles. They had to fly in a cramped position. Even more vital, the clearance for seat ejection was slight.

Postproduction Modifications **Mid-1952**

The Air Force got Lockheed to correct the ejection seats and cockpits of 330 F–94 (A and B) aircraft for some $4.5 million. Minor improvements, already scheduled by the Air Force, would be done concurrently with the Lockheed modification.

Total F-94As Accepted

109

Acceptance Rates

All F–94As were accepted by the Air Force between December 1949 and December 1950—14 in FY 50, and 95 in FY 51.

Flyaway Cost Per Production Aircraft [5]

$258,123.00—airframe, $193,721; engine (installed), $45,227; electronic, $4,014; armament, $15,161.

Subsequent Model Series

F–94B

Other Configurations

None

Phaseout **1954**

A few ANG squadrons, federalized during the Korean War, flew F–94s in late 1951. Upon reverting to inactive status, their planes stayed with active Air Defense Command units.[6] Nonetheless, no F–94As remained in the USAF inventory in mid-1954.

F-94B

Previous Model Series

F–94A[7]

New Features

Gyroscopic instrument (Sperry Zero Reader) for more accurate landings in bad weather; high pressure oxygen system; improved

---

[5] Excluding the cost of ordnance and government-furnished aeronautical equipment (GFAE).

[6] ADC was established on 21 March 1946. It lost its major air command status and became an operational command under CONAC in December 1948, but re-emerged as a major air command on 1 January 1951.

[7] The F–97A (redesignated F–94C) was ordered right after the F–94A. The third model followed the F–94A in production and became the F–94B.

hydraulic system; and larger, better-shaped, external fuel tanks. These were mounted along the airplane's center line instead of being suspended from the wings, as on the F–94A.

First Flight (YF-94B) **December 1950**

A converted F–94A, the 19th production, flew the maiden flight. F–94Bs began reaching the operational forces a few months later.

Enters Operational Service **April 1951**

With ADC's 61st Fighter Interceptor Squadron at Selfridge AFB.

Operational Problems

Despite its new features, the F–94B closely resembled the F–94A. The two had similar engines and cockpits, the same configuration weaknesses, and deficient fuel systems. Thus, they shared identical operational problems and required like postproduction modifications. Lacking adequate anti-icing equipment, neither the F–94A nor F–94B could qualify as an all-weather interceptor.[8] Pending something better, ADC welcomed the B.

War Commitments **January 1952**

A handful of F–94Bs soon joined the 15 F–94As allocated to the Far East Air Forces in March 1951. The aircraft were so few, however, that they could not be easily spared. Hence, they did not enter the Korean war until late December 1951, when the 68th FIS posted two F–94s on strip alert at Suwon Air Base.[9] Even then the aircraft's involvement was limited to local air defense scrambles under positive ground-radar control. The new F–94s were fitted with the latest fire-control system.[10] The Air Force, therefore, did not want them to fly over enemy territory where this secret electronic equipment could be compromised. The restriction was not lifted until nearly a year later—after continued B–29 losses were tied to the ineffectiveness of fighter-escorts equipped with the older airborne-intercept radars. The 319th FIS

---

[8] The B's windshield—but not the A's—did have some kind of anti-icing system.

[9] The Air Force hurried the conversion of FEAF's old F–82s to more modern F–94Bs. In addition, it deployed the 319th FIS to Korea. This unit's F–94Bs went into operation at Suwon on 22 March 1952.

[10] Produced by the Hughes Aircraft Company, the E–1 was the first in the E series of sophisticated fire-control systems that were to equip more modern planes. The Air Force ordered the system in June 1948, when it asked that the AN/APG–3 radar (being developed for the tail defense of the B–36) be adapted to the Northrop F–89. A November amendment of the June contract extended the requirement to the F–94. The modified AN/APG–3 radar was redesignated AN/APG–33 and the entire system, including its A–1C gunsight, became the E–1 in late 1949. It was installed in early F–89s as well as F–94As and –Bs. Low-powered, the E–1 was fairly primitive alongside the E–5 of the rocket-firing F–94C. The system was nevertheless a pioneer achievement.

in November 1952 began using some of its F-94Bs as a screen between the Yalu and Chongehon rivers. Soon after, F-94s also flew within a 30-mile radius of the B-29 targets. Enemy planes usually retreated rather than come up against F-94 barrier patrols.

Appraisal

Although not too successful against low-flying aircraft, few planes proved as reliable as the F-94 against the enemy in the Korean war, even in nasty weather and darkness. Besides B-29 escort duties and enemy fighter interception missions, F-94s protected B-26 light bombers and could fly deep into North Korea when most other aircraft were grounded due to bad weather. Korean veterans as a rule praised the F-94. It was rugged and could fly many hours without maintenance.

Attrition

The Air Force lost 28 F-94s between January 1952 and 27 July 1953—the day the war ended. Only one of the 28 losses was due to direct enemy action.[11] During the same period, F-94 pilots claimed four enemy planes destroyed.

Total F-94Bs Accepted

356, plus 1 prototype—a converted F-94A.[12]

Acceptance Rates

The Air Force accepted 176 F-94Bs in FY 51 and 180 in FY 52—the last four in January 1952.

Flyaway Cost Per Production Aircraft

$196,248.00—airframe, $123,422; engine (installed), $31,336; electronics, $7,635; ordnance, $2,947; armament, $30,908.

Subsequent Model Series

F-94C

Other Configurations

None

Phaseout

The F-94B, like the F-94A, left the active force by mid-1954. The Guard still flew the two models in late 1957.

Milestones **30 January 1953**

Using the E-1 fire-control system, the F-94 made its first Korean kill at night, destroying a conventional, but speedy LA-9. The

---

[11] Air Force-wide there were 51 USAF/ANG F-94 major accidents in fiscal year 1953, 34 of then attributable to pilot errors.

[12] 150 F-94Bs were ordered under AF Contract 9844 and 206 under AF Contract 14804. The YF-94B was booked against the initial F-94 contract (AF-1849).

Starfire pilot (Capt. Ben L. Fithian) and observer (Lt. Sam R. Lyons) never saw the enemy plane until it burst into flames. F–94s shot down three other elusive enemy jets before the armistice.

F-94C

Manufacturer's Model 880-75-13

Previous Model Series

F–94B

New Features

Pratt & Whitney J48–P–5 or –5A engine (8,300-lb thrust with afterburner; 6,250-lb, without); thinner wings, with increased dihedral; sweptback horizontal stabilizer; aft dive flaps, drag chute; and longer nose with radome in retractable shield. All-rocket armament accommodated 48 2.75-inch folding-fin aerial rockets—24 in a ring of firing tubes around the nose and 24 in two cylindrical pods. One pod was located on each of the two wings, midway between root and tip. Also featured were wing and horizontal stabilizer thermal de-icing, single-point refueling, greater fuel capacity, as well as the Hughes E–5 fire-control system and Westinghouse W–3A autopilot (for instrument approach).

First Flight (Prototype) **18 January 1950**

The prototype flight took place 11 months before the YF–94B's first official flight. Converted F–94As were used in each case.[13]

Production Decision **February 1950**

The USAF decision for a redesigned F–94 (referred to as the F–97A) followed reappraisal of the F–94 program and January 1950 plans calling for haste in supplying the air defense forces with better and more of the Lockheed interim interceptors.[14]

Redesignation **12 September 1950**

The F–97A, endorsed by the Air Force in February 1950, formally became the F–94C—third, biggest, and last of the F–94 model series as well as the final upshot of the basic Shooting Star design.

---

[13] The entire F–94 program finally totaled 852 productions—109 F–94As (against a first order for 150), 356 F–94Bs, and 387 F–94Cs (originally known as F–97As). Air Force records, however, showed only 2 prototypes (1 YF–94B and 1 YF–94C) officially accepted—others were accounted for as production aircraft, or charged to another program (as were the F–94A prototypes, developed from F–80C and T–33 productions).

[14] The Air Force realized a drastically improved F–94A was not there for the asking. It then settled for a third, but "in-between type," that preceded the so-called F–97A—the F–94B, which still fell short of the Air Force's early 1950 expectations.

Development Problems **1950–1951**

The F–94C ran immediately into trouble. To begin with, the first production deliveries were scheduled for 1951—far too early. Both the Pratt & Whitney J–48 engine and laminar wings specifically earmarked for the F–94C, were not likely to be fully developed when needed. Other improvements or new components (many also intended for the F–94B) were slipping. The automatic approach system was not ready; testing of the 250-kilowatt-radar, rocket-nose, and collision-course sight was not due until 1951; development of an advanced fuel purging system showed scant progress, and the only autopilot available was too big even for the larger F–94C.

First Flight (Production Aircraft) **October 1951**

Although this plane was not accepted by the Air Force until May 1952, it did not go directly to the operational forces.

Testing **1951–1952**

The Air Force allocated to the testing program the F–94C prototype (first flown as the YF–97A in January 1950 and accepted in October), together with 9 other aircraft received by the end of June 1952. None of these "test productions" performed well. ADC concluded that low speed (some 40 knots less than the F–89) and poor maneuverability downgraded the F–94C. Nevertheless, it would be acceptable if these deficiencies were corrected.[15]

Engine Problems **1952**

On its first trial in August 1951, the F–94C's J48–P–5 engine had passed its 150-hour qualification test, but its afterburner had warped and cracked. After much testing and redesign, the engine finally passed new qualification tests in May 1952 with afterburner intact. Fuel burner nozzle failures occurred soon afterward. Since it was impossible to find defective nozzles by visual inspection, the F–94Cs were grounded.[16] Despite fairly good engine performance after some modifications, the Air Force in mid-1952 still sought to enhance the rate of climb and high-altitude reliability of the P–5. It considered switching to the higher thrust J48–P–8, but installation difficulties wiped out the project.

Required Improvements **August 1952**

A joint study (Headquarters USAF, Air Proving Ground Command (APGC), ARDC, and ADC) called for variable position dive

[15] Some of them—the unsatisfactory fuel system in particular—were reported by test pilots of the Air Research and Development Center (ARDC) as resulting from poor design and substandard quality control during production. Others reflected a variety of causes that combined to erode the plane's efficiency.

[16] Fitting all engines with improved nozzles solved the problem before the end of 1952.

brakes, aileron spoilers, a better drag chute, and further improvement of the engine reliability. The study also recommended speedy installation of the aircraft's new rocket armament (early F–94Cs still carried machineguns) and additional rockets.

Immediate Modifications **1952**

By mid-October 1952, the F–94C's flight characteristics and controls were improved. More than $3.5 million had been allotted to modify the cockpits of early F–94Cs,[17] and work was underway to correct the aircraft's inadequate de-icing boots and faulty stall warnings. Lockheed had also arranged for field installation of the variable position dive brakes and aileron spoilers. Drag chute improvements were progressing and ways to upgrade the engine's reliability were under review. Armament difficulties, however, remained unsolved.

Armament Problems **Mid-1952**

The success of the F–94C's all-rocket armament hinged on rocket accuracy and interceptor performance reliability. The F–94C and its rockets had neither.[18] Worse, the P–5 engine flamed out when the full-nose load of 24 rockets was salvoed above 25,000 feet. If only 12 rockets were fired, a near flameout still occurred that slowed the interceptor speed. The Air force wanted the problems cured and the rocket load doubled. Both could be done. In fact, the mounting of additional rockets in wing pods had been considered since 1951. Nonetheless, it was unlikely the F–94C would get its extra rockets before the 163d production.

Program Reduction **1952**

Improvements notwithstanding, two of the four production contracts (the first, definitized on 27 July 1950, dealt with the F–97A) were cancelled late in the year, cutting F–94C procurement from 617 to 387.[19]

Production Modifications **1953**

In the spring (beginning with the 100th production—not the 163d), F–94Cs came off the assembly line with wing pod "sidearms." Each pod packed 12 of the Aeromite-developed FFARs. The long cylinder pods measured 9 feet 6 inches and their fiberglass nose covers protruded about 6 feet from the wing leading edge. Before the rockets left the pods, the fiberglass covers

[17] Some 260 F–94Cs would probably feature the F–94A and F–94B small cockpits and the Air Force did not expect $3.5 million to fill the bill.

[18] The F–94C's all-rocket armament had been a key selling point. Admittedly, a salvo of rockets would cause more damage than a burst of machinegun fire.

[19] The Air Force considered cancelling the entire program in July. It held off because of anything better and the need (in the midst of the Korean War) to keep Lockheed in production.

disintegrated due to rocket-generated gas pressure. The production-improved F–94Cs also came with new ejection seats that would lift both the pilot and radar observer well above the cockpit sill.

Enters Operational Service **7 March 1953**

With ADC's 437th FIS at Otis AFB. As the first rocket-bearing interceptor, the F–94C generated less enthusiasm than expected.[20] Nearly 2 years behind schedule, it showed limited performance. And, clearly, its basic design could not be stretched further to meet future needs.[21]

Initial Operational Capability **1953**

The 437th FIS attained initial operational capability in June.

Operational Deficiencies **1954**

In mid-1954, squadron operational suitability tests confirmed the F–94C's poor weather-proofing[22] and disclosed leaky fuel tanks. They also revealed the need to improve the E–5 fire-control system.

Postproduction Modifications **September 1954**

Known as Hop–Up, these modifications resolved the F–94C's recently confirmed shortcomings. Early F–94Cs also exchanged their ejection seats for the safer ones featured by later productions. The Hop–Up modification of the E–5 eventually added an optical sight to the system.

End of Production **May 1954**

With delivery of the last two aircraft.

Total F–94Cs Accepted

387—plus 1 prototype

Acceptance Rates

The Air Force took delivery of 9 F–94Cs in FY 52, 153 in FY 53, and 225 in FY 54. The YF–94C had been accepted in October 1951.

---

[20] Maintenace crews praised the F–94C, because they could get to its electronics equipment easily. Pilots generally liked the aircraft, commenting that the J48–P–5 engine "wheezed, coughed, spurted, and blurped at altitude; but it never quit running."

[21] Intended as a "quick-fix" all-weather interceptor to fill the air defense gap until the F–89 was ready, 1949 planning had envisioned an operational F–94C in 1951. Moreover, the F–94C (like the F–94A and B) could not destroy any bomber superior to the Russian TU–4 that compared with the B–29.

[22] During continuing rain in late 1953, 80 percent of the alert aircraft at one base went out of commission. Moisture in the cockpit had short-circuited the electrical and fire-control systems.

Flyaway Cost Per Production Aircraft

$534,073.00—airframe, $380,755; engine (installed), $90,147; electronics, $7,058; ordnance, $518; armament, $55,595.

Subsequent Model Series

None

Other Configurations

F–94D. A single-seat fighter-bomber for long-range ground support. The D would have a high-thrust centrifugal flow turbojet engine with afterburner, plus autopilot and airborne equipment to allow automatic approach and tactical control from the ground. Authorized for procurement in mid-1951 (when the Korean War started), one F–94D prototype was developed (through conversion of an early F–94 production), but the 112 F–94Ds on order were all cancelled.

Phaseout **February 1959**

Despite mediocre performance, the F–94C lasted a long time as a first-line interceptor. The Air Force wanted to get rid of the aircraft,[23] but could ill afford it. The F–94C in mid-1954 (when ADC counted a peak 265) was still regarded as the best two-man interceptor at low altitudes.[24] The F–94C finally disappeared from USAF rolls in early 1959; from the ANG's in mid-1960.

PROGRAM RECAP

USAF records revealed a grand total of 854 F–94s—2 prototypes, 109 F–94As, 356 F–94Bs, and 387 F–94Cs. All aircraft were ordered into production for the Air Force's own use.

---

[23] At one time during 1955, 48 percent of the Air Force's remaining F–94Cs were grounded for lack of parts.

[24] Despite many structural modifications, the F–89 operated poorly, particularly at low level; and the Convair F–102 (originally due to enter service in mid-1953) was several years away. As for the development of a low-altitude surface-to-air missile (investigated under Project LASAM), this was out of the question insofar as the Air Force was concerned. It planned instead to test low-altitude seekers that ADC could possibly use on its future Bomarcs.

TECHNICAL DATA

F-94A, F-94B, and F-94C

Manufacturer	(Airframe)	Lockheed Aircraft Corporation, Burbank, Calif.
	(Engine)	Allison Division of General Motors Corporation, Indianapolis, Ind. (F-94A/B). Pratt & Whitney, East Hartford, Conn. (F-94C).
Nomenclature		Fighter Interceptor.
Popular Name		Starfire

Characteristics	*F-94A*	*F-94B*	*F-94C*
Engine, Number & Designation	1 J33-A-33	1 J33-A-33	1 J48-P-5
Length/Span	40.1 ft/38.9 ft	40.1 ft/37.5 ft	44.5 ft/37.3 ft
Weight (empty)	9,557 lb	10,064 lb	12,708 lb
Max. Gross Takeoff Weight	15,710 lb	16,000 lb	24,200 lb
Max. Speed (sea level)	526 kn	511 kn	556 kn
Combat Speed (Basic Mission)	474 kn	426 kn	454 kn
Rate of Climb (sea level)	4,250 fpm	6,850 fpm	7,980 fpm
Service Ceiling	46,000 ft	48,000 ft	51,400 ft
Combat Range (Basic Mission)	937 nm		12,000 st. miles
Armament	4 .50-in machine guns	4 .50-in machine guns	24 2.75-in FFARs + 12 ea in 2 wing pods
Max. Bomb Load	2,000 lb	2,000 lb	2,000 lb
Crew	2	2	2

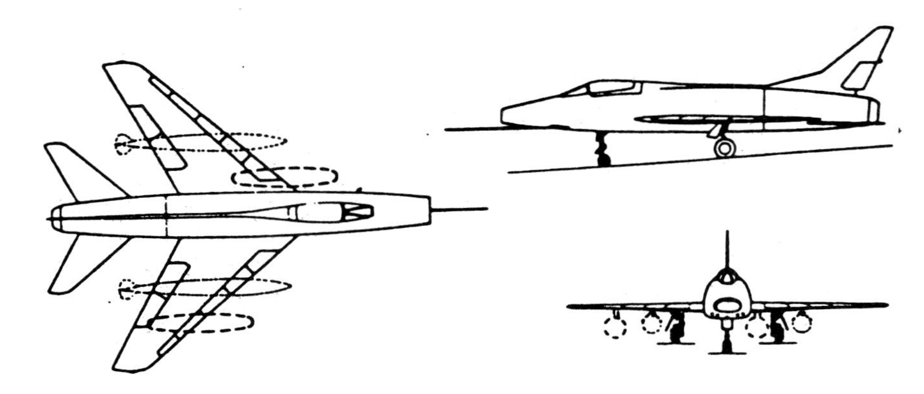

NORTH AMERICAN F–100 SUPER SABRE

Evolved from the F–86 Sabre. The North American F–100 was the forefather of the Air Force's Century Series of fighters.

F–100A: This day fighter was the world's first supersonic airplane ever produced.

F–100C: Differed from the F–100A by carrying extra fuel drop tanks and additional stores (bombs and rockets), as called for by the aircraft's secondary fighter-bomber role.

F–100D: In contrast to the F–100C, the F–100D served primarily as a fighter-bomber. It became the major production type of the Super Sabre series.

F–100F: Tandem two-seat cockpit with dual controls. Only two of the F–100D's four built-in 20 mm. M–39 guns were retained.

Both the F–100D and F–100F proved their worth in SEA.

In 1966, modified F–100Fs began attacking the North Vietnamese Fan Song fire control radars.

NORTH AMERICAN F-100 SUPER SABRE

Manufacturer's Model NA-192

Basic Development **1949**

Evolved from the F-86 Sabre. North American designated its undertaking Sabre 45 because of the aircraft's 45 degrees of wing sweepback.

Advanced Development Objective **September 1950**

Unsolicited Proposal **January 1951**

North American submitted Sabre 45 design for consideration as supersonic day fighter.

General Operational Requirements **27 August 1951**

Called for an air superiority weapon to be operational preferably in 1955 and not later than 1957.

Go-Ahead Decision **October 1951**

The Air Force Council pressed for the development of revised Sabre 45. This decision ran counter to the belief of key development personnel that the aircraft would not meet the simplicity and cost requirements, basic to a day fighter. To obtain quickly a new fighter that would substantially surpass the F-86, the Air Force Council also agreed with the Aircraft and Weapons Board's recommendations to buy it in quantity prior to flight-testing, even though this ran the risk of extensive modifications in the future.

Mockup Inspection (Sabre 45) **7 November 1951**

The Mockup Board received more than 100 airplane configuration change requests. The Board also identified several armament deficiencies and requested a number of modifications to increase the "kill" potential of the aircraft.

Official Designation **30 November 1951**

The revised Sabre 45 was standardized as the F-100.

Initial Contract Date **3 January 1952**

The Air Force issued a letter contract for two F-100A prototypes.

First Contract for Production **11 February 1952**

The Air Force rushed through a second letter contract to procure 23 F-100As with fiscal year 1952 funds.

Mockup Inspection (F-100A) **21 March 1952**

Concentration on F-84 and F-86 improvement and faster production during the Korean War slowed down design of the F-100. However, the revised mockup featured most of the changes requested by the Air Force in late 1951.

Second Production Contract **August 1952**

Having found the revised mockup basically satisfactory, the Air Force directed procurement of 250 additional F–100As.

First Flight (Prototype) **25 May 1953**

The prototype flight was accomplished 7 months ahead of date set by contractor. In a subsequent flight, the first YF–100A reached a speed of Mach 1.05 while equipped with a derated prototype engine (one Pratt & Whitney XJ–57–P–7 turbojet not tuned up to its full power). However, by the time initial flight testing of the prototype was completed on 25 September, three major deficiencies were confirmed, all of which required correction before the F–100A could be considered an acceptable combat weapon system. The second prototype flew on 14 October, later than expected but still ahead of the original schedule.

First Flight (Production Aircraft) **29 October 1953**

Two weeks after the first flight of the second prototype.

Flight Testing **November 1953–December 1955**

The first F–100A was subjected to considerable testing in order to develop "fixes" for the deficiencies disclosed during the prototype's flight tests, but a general strike by the North American labor force during the last 3 months of 1953 impeded progress by delaying delivery of early production aircraft earmarked for the USAF flight test program. During the same period, a North American pilot demonstrated the aircraft's high-speed guarantees by reaching Mach 1.34 during level flight at 35,000 feet. In late 1955, despite the many improvements made during the 2 intervening years, the F–100A was evaluated by the Air Proving Ground Command as superior in performance to other fighters in the USAF inventory, but of limited tactical capability because of functional deficiencies. The month-long operational suitability tests conducted under Project Hot Rod—a project initiated because of the difficulties encountered with the Convair F–102 interceptor—once more confirmed the F–100A's shortcomings and the inadequacies of the tactical air control system. APGC also concluded that a fighter-day squadron equipped with F–100A aircraft could operate substantially as well as an F–86 squadron, but did require an augmentation of support facilities and personnel.

Program Change **December 1953**

In spite of its serious flight control and stability deficiencies, the F–100A was still urgently needed by the Tactical Air Command. Greatly concerned by concurrent slippages in the F–84F program, TAC also recommended production of a day fighter with a secondary fighter-bomber capability to satisfy forthcoming Air Force requirements as well as those of the foreign countries covered by the Mutual Development Assistance Program. In consideration of such factors, the Air Council directed the deletion of 70 F–100As and production of an equivalent number of a tactical-bomber version of the aircraft.

Early Modifications **December 1953**

Black boxes were incorporated in the yaw and pitch control axis of the F–100A to eliminate stability and control problems at certain speeds. Glass was added to the side panels of the forward cockpit to increase visibility, but further improvement of this third major deficiency was also under study. Two other major modifications were approved. The first, suggested by North American, involved the installation of integral fuel wings on future F–100A productions to provide the aircraft with a radius equivalent, on internal fuel, to that obtained with two 275 gallon tanks. The other, as proposed by TAC in mid-1953, would give forthcoming F–100As both a conventional and nuclear bombing capability.

First Acceptance (Production Aircraft for Operational Inventory) **September 1954**

This F–100A and 69 others differed from the prototype aircraft in having a shorter fin and rudder of increased chord. In an attempt to overcome continuing control difficulties in the roll, the shape of the vertical tail surfaces of the other 133 F–100As built was again changed. The Air Force began to take delivery of the latter aircraft in the spring of 1954, but the initial productions were allocated to the testing program. Unmodified F–100As were the first to be released for operational use. They began reaching TAC on 18 September.

Second Program Change **September 1954**

Because of improvements in Soviet fighters, the Air Force decided to accelerate the F–100 production and to procure a third model series of the aircraft. North American was directed to open a second production source at Columbus.

Enters Operational Service **27 September 1954**

With TAC's 479th Fighter Day Wing, at George AFB, as an interim aircraft pending replacement by modified F–100A versions and subsequent model series. The wing did not acquire an initial operational capability until September 1955, but the operational F–100As gave TAC's pilots valuable experience in supersonic flight.

Significant Operational Problems **10 November 1954**

All F–100A aircraft were grounded following six major accidents caused by still unsatisfactory yaw characteristics, structural failures induced by aerodynamic forces exceeding the airframe's limits, and malfunctions of the flight control system's hydraulic pump. Concurrently, the aircraft coming off the production line were kept in storage to await corrective modification. Production, which had been expanded 2 months before, was limited to 24 aircraft per month. Although the Air Force partially lifted the imposed flying and production restrictions in February 1955 and aircraft deliveries were resumed in April, the IOC of most of the F–100A squadrons was set back about 6 months.

Subsequent Model Series

F–100C

Other Configurations **December 1954**

YF–107A (F–100B). The model series between the F–100A and the F–100C, the F–100B, as called for on 16 December 1954 by GOR 68, was conceived as a tactical fighter-bomber as well as an air superiority day and night fighter. Three prototypes were built, but they were so extensively redesigned that their intended designation was changed to YF–107A before the first example flew on 10 September 1956. A unique feature of the YF–107A (powered by a J–75–P–11 axial flow gas turbine engine with afterburner) was the engine inlet duct, located on the upper fuselage behind the cockpit canopy, which incorporated a wedge and a two-position ramp to ensure optimum propulsion during high speeds. Another unusual feature of the YF–107A configuration was a logistics pod, proposed by North American to increase the aircraft's ground force support capability. According to North American, the YF–107A airframe's pod cavity could also be used to carry a power plant to start transient aircraft. In mid-1956 the Air Force considered the YF–107A as a possible substitute for the troublesome F–105 being developed by the Republic Aviation Corporation and testing of the three prototypes was accelerated. In February 1957, however, the F–107 program was discontinued because, despite recurring slippages, the Republic F–105 was still significantly ahead of the North American plane from a production standpoint. GOR 68 was cancelled on 22 March 1957 and the three YF–107As were transferred to the National Aeronautics and Space Administration (NASA) for further research in high supersonic speed ranges.[1]

Mid-1954

F–100BI. An interceptor version of the F–100B also was considered before that aircraft matured as the prototype F–107A. In July a mockup of the future F–100BI, as it was referred to, was completed as a potential backup for the F–102 interceptor being produced by Convair. Development of the aircraft did not material-

[1] One YF–107A is now on display at the Air Force Museum.

ize when it became evident that the known deficiencies of the F–100A, regardless of the improvements expected from the subsequent model series, would prevent the F–100BI from satisfying the Air Defense Command's operational requirements more fully than the F–102 interceptor already under contract.

1961

RF–100A. Another configuration of the F–100A came into being when four of the aircraft were fitted with reconnaissance equipment. The new RF–100As were delivered to Nationalist China in late 1961 under the auspices of the Military Assistant Program.

End of Production **April 1955**

The Air Force took delivery of the last 23 F–100As in July 1955.

Total F-100As Accepted

203

Acceptance Rates

Fifteen F–100As were accepted in FY 54, 165 in FY 55, and 23 during the first month of FY 56.

Flyaway Cost Per Production Aircraft

$1,014,910.00—airframe, $748,259; engine (installed), $217,390; electronics, $8,549; ordnance, $20,807; armament, $19,905.

Average Maintenance Cost Per Flying Hour

$215.00

Total RDT&E Cost

$23.2 million. When the F–100 program ended, prorating this cumulative R&D cost boosted every F–100 model's unit price by $10,134.00.

Phaseout **1958-1961**

F–100As began leaving the Air Force tactical inventory in 1958 when 47 aircraft were transferred to the ANG. In mid-1959, the military assistance program allocated 15 F–100As to Nationalist China and TAC prepared to store most of the remaining aircraft at Nellis AFB. In 1960, 65 additional F–100As were given to the Chinese Nationalist Air Force. The ANG inventory reached its full quota of 70 F–100As during the same year. By the end of 1961, 47 major flying accidents and the modification or cannibalizing of a few of the other aircraft accounted for the active fleet's entire phaseout.

Reactivation **1961-1962**

F–100As rejoined the Air Force's operational inventory, as ANG and AFR units were recalled to active duty because of the Berlin crisis. In early 1962, despite the aircraft's operational deficiencies, the Air Force decided to extend the F–100's service life. Many of the ANG aircraft which came under the operational control of TAC, after the release of the ANG personnel, were retained in the command's inventory.

Final Disposition **1962–1970**

Thirty-eight of the aircraft repossessed from the ANG were subsequently transferred to Nationalist China, bringing to 118 the total of F–100As furnished to that country by the Military Assistant Program. Most of the other F–100As retained by the Air Force were used for aircrew training. The Air Force gave up its last F–100A in early 1970, 3 years after the ANG had lost its remaining few through attrition.

Record Flight **29 October 1953**

The first of the two YF–100A prototypes set a world speed record of 755.149 mph in the last such record established at low altitude.

Other Milestones

The F–100A Super Sabre was also first as the Air Force's Century-series fighter, and as an operational fighter capable of level supersonic performance.

F-100C

Manufacturer's Models NA-214, -217, and -222

Previous Model Series

F–100A

New Features

Fuel tanks inside the wings. Pylons to hold extra fuel drop tanks and additional stores (bombs and rockets), as called for by the aircraft's secondary fighter-bomber role. The first F–100Cs, like the F–100As, were equipped with the Pratt & Whitney J–57–P–7 engines. Others, before the 101st production, were powered by the J–57–P–39s. The later version of the F–100C incorporated the increased thrust of the J–57–P–21. The F–100C also differed from the F–100A by being fitted for the probe and drogue type of in-flight refueling.

Definitive Contract for Production **February 1954**

The Air Force eventually bought 476 F–100Cs, using FY 53 funds for the first 70, FY 54 funds for the next 381, and FY 55 funds for the last 25.

First Flight (Prototype) **March 1954**

First Flight (Production Aircraft with P-7 Engine) **17 January 1955**

The aircraft was accepted by the Air Force in April 1955. Production of the first F–100Cs, totaling 100 aircraft equipped with J–57–

P–7 or –P–39 engines, was completed in September of the same year.

Enters Operational Service **14 July 1955**

With the 450th Day Fighter Wing (later the 322d Fighter Day Group) at Foster AFB, Tex.

First Flight (Production Aircraft with P-21 Engine) **September 1955**

Two months after the –P–7 engine-equipped F–100C entered operational service and 2 months before being accepted by the Air Force.

Flight Testing **1955**

Functional development testing (Phase VI) of the F–100C started in February with the first production (J–57–P–7 engine-equipped) aircraft. The tests confirmed that the F–100C, with many of the features of the F–100A day fighter from which it was developed, could be expected to fill the bomber role only until a more suitable fighter-bomber could be added to the Air Force inventory. Operational suitability testing of the later F–100C productions was conducted toward the end of the year. The tests disclosed that the aircraft's chief advantage over the earlier F–100A and F–100C configurations derived from the increased thrust delivery of the J–57–P–21 engine. The tests also indicated that earlier configuration deficiencies were still present, not the least of which was the susceptibility of the Pratt & Whitney J–57 engine to compressor stall. On the other hand, the OST reports pointed out, the F–100C was an excellent vehicle for the low-altitude bombing system (LABS) because its maximum ground speed of 1,050 feet per second was considerably higher than the delivery speed of contemporary operational fighters. Another worthy feature of the F–100C, shared by all other F–100 configurations, was the aircraft's nose-wheel steering system which permitted safe taxiing even in cross winds up to 30 knots per hour.

Modifications **1955**

Like the F–100A, when used in its primary day fighter role, the F–100C at high speeds had the tendency to yaw and then go into an uncontrollable roll. Beginning with the 146th F–100C production, significant improvement was obtained with the installation of an hydraulically activated and electrically controlled yaw damper. Assisted by North American teams, the Air Force retrofitted the first 145 F–100Cs with the device. Similarly, damping of longitudinal oscillations was increased by the addition of a pitch damper in the horizontal stabilizer control system. Factory incorporation of the pitch damper started with the 301st F–100C at a cost of almost $10,000.00 per aircraft. Another modification to reduce the F–100C's landing speed, an increasingly critical jet aircraft problem, was given up. The modification, North American revealed, would require replacement of the aircraft's wings. The Air Force concluded that the cost involved would be out of proportion to the benefit received.

Operational Problems **December 1955**

An asset of the F–100C over the F–100A was the aircraft's capability to carry extra fuel. Fuel tanks were located in the fuselage as well as in the wings and external fuel was carried in two 275-gal tanks which could be supplemented by two 200-gal tanks. The additional 200-gal tanks permitted greater range but resulted in a loss of directional stability which was most critical at speeds in excess of Mach .8 when these tanks were used on the inboard stations in conjunction with the 275-gal tanks. Remedial action through enlargement of the aircraft's stabilizer—a feature of subsequent F–100 model series—was disapproved because of the excessive cost and time involved. Instead, after testing showed that larger external tanks did not affect the F–100C's longitudinal stability, the Air Force prohibited the use of the 200-gal tanks and directed replacement of the 275 and 200-gal tank combination by 450-gal external tanks. During the same period, Pratt & Whitney improvised a partial remedy for compressor stalls in the F–100's J–57 engine by installing a pressure bleed off which served to release the accumulated gases and prevent internal explosions.

End of Production **April 1956**

Production ended after the 476th aircraft—451 built by the North American's Inglewood plant in California, and 25 by the contractor's second plant at Columbus, Ohio.

Subsequent Model Series

F–100D

Other Configurations

None

Acceptance Rates

Sixteen F–100Cs were accepted in FY 55, 459 in FY 56, and one in the first month of FY 57.

Last Acceptance **July 1956**

Total F–100Cs Accepted

476

Flyaway Cost Per Production Aircraft

$663,181.00—airframe, $439,323; engine (installed), $178,554; electronics, $12,050; armament, $21,125; ordnance, $12,125.

Average Maintenance Cost Per Flying Hour

$249.00

Special Utilization **1956**

The Air Force began to re-equip its Air Demonstration "Thunderbirds" Squadron with supersonic F–100Cs. The team retained the C-model Super Sabre until 1964.

Oversea Deployments **December 1956**

More than 150 F–100Cs had reached the USAFE inventory, 55 at Bitburg, 6 at Furstenfelbruck, 30 at Landstuhl, and 26 at Hahn, all air bases located in West Germany. Thirteen USAFE F–100Cs were at Sidi Slimane AB, in Morocco, and 26 at Camp New Amsterdam in the Netherlands.

Other Transfers **Mid-1959**

Four F–100Cs reached the ANG in FY 60, 89 more the following year. The aircraft with their units were returned to TAC's operational control during the Berlin crisis. Soon afterwards, in contrast with USAF retention of some of the recalled F–100As, F–100C transfers to the ANG were resumed. The Guard's F–100C inventory began climbing steadily from 122 aircraft in mid-1963 to its authorized peak of 210 in mid-1966. The USS Pueblo incident in January 1968 brought another recall of the Air National Guard, including the temporary mobilization of eight F–100C groups for a total of 200 aircraft. However, as called for by USAF planning, the ANG inventory in late 1970 again totaled 210 F–100Cs. Seventeen of these aircraft were used for training. More than 90 percent of the others were combat ready.

Problems and Additional Modifications **1961–1966**

The F–100's initial deficiencies, the extended retention of the aircraft, the shortages and requirements created by the war in Vietnam, all were to cause numerous modifications of the weapon system. In 1961 the lack of J–59–39 engine spares made it necessary to replace the engine of numerous F–100Cs. In 1962 the aircraft's capability to carry two MA–3 launchers was increased to six and another modification was accomplished to exchange the F–100C's AB/APG–30A radar for the more modern AN/ASC–17. Meanwhile, the F–100 fuel tank problem, identified in 1955, persisted. The Air Force directed as an initial solution the use of 450-gallon tanks, but these proved expensive and scarce. A TAC recommendation to replace 450-gallon tanks with 335-gallon ones was later approved, but still posed many technical difficulties. In addition to the known deficiencies calling for further improvement, other problems were either defined or took on added importance in the following years. Foremost in the mid-sixties, was the F–100C's inability to deliver all of the primary non-nuclear weapons in the Air Force arsenal. Late in 1965, only 125 ANG F–100Cs could use the CBU bombs and AIM–9B Sidewinder missiles. Despite TAC efforts to improve the armament systems of the aircraft allocated to the Guard, the modifications scheduled for 1966 were postponed for over a year because of a shortage of adapters and Aero 3B launchers. During the same period, the operational capability of the ANG's F–100Cs also was limited by the scarcity of MJ–1 bomb lifts and MHU–12H trailers.

Phaseout **June 1970**

In spite of the 1962 decision to extend the F–100 service life, the F–100Cs were quickly supplanted by the F–100Ds. Eighty-five major flying accidents, the cannibalizing of 18 aircraft, re-equipping of the Thunderbirds, and priority modernization of the ANG tactical fighter units, almost entirely depleted the inventory of the regular forces. The Air Force used most of its few available F–100Cs for training until March 1970, when the last three flew their final missions. Two of the three F–100Cs remaining in the training program had accumulated a combined total of 4,929 flying hours since the fall of 1958. Transfer of these aircraft and of 12 other F–100Cs to the Air National Guard completed the fleet's phaseout from the Air Force inventory.

Record Flight **20 August 1955**

An F–100C established a world speed record—the first above Mach 1—at 822.135 mph.

Other Milestones **4 September 1955**

F–100C won the Bendix Trophy transcontinental race, 2,325 miles at average speed of 610.726 mph.

13 May 1957

Three USAF F–100C Super Sabres set a distance record for single-engine jet aircraft, flying 6,710 miles from London, England to Los Angeles, Calif., in 14 hours and 4 minutes, using in-flight refueling.

F-100D

Manufacturer's Model NA-223, -224, -235, -245.

Previous Model Series

F–100C

New Features

Increased wing and vertical tail area, additional electronic equipment, autopilot, provision for "Buddy" tanker refueling equipment, two 450 gallon air-refuelable external tanks, and inboard landing flaps.

Basic Development **May 1954**

TAC's request for a more sophisticated fighter-bomber led to an Air Force study of a third configuration in the 100-series—the F–100D. In contrast to the F–100A and F–100C, the F–100D would serve primarily as a fighter-bomber and only secondarily as a day fighter.

Initial Contract for Production **October 1954**

Additional procurement was directed in March and December 1955. On the latter date, however, total procurement dropped from scheduled peak of 1,604 F–100Ds. The decrease resulted from the Air Force's decision to purchase a two-seat trainer version of the aircraft.

Special Armament Tests **December 1955**

Six F–100Cs were modified to test the possibility of arming the F–100D with infrared missiles. Some of the prototyped F–100Cs were equipped with the Hughes GAR–1B infrared seeker models of the air-launched Falcon missiles; others, with the GAR–8 (later redesignated AIM–9B) Sidewinders being developed by Philco and General Electric. Testing of the two combinations resulted in the September 1956 selection of the Sidewinder to increase the F–100D's potency in the intercept role. Provisions for installation of the air-to-air Sidewinders started with the 184th F–100D production, when provisions for center line special stores also began.

First Acceptance **November 1955**

The delivery of all F–100Ds earmarked for testing was completed in the spring of 1956.

First Flight (Production Aircraft) **24 January 1956**

The aircraft had been built by the Inglewood plant. The first F–100D completed by the North American's second production line at Columbus first flew on 12 June 1956.

First Acceptance (Production Aircraft) **April 1956**

Deliveries to TAC units at Langley AFB began in September. By the end of the year 79 F–100Ds were in TAC's operational inventory.

Initial Problems and Directed Modifications **27 June 1956**

The Air Force identified for North American several major deficiencies of the F–100D. Included were the failings of the Sundstrand Constant Speed Drive (designed to provide the aircraft's electrical system with constant frequency electricity), the incomplete tie-in between the autopilot and low-altitude bombing systems, the inaccuracy of the MA–3 fire control and, depending on its load, the gravitational pull ("G" force) sustained by the F–100D when flying at subsonic speed above 32,000 feet. Despite TAC's concern, a large number of F–100Ds entered the operational inventory before these and other F–100D shortcomings could be rectified.

Improvement Slippages **July 1956**

In spite of considerable efforts, improvement of the F–100D's autopilot was delayed. Installation of the improved autopilot, scheduled to begin with the first production-provisions for Sidewinder missiles and center line special stores, slipped from the 184th F–100D production to the 384th. In-service F–100Ds were subsequently retrofitted.

Enters Operational Service **29 September 1956**

With TAC's 405th Fighter-Bomber Wing at Langley AFB.

Oversea Deployments **December 1956**

TAC's recommendation that F–100D oversea deployments be postponed was overruled. USAFE acknowledged the aircraft's deficiencies and needed modifications, but pointed out that the F–100D, as it was, still represented an improvement of its forces. Too, in anticipation of the command's conversion to F–100Ds, modification of the USAFE F–84F and F–86F fighter-bombers had already been stopped. The Far East Air Forces took side with USAFE, and by the end of December 136 F–100Ds had reached the oversea theaters—the 46 FEAF F–100Ds were at Itazuke AB; the 70 USAFE F–100D aircraft were at Etain and Chaumont, France, and at Boulhaut and Sidi Slimane Air Bases in Morocco.

Other Modifications **1957-1959**

High-altitude maneuver problems were solved in early 1957. Necessary adjustments were first included in the aircraft's 225th production and earlier F–100Ds were retrofitted. Various engineering changes to improve the F–100D's Constant Speed Drive (CSD) were not so successful. To minimize the danger of in-flight case rupture, the Air Force in June 1957 directed that the CSD be placed on a separate oil system. Modification of the aircraft already released from the factories was completed in February 1958. Sixty-five F–100Ds were modified to increase their striking power by using the GAM–83 Bullpup air-to-surface missiles. This additional modification was completed in late 1959 as programmed, but the Bullpup deliveries fell behind schedule. The first GAM–83-equipped F–100D squadron became operational in December 1960 and three more by June 1961.

Other Special Features

Boosted by a 150,000-lb Astrodyne rocket, the F–100 first demonstrated zero-length launching on 7 June 1957 at Edwards AFB. Final F–100D productions incorporated equipment for the zero-length launches from atomic shelters.

End of Production **1957-1959**

Production of the F–100D, scheduled to end in early 1958, was stretched out to keep North American's labor force in being. In April 1957 production began to drop gradually from a monthly average of 45 aircraft to about five in October 1958. This low rate of production remained in effect until August 1959, when the Air Force took possession of the last five F–100Ds built by the Inglewood factory. The Air Force stretch-out directive did not cover the North American's second production line. As initially programmed, F–100D productions at Columbus ended in December 1957.

Subsequent Model Series

F–100F

Other Configurations

None. A number of other single-seat versions of the Super Sabre were proposed but failed to materialize, including the all-weather F–100J offered to Japan through the Foreign Military Sales Program, the F–100L with a J–57–P–55 engine in place of the –21A, and the F–100N, a simplified D-model with reduced electronic equipment.

Acceptance Rates

One hundred and thirteen F–100Ds were accepted from the Inglewood factory in FY 56, 576 in FY 57, 166 in FY 58, 75 in FY 59, and 10 in FY 60. Two F–100Ds, built in Columbus, were accepted in FY 56, 212 in FY 57, and 120 in FY 58.

Last Acceptances

From Columbus, December 1957; from Inglewood, August 1959.

Total F–100Ds Accepted

1,274—940 from Inglewood and 334 from Columbus.

Flyaway Cost Per Production Aircraft[2]

$697,029.00—airframe, $448,216; engine (installed), $162,995; electronics, $10,904; ordnance, $8,684; armament, $66,230.

Average Cost Per Flying Hour

$583.00

Average Maintenance Cost Per Flying Hour

$249.00

Postproduction Problems **1959–1962**

Parts shortages and some of the J–57 malfunctions were alleviated but problems with the engine bearings and the aircraft's afterburner fuel system remained unsolved. Moreover, deficiencies persisted in the pylon assembly. Testing disclosed that correction of these deficiencies would not stop inadvertent bomb releases due to improper bomb-loading procedures. Procurement of additional pylons for war reserve was therefore postponed. Air refueling of the

[2] Excluding $10,134 of prorated RDT&E cost and cumulative modification costs specifically spent on certain F–100 models, i.e., $224,048 on each F–100C; $110,599 on each F–100D; and $105,604 on each F–100F.

F–100D also did not work as well as first expected. Recurring losses of probes during high speed and high "G" force maneuvers caused the removal of refueling probes from all F–100Ds, except for air refueling missions, pending reinforcement of the aircraft's underwing structures. In late 1962, a shortage of 450-gallon tanks and the depletion of TAC's 335-gallon tank reserves compounded the difficulty of standardizing the F–100 fleet.

Postproduction Improvements **1962–1965**

Like previous F–100 model series, the D's combat life was extended in 1962, and the aircraft's capability to deliver non-nuclear weapons was increased. Necessary modifications, applied also to the F–100Fs, were completed in April of the same year. Another much more extensive modification program, referred to as High Wire, ensued. The main purpose of the High Wire work, accomplished by both the Air Force and North American, was to standardize a weapon system which had been modified on so many occasions that individual aircraft differed from each other. The High Wire modifications, requiring about 60 workdays per aircraft, were applied to some 700 F–100s and completed in mid-1965. Overall cost reached $150 million, but the results were gratifying.

Unrelenting and New Difficulties **1965**

Regardless of the remarkable High Wire achievements, the F–100Ds, as well as all other F–100s, continued to present operational problems. Malfunctions of the aircraft's landing gear and the unreliability of its drag chutes accounted for a number of accidents. In addition, while compressor stalls in the J–57–21 engine still occurred, of new concern was the engine itself, which had gone beyond its reliable service life and for which no replacement was available. Complete overhaul of the engines, as subsequently directed, took care of this new problem, but not without trials. Some of the Aerodex-overhauled J–57 engines proved to be unsatisfactory, and a continuing shortage of spares further slowed down the F–100 inspection and repair as necessary (IRAN) cycle.

Combat Deployments **1965**

Several F–100 aircraft, belonging to the Thirteenth Air Force in the Phillipines, were initially deployed in Thailand in May 1962 to restrain Communist forces overrunning most of Northwest Laos. However, F–100 operations over North Vietnam did not start until 1965. The Air Force used F–100 jets in South Vietnam in February of the same year, also for the first time. F–100 deployments to Southeast Asia (SEA)[3] were accelerated soon afterwards, and by 30 June 1967 only five F–100 squadrons remained in the United States.

---

[3] Republic of Vietnam, Thailand, Laos, and Cambodia.

Structural Modifications **1966-1969**

A second decision in 1966 to keep the F–100s in the USAF inventory longer than ever anticipated prompted the Air Force to investigate the extent and cost of the structural modifications needed to stretch the F–100-designed service life of 3,000 flying hours to a ceiling of 5,500 hours. This was later increased to 7,000 hours to permit retention of the D and F model series through 1971. Because of the F–100's high rate of weapon deliveries in SEA, the Air Force, assisted by North American, also began in early 1967 to examine the structural condition of the aircraft's wings. They also examined the possibility of redesigning the wing lower skin should this be needed due to the aircraft's extensive combat use. In mid-1967, the urgent need for safety improvements was confirmed when one aircraft crashed because of wing failure. The accident led the Air Force to ground a number of F–100s, pending reinforcement of their wings with external straps. In the final months of 1967, the Air Force came up with a complete F–100 structural modification program. By 1969, modification of the wing center section was completed on 682 of the program's 882 aircraft. Modification of the F–100's lowest wing outer panel—considered mandatory by the Air Force before the aircraft reached a total of 4,000 flying hours—also went well.

Special SEA Modifications **1967-1968**

As operational requirements rose, various modifications were undertaken to raise the combat capability of the F–100 aircraft, some of which reached almost 14 years of age. The aircraft's weapon release and firing system were improved; new guns and a more accurate target-marking system were provided. Combat Skyspot, a modification program first implemented in April 1966 and covering most of the USAF SEA aircraft, was completed. The modification, which included the equipping of each aircraft with Motorola's new SST–181X band radar transmitter, gave a ground-directed bombing capability to all F–100s operating at night or in bad weather.

Attrition **July 1956-June 1970**

The Air Force lost over 500 F–100Ds, with many of the accidents occurring during the first 2 years of the aircraft's operational service. In the following years, numerous modifications and an intensive training program to curtail pilot errors reduced accident rates. This trend was reversed in the late sixties as F–100D combat operations increased. In 1 year, more than 50 F–100Ds were lost in the war.

Phaseout **Mid-1972**

The ANG received its first F–100Ds in 1969 but by mid-1970 had only 20. USAF plans called for keeping most of its 364 operational F–100Ds through 1971. However, phaseout of F–100D/F fighters in South Vietnam was stepped up.[4] Hence, by mid-1972 only 12 F–100Ds remained on USAF rolls while the Guard boasted 335.

Other Countries

The Air Force lost 203 of its 1,274 F–100Ds to the Military Assistant Program. The aircraft, used to modernize NATO forces, were all equipped—at a cost of $17,755. per aircraft—with the ARN–21 UHF navigation equipment, commonly adopted by the Air Force and the allied air forces. Another modification, one that would allow use of the early GAR–8 Sidewinder missiles, was only approved for 150 of the aircraft. It was completed in 1960 at a total cost of some $2 million. France, the first recipient country, was given 68 F–100Ds; Denmark followed, with the allocation of 48 aircraft. The F–100D Military Assistance Program was also extended to Turkey which received the highest number—87 aircraft.

Other Uses

The F–100Ds played an important role in the Air Force critical training of SEA replacement crews. In mid-1970, 44 F–100Ds remained assigned to the training programs conducted at Luke and at Cannon AFB, N. Mex.

Special Assignment

The Air Force Thunderbirds squadron began replacing its F–100Cs with F–105 Thunderchiefs in early 1964, but a major F–105 flying accident in May prompted the Air Force to re-equip its precision flying team with eight F–100Ds, modified for demonstration purposes. The team received its new Super Sabres in July and resumed its demonstrations 30 days later. The Thunderbirds flew F–100Ds until November 1968 when they started to transition into the faster, higher-flying F–4E Phantoms.

Milestones **26 December 1956**

Buddy refueling was first achieved between two F–100D aircraft.

F-100F

Manufacturer's Model NA-243.

Previous Model Series

F–100D

New Features

Tandem two-seat cockpit with dual controls. Only two of the F–100D's four built-in 20-mm M–39 guns.

---

[4] F–100D/F fighters from the 35th Tactical Fighter Wing redeployed from Phan Rang AB, to the United States in July 1971.

Basic Development **8 September 1955**

North American Aviation proposal to modify an F–100C to a trainer fighter version at no cost to the Air Force.

Production Decision **November 1955**

The Air Force Council decision stemmed from the alarming rate of F–100 flying accidents which indicated the urgent need of a two-place supersonic trainer to replace the Air Force's standard jet trainer—the 7-year-old T–33, a variant of the Lockheed P–80 "Shooting Star," first developed in the latter part of World War II. The decision vindicated, at least temporarily, those who had advocated a two-seat trainer version for each fighter aircraft.

Initial Contract for Production **December 1955**

For 259 two-place aircraft. The contract was accompanied by a reduction in F–100D procurement.

Mockup Inspection **January 1956**

The inspection covered only the aircraft's cockpit.

First Flight (TF-100C) **6 August 1956**

This was the conversion trainer proposed by North American. Designated TF–100C, the aircraft, which lacked all operational equipment, served as the prototype for the F–100F.

First Flight (Production Aircraft) **7 March 1957**

This was the F–100F, derived from the single-seat F–100D tactical fighter bomber and designed to combine this role with that of combat proficiency trainer.

First Acceptance **January 1958**

This was the first F–100F, its delivery having been preceded, beginning in May 1957, by that of a number of F–100 trainers which were subsequently brought up to the F–100F's dual configuration. The aircraft entered TAC's operational inventory almost immediately, and by December 1958 the new F–100Fs had reached most of the oversea commands' F–100D units.

Flight Testing **1958-1959**

Because of its similarity to the F–100D, testing of the F–100F, like its operational use, could be speeded. Only limited performance and qualitative (stability and control) tests were conducted, and those were completed in May 1958. The Category II performance tests, also curtailed, were completed 1 year later.

End of Production **1959**

As with the F–100D and for the same reasons, the Air Force slowed down production of the F–100Fs. Delivery of the last one in September represented a slippage of several months from previous production schedules.

Total F-100Fs Accepted

The Air Force accepted 339—a total finalized in October 1958, after numerous program changes. Included in this number were 45 aircraft, specifically purchased for the Military Assistance Program.

Acceptance Rates

Fourteen two-seaters were accepted for the Air Force in FY 57, 227 in FY 58, and 53 in FY 59. Fourteen F–100Fs were accepted for the MAP in FY 58, 16 in FY 59, and 15 in FY 60.

Flyaway Cost Per Production Aircraft

$804,444.00—airframe, $577,023; engine (installed), $143,527; electronics, $13,677; ordnance, $3,885; armament, $66,332.

Average Cost Per Flying Hour

$583.00

Average Maintenance Cost Per Flying Hour

$249.00

Subsequent Model Series

None

Other Configurations

None. In 1964 North American attempted to establish a production line in France for some 200 two-seat Super Sabres designated F–100S by the manufacturer. The proposed F–100S utilized the basic F–100F airframe and a Rolls-Royce RB 168–25R Spey turbofan in place of the J–57–P–21 or –21A to improve performance. As in the case of the proposed F–100J, L, and N versions, the project did not materialize.

Postproduction Problems and Improvements **1959-1965**

Engine malfunctions, spare and part shortages, and F–100D component deficiencies were experienced by the aircraft's two-seat model. Consequently, F–100D modification programs encompassed the F–100Fs. In 1959 fifteen of the aircraft were modified to increase their striking power through use of the GAM–83 Bullpups. In 1962 all F–100Fs were modified to increase their nonnuclear combat capability.

Structural Modifications

The F–100 service life's several extension decisions and resulting structural modifications of necessity were applied to the F–100F, because this last model in the series was of the D vintage, with the same airframe and wings.

Special SEA Modifications

Seven F–100F aircraft—designated "Wild Weasel I"—were modified to carry special equipment. This included the APR–25 vector radar homing and warning (RHAW) receiver to detect S-band signals (emitted by SA–2 fire control radar and early warning/ground controlled intercept radar), and C-band signals (from improved SA–2) and the X-band airborne intercept radar. They also were equipped with the APR–25 (WR–300) L-band warning receiver to indicate missile guidance emissions, and the IR–133 panoramic receiver that could detect S-band signals at a greater range than the APR–25. The KA–60 panoramic camera and a dual-track tape recorder also were installed in the Wild Weasel I aircraft.

Wild Weasel Deployments **1965–1966**

Four aircraft were deployed from Eglin to Korat, Thailand on 21 November 1965 and assigned to the operational control of the 388th Tactical Fighter Wing. They began to fly war missions on 3 December. Three additional Wild Weasel I aircraft were deployed to the SEA theater on 27 February 1966, also to participate in the "Iron Hand" anti-SAM air campaign.

Other Combat Modifications **1966**

F–100Fs were equipped with the AGM–45 Shrike missile. In April the Wild Weasel planes themselves began attacking the North Vietnamese Fan Song fire control radars.

Attrition **July 1958–June 1970**

F–100F accident rates followed the F–100D's pattern, with 31 losses registered during the first 2 years of the aircraft's service life. Accident rates decreased subsequently, but the losses began again to rise in the mid-sixties. By June 1970 a total of 74 aircraft, one fourth of the Air Force's 294 F–100Fs, had been lost in major accidents.

Phaseout **Mid-1972**

Like the F–100D, the F–100F was practically out of USAF inventory by mid-1972. The ANG had received an initial increment of six F–100Fs in 1958, but little more until the late sixties. In June 1972, however, the Guard had 550 F–100s, 100 of then F–100Fs. Five ANG squadrons had already completed the installation of F–102-type afterburner on their assigned F–100s. This modification—service-tested by the Air force—helped solve the F–100's chronic compressor stall problem and reduced engine bay temperatures. Although available F–102 afterburners were being overhauled, $8 million worth of new flap-type afterburners had to be ordered. Yet, the Air Force believed the latest F–100 modification would pay for itself in 2 years.

Other Countries

A number of F–100Fs were flown by the Danish, French, and Turkish air forces.

Milestones **7 August 1959**

Two USAF F–100Fs made first flight by jet fighter aircraft over North Pole.

PROGRAM RECAP

The Air Force accepted a grand total of 2,294 F–100s—45 F–100Fs for the Military Assistance Program; the rest, for its own use. Among the USAF 2,249 F–100s were 2 F–100A prototypes, 203 F–100As, 476 F–100Cs, 1,274 F–100Ds, and 294 F–100Fs.

TECHNICAL DATA

F–100A/C/D and F–100F

Manufacturer	North American Aviation Inc., Inglewood, Calif. and Columbus, Ohio (F–100C and D).
Nomenclature	Supersonic Tactical Fighter (F–100A/C). Supersonic Tactical Fighter-Bomber (F–100D). Supersonic Tactical Fighter-Bomber and Combat Trainer (F–100F).
Popular Name	Super Sabre

Characteristics	*F–100A*	*F–100C*	*F–100D*	*F–100F*
Length/Wing	48 ft/39 ft	47 ft/39 ft	49 ft/39 ft	52.5 ft/39 ft
Takeoff Weight	32,500 lb	37,000 lb	39,750 lb	40,100 lb
Takeoff Ground Run	6,150 ft	4,590 ft	5,030 ft	5,210 ft
Max. Speed at 35,000 ft	710 kn	803 kn	790 kn	790 kn
Radius	510 nm	500 nm	460 nm	450 nm
Engine, Number & Designation	1 J–57–P–7	1 J–57–P–21	1 J–57–P–21A	1 J–57–P–21
Crew	1	1	1	2
Combat Ceiling	49,000 ft	49,000 ft	47,700 ft	47,300 ft
Rate of Climb (sea level)	4,200 fpm	4,600 fpm	4,100 fpm	4,000 fpm
Guns	4 20-mm M–39s	4 20-mm M–39s	4 20-mm M–39s	2 20-mm M–39s
Rockets	14 2.75″ FFARs	42 2.75″ FFARs or 2 AIM–9B/E/J	38 2.75″[5] FFARs or 4 AIM–9B/E/J	38 2.75″[5] FFARs or 4 AIM–9B/E/J
Max. Bomb Load	5,000 lb	5,000 lb	7,040 lb	5,000 lb
Special Stores	1 MK–7 (Wg Station)	1 MK–7 (Wg Station)	1 MK–28 or MK–43/57/61 (C/L Pylon)	1 MK–7 or 1 MK–28/43/57/61 (C/L Pylon)

---

[5] In LAU–3/A launchers.

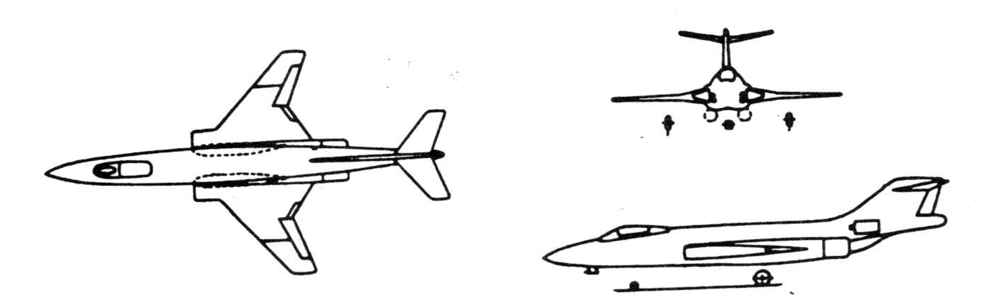

McDONNELL F–101 VOODOO

F–101A: The supersonic, single-seat F–101A Voodoo was developed from the experimental F–88.

F–101C: Looked like the A, but its structure had been strengthened.

RF–101: The most distinctive feature of the RF–101A was its nose, which had been lengthened for the installation of photographic equipment.

RF–101C: Retained the F–101C's capability of delivering nuclear weapons. The single-place, supersonic RF–101C soon established itself as the Air Force's reconnaissance workhorse.

F–101B: The interceptor version of the Voodoo had an elongated cockpit, permitting sitting of observer behind pilot. Moreover, it carried missiles and rockets. One out of every four F–101Bs (TF–101Bs), were fitted with dual-control kits for pilot training. Late F–101B productions featured a number of modifications and were identified as F–101Fs in 1961.

McDONNELL F-101 VOODOO

Manufacturer's Model 36W
Weapon System 105A

Basic Development **June 1946**

McDonnell's detail design of a strategic penetration fighter intended to escort bombers of the recently established—21 March 1946—Strategic Air Command. The Air Force ordered two prototypes of McDonnell's original Voodoo under the designation XF–88. The first XF–88 flew on 20 October 1948, some 6 months after the contracted delivery date. This initial slippage, the contractor claimed, was the result of changes in the prototype's structural design. The change from straight wing to a 35-degree wing-swept back, along with the danger of compressor stalls at high speed, caused McDonnell engineers to alter the shape of the ducts through which air entered the turbine engines. The second XF–88, with short afterburners boosting the thrust of its J–43–WE–22 engines, did not fly until 2 years later.

Program Cancellation **August 1950**

The Air Force cancelled the XF–88 contract a few months after the second prototype's first flight. The decision was due primarily to the shortage of funds that had been forewarned by President Truman in mid-1948 and to the United States endorsement of defense plans brought back from Europe by Secretary of Defense James V. Forrestal in the fall of the same year. These plans, urging greater use of the atomic bomb, meant that more atomic power had to be packed into SAC's forces. Hence, most of the Air Force money was spent on the B–36, one of the bombers that the F–88 had been designed to escort. Although the F–88 had failed to perform satisfactorily in its intended roles of escort fighter and ground support plane, many desirable qualities were attributed to its prototypes. Nevertheless, there were other reasons for cancelling production. A significant number of Republic's F–84Es, under contract since late 1948, had already entered USAF inventory and could satisfy immediate requirements for a penetration fighter. Moreover, a new model series of the proven North American Sabre, the F–86D—flown in December 1949—was expected to meet the urgent requirements for a better interceptor.

Program Reactivation **January 1951**

The Air Force, pending development of a new fighter, planned to replace the F–84E with the F–84F, the production of which had been decided. SAC, however, did not support these plans and wanted a long range fighter capable of escorting the transoceanic B–36s. On 12 January SAC outlined the minimum characteristics of the interim aircraft needed for the period 1952–1953. Headquarters USAF agreed to evaluate several contractor offers which might more nearly satisfy SAC.

General Operational Requirements **6 February 1951**

This GOR, published as Skeleton GOR 101, was subsequently expanded as GOR 101-2 to cover the aircraft's next model series. Both GORs were cancelled in November 1958, when the Air Force decided to terminate the F-101 production—the F-101B interceptor, excepted. New requirements, if any, would be met by modifying existing F-101s.

Competitors and Selection **May 1951**

Included in the contractor's offers in response to GOR 101 were Lockheed's F-90 and F-94, an improved configuration of the McDonnell F-88, North American's F-93, Northrop's improved F-89, and three Republic submissions—the F-91, the already purchased F-84F, and another version of the F-84F that would be equipped with a turboprop engine. McDonnell's new F-88 was chosen, but the Air Force did not commit itself to go to production until several months later.

Production Go-Ahead **October 1951**

The October production decision was the result of Korean War experiences. Existing fighters had proved unsatisfactory as escorts for B-29s. Between June 1950 and September 1951, American pilots flew a mix of fighters and downed 13 Russian-built MIGs for every plane lost, a ratio reflecting superior flying skill rather than better equipment.[1] The Air Force thus found itself facing two problems: development of a satisfactory escort fighter and replacement of the F-84s and F-86s used in Korea. In October 1951, it released fiscal year 1952 funds, previously allocated to the F-84F and F-86F aircraft, to get McDonnell's new F-88 into production without further delay. Moreover, instead of procuring the Voodoo solely as an interim fighter while an "ultimate" long range fighter was being developed, the Air Force decided that the latter would be obtained by improving early Voodoo productions. The first production aircraft would have the same airframe as the "ultimate" series, but the first aircraft would only incorporate "available" production-type equipment, systems components, and engines. Then, as more advanced equipment became available, the airframes would be modified to receive them.

Production Policy **26 November 1951**

The Cook-Craigie production policy, outlined for the Convair F-102, was extended to the new Voodoo. This meant that the initial production run of the basic aircraft would be kept to the minimum

---

[1] The F-86's final boxscore was 14 to 1.

needed for comprehensive testing. While these aircraft were being assembled, preparations would be made for full scale production of a version that would incorporate the changes judged necessary because of the test program. The test airplanes already produced would then be reworked on the production line into the approved configuration. The leading objectives were to eliminate the faults in a basic design before many aircraft had been built and to get operationally effective weapon systems into tactical use as quickly as possible.

Official Designation **30 November 1951**

The improved Voodoo bore the designation F–101. The Air Force Council directed the new designation because of the significant differences between the F–88 and the new configuration proposed by McDonnell in May 1951.

F101A

Contractual Arrangements **1952**

McDonnell accepted on 15 January the initial F–101A letter contract offered by the Air Force on condition that the final contract would be of the fixed price, incentive type. The Air Force accepted McDonnell's terms and signed such a contract on 11 June 1952. Cost increases, judged excessive by the Air Force, led to a renegotiation of the contract. It was finally concluded in November 1956 as a modified fixed price-incentive contract, in which the cost ran about 5 percent more than the target cost. McDonnell made neither the 10 percent maximum profit, nor the 8 percent target profit permitted by the original F–101 contract. The contractor's profit reached 6.85 percent of the total cost, or about as much as a cost-plus-fixed fee contract would have allowed. Other F–101 contracts followed almost the same buying pattern. As with the original model, the manufacturer began production under a temporary letter contract which was later replaced by a more formal, negotiated agreement. The Air Force endorsed the LC procedure only to make sure that the contractor's work would not be delayed by time consuming negotiations.

Contractor's Production Proposal **March 1952**

McDonnell proposed building and testing the first 33 F–101As as 6.33 g[2] airplanes; then making necessary modifications on the next 30 airplanes to bring them up to the 7.33 g strength requirements specified by GOR 101. The Air Force agreed in principle, but negotiations over design details for making the Voodoo a strategic fighter—one that could not only escort bombers but also could act

---

[2] One g is the measure or value of the gravitational pull of the earth or of a force required to accelerate or decelerate at the rate of 32.16 feet per second per second any free moving body.

as an atomic bomber and at all times be able to engage in air-to-air combat—were to consume almost another 2 years.

Mockup Inspection **21 July 1952**

The Air Force Board approved close to 90 requests for alteration, half of which concerned items required by contract and, therefore, mandatory on the first airplane. This first inspection was supplemented in the following 12 months by several others, including that of an atomic weapons mockup held on 17 and 18 March 1953.

Production Hold Order **May 1954**

The Air Force decided that release of FY 54 funds allocated to the F–101 would be held in abeyance until the end of the Category II flight tests, then expected to be sometime in March 1955. This suspension of funds resulted in a postponement of mass production. The armistice in Korea enabled the Air Force to move more deliberately in committing itself to a particular design. This less frenzied approach was dubbed the "fly-before-you-buy policy," a catchphrase that accurately reflected the shift of emphasis from a crash production to a peacetime, more economical research and development program.

First Delivery **August 1954**

The aircraft was delivered as programmed in early 1952.

First Flight **29 September 1954**

The aircraft was flown at Edwards AFB through the programmed flight test profile with encouraging results and attained Mach 1.07 in dive. Three other F–101As were accepted by the Air Force before the end of the year. They immediately began to undergo Category I flight tests.

Production Resumption **28 October 1954**

The Air Force lifted its production hold order and gave McDonnell an early 1957 operational deadline.

Flight Testing **1954–1956**

Category II flight tests, started in January 1955, confirmed deficiencies first identified during the Category I flight tests of late 1954. Foremost in the problems encountered, and which proved to be much more difficult to overcome than anticipated, were the compressor stalls of the two Pratt & Whitney J57–P–13 turbojet engines (that had replaced the less powerful J–43–WE–22 engines of the F–88 prototypes) and the aircraft's tendency to "pitch up." Despite ensuing corrective efforts, by mid-1956 the continued testing of 29 F–101As thus far accepted by the Air Force showed a number of still unsolved structural, propulsion, aerodynamic, and armament problems.

New Production Stoppage **May 1956**

McDonnell's failure to fix the aircraft's malfunctions led the Air

Force once again to halt production. The hold order was of short duration, but the F–101A production and that of the aircraft's reconnaissance version remained limited to a total of eight airplanes per month through the end of October 1956.

Early Structural Problems **June 1956**

In September 1955 McDonnell had informed the Air Force that F–101A production had proceeded much faster than the test program so that the two were out of phase. Contrary to past expectations, it would be impossible to get a 7.33-g F–101 from the production line prior to production of the 116th airframe. The 115 6.33-g airframes built, including those of the aircraft already accepted by the Air Force, could still be brought up to the 7.33-g load specification of GOR 101, but they would have to be torn down and practically rebuilt. Furthermore, so much redesign work would be necessary that most of the 7.33-g airplane parts would not be interchangeable with the parts of the former 6.33-g aircraft. After investigating every possible modification, including cost and time required, the Air Force decided in June 1956 that it would accept the 6.33-g aircraft. When accepted, this type of aircraft would not be able to engage in aerial maneuvers at a gross weight in excess of 37,000 pounds. The immediate concern, however, was to get an aircraft that would meet even these reduced operational requirements.

Special Identification **September 1956**

Three months after the June decision to accept the 6.33-g aircraft, Headquarters USAF approved designation of the 7.33-g F–101 as the C model series. Except for one aircraft used in development of the F–101's interceptor version, all 6.33-g aircraft received the A suffix assigned to the initial F–101s and to their reconnaissance counterparts.

Modification Progress **September 1956**

Since the end of May 1956 McDonnell had been running a modification rather than a production line, incorporating more than 300 Air Force-approved design changes and some 2,000 engineering improvements of its own in the aircraft that were in production. Although the first of these modified aircraft would not be ready for delivery before the end of November, it looked as if the contractor was finally getting a fix for pitch-up, the most serious deficiency of the aircraft and the one that took longest to correct.

Hold-Order Release **26 November 1956**

Satisfied with the active inhibitor (pitch-up device) installed by McDonnell, the Air Force decided that production for the combat inventory could proceed and completely rescinded the May production restrictions. The decision marked the conclusion of a 3-month review of the entire F–101 program, including funding, schedules, requirements for the aircraft, and any alternatives available to the Air Force.

Program Changes **December 1956**

The Air Force final endorsement of the F–101 was accompanied by several changes. The peak production rate projected for the Voodoo interceptor and the F–101A program was reduced, with the last 96 F–101As scheduled to be converted to the reconnaissance configuration. This conversion was associated with an accompanying decision to delete the RF–104 and RF–105 from the Air Force budget. Reduction of the F–101A program also reflected the impact of SAC's 1954 cancellation of its original requirements, the forthcoming reassignment of the aircraft, the 7.33-g F–101Cs included, to the Tactical Air Command, and TAC's mild enthusiasm toward its new acquisitions. Initially developed as a strategic penetration fighter, intended to escort SAC bombers and therefore designed to operate from permanent installations, the F–101A, as well as the F–101C, would be difficult to adapt to TAC's doctrine of dispersal because their weights and takeoff/landing needs would not permit them to deploy to or from temporary or hastily prepared runways. Too, the F–101A and F–101C were only nuclear fighter-bombers, incapable of delivering conventional bombs.

First Acceptance (Production Aircraft) **2 May 1957**

This was the 41st F–101A built, but the first one accepted for the operational inventory.

Enters Operational Service **2 May 1957**

The aircraft became operational at Bergstrom with the 27th Fighter-Bomber Wing, a SAC unit which, like the aircraft, was to be transferred to TAC on 1 July 1957. The whole complement of F–101As were used ultimately to equip three squadrons of TAC's 81st Tactical Fighter Wing.

Subsequent Model Series

F–101B

Other Configurations

RF–101A, F–101C, RF–101C, RF–101G, and RF–101H.

End of Production **October 1957**

With the delivery of the last seven aircraft.

Total F-101As Accepted

Of 77 accepted, only 50 reached the combat forces. The others, referred to as "preproductions," were allocated to the experimental and test inventory.

Acceptance Rates

Fifteen F–101As were accepted in FY 55, 14 in FY 56, 13 in FY 57, and 35 in the first 4 months of FY 58.

Flyaway Cost Per Production Aircraft

$2,906,373.00—airframe, $2,364,143; engines (installed), $429,016; electronics, $25,249; ordnance, $15,300; armament, $72,665.

Average Maintenance Cost Per Flying Hour

$362.00

Phaseout **1966-1970**

The F-101A began leaving the USAF inventory in 1966, when 27 of the aircraft were transferred to the Air National Guard. By mid-1970, several major flying accidents, the cannibalization of a dozen aircraft, and a number of conversions accounted for the rest of the F-101As.

F-101C

Manufacturer's Model 36W
Weapon System 105

Previous Model Series

F-101A. Although bearing an earlier suffix letter, the F-101B interceptor was predated by the F-101C.

New Features

The only major difference between the A and C models was the strengthening of the internal structure of the F-101C to the 7.33 g specified by GOR 101.

Contractual Arrangements **March 1956**

Production of the F-101C, so designated in September 1956, was in fact initiated by a March 1956 letter contract, calling for an additional number of F-101As. In December of the same year, however, the combined F-101A and C program was reduced to a total of 124 aircraft.

First Acceptance (Production Aircraft) **August 1957**

This was the first of the aircraft accepted for the combat forces.

Enters Operational Service **September 1957**

The 523d Tactical Fighter Squadron (TFS) of the 27th Fighter Bomber Wing received the first aircraft.

Subsequent Model Series

None, except for the F-101B model.

Other Configurations

RF-101C, RF-101G, and RF-101H.

End of Production **May 1958**

With delivery of the last aircraft.

Total F-101Cs Accepted

47

Acceptance Rates

All 47 F–101Cs were accepted by the Air Force during fiscal year 1958.

Flyaway Cost Per Production Aircraft

$1,276,145.00—airframe, $803,022; engines (installed), $287,764; electronics, $61,079; ordnance, $441; armament, $123,839.

Average Maintenance Cost Per Flying Hour

$362.00

Oversea Deployments **1958**

By the end of the year, 17 F–101Cs had been deployed to Europe. The USAFE Voodoos were stationed in England with the Royal Air Force at Bentwaters.

Phaseout **1966**

For all practical purposes, the F–101C left USAF inventory in mid-1966, when 31 of the 47 7.33 g aircraft were assigned to the ANG. Several major flying accidents and a number of conversions during the preceding years accounted for most of the original fleet.

First Record Flight **12 December 1957**

An F–101C established an FAI[3] world speed record at 1,207 mph, at Edwards AFB. Moreover, McDonnell's Voodoo remained the fastest tactical fighter in operational service until the advent of the F–104. At the time of its introduction into service it was also the heaviest single-seat fighter ever accepted by the Air Force.

Other Milestones **1958**

In addition to speed, a striking feature of the F–101 was its 1,000-mile unrefueled range. The aircraft could also be refueled in-flight by the flying boom or the probe and drogue methods. On 28 May 1958 two F–101Cs from Bergstrom AFB, Tex., made a nonstop, round trip flight of 5,600 miles. On 28 June, four F–101Cs flew nonstop from Andrews AFB, Md., to Liege, Belgium, at an average speed of 640 mph. In August of the same year, a flight of seven Voodoos completed a 6,100-mile nonstop deployment from Bergstrom to Bentwaters, England.

RF–101A

Manufacturer's Model 36X

Weapon System 105L

Previous Model Series

F–101A

General Operational Requirements **6 February 1951**

The reconnaissance version of the future F–101A was included in

[3] Fédération Aéronautique Internationale (FAI). An international organization founded in October 1905 in Paris for the purpose of authenticating aeronautical flights, both civilian and military, and promoting good will and understanding among world aviation interests.

the initial GOR of February 1951. Soon thereafter, McDonnell expressed doubts about the basic aircraft's capability of satisfying the reconnaissance configuration requirements.

Letter Contract **January 1953**

Procurement of the RF–101A was initiated by a letter contract covering the production of two prototypes. A formal contract was not negotiated until the following year.

Mockup Inspection **12-13 January 1954**

The RF–101A mockup inspection took place about 18 months after the first mockup inspection of the basic F–101.

First Flight (YRF-101A) **May 1954**

The Air Force accepted delivery of the second prototype the following month.

Configuration Changes **May 1956**

The December 1955 reassignment of the future RF–101As from SAC to TAC generated a number of configuration changes in order to satisfy TAC's request for additional electronic devices.

First Flight (Production Aircraft) **June 1956**

This aircraft, identified as the RF–101A–20, and two other productions had the 1,773-Imperial gallon fuselage fuel tank capacity of the F–101A.

Production Modifications **April 1957**

The fourth production aircraft—the RF–101A–25, first delivered in April 1957–and all subsequent RF–101A productions were built to the same specifications and grouped under the same block number. Their fuselage fuel tank capacity was supplemented by two 75-Imperial gallon tanks—one in each wing. Otherwise, being the reconnaissance version of the F–101A, there was little dissimilarity between the two. The RF was lighter, however, and had retained the bombing capability of the F–101A.

New Features **April 1957**

The most distinctive feature of the RF–101A was its nose, which had been slightly lengthened for the installation of photographic equipment. This equipment—initially unavailable or scarce—normally comprised a long focal length Fairchild KA–1 framing camera, one vertical and two side oblique Fairchild KA–2 framing cameras, and one CAI KA–18 strip camera.

Enters Operational Service **6 May 1957**

The aircraft was assigned to the 363d Tactical Reconnaissance Wing (TRW) at Shaw AFB as a replacement for the RF–84F, which was being transferred out of the Tactical Air Command. Although harboring distinct advantages over the subsonic RF–84Fs, the new, high-performance RF–101As were delivered without certain equipment vital to the accomplishment of the reconnaissance mission and their picture-taking capability would be limited until photographic production items became available. Even then it was doubtful whether the RF–101A could compensate for the RB–57, which was also being phased out of the reconnaissance inventory. The RF–101A, at best, was considered as a sort of consolation prize for the RF–104 and RF–105, both of which had been scratched from the Air Force's future reconnaissance forces.

Subsequent Model Series

RF–101C.

Other Configurations

RF–101G—an F–101A modified for reconnaissance. The F–101 airframe of the RF–101G, so designated in 1966, was extensively modified to accommodate photographic and electronic components far superior to those of the original RF–101As. Although it also involved significant airframe modifications, several of the 35 RF–101A productions were brought up to the G standard.

End of Production **1957**

The last two RF–101As were accepted by the Air Force in October.

Total RF–101As Accepted

35

Acceptance Rates

Twenty RF–101As were accepted in FY 57, and 15 during the first 4 months of FY 58.

Flyaway Cost Per Production Aircraft

$1,604,963.00—airframe, $1,150,903; engines (installed), $288,466; electronics, $32,566; ordnance, $591; armament, $132,457.

Flyaway Cost Per Modified Aircraft (RF–101G)

$2,979,745.00—airframe, $2,387,899; engines (installed), $429,016; electronics, $106,630; armament, $56,200; ordnance, none.

Average Cost Per Flying Hour (RF–101A)

$853.00

Average Maintenance Cost Per Flying Hour (RF–101A)

$322.00

Phaseout **1971**

Like the F–101As from which they derived, the few RF–101As produced had a limited impact on the Air Force's operational capability. Between 1960 and 1970, eight of them were supplied to Nationalist China through the Military Assistance Program. Several flying accidents, the cannibalization of a few others, and transfer of one RF–101A to the Air National Guard in 1966 further depleted the 35-aircraft fleet. In June 1970 six of the 14 RF-101As remaining in the regular reconnaissance forces were used for training, but all RF-101s were phased out of USAF inventory during the following year. The RF-101Gs, including the two or three RF-101As converted to the G configuration, were allocated to the Guard almost as soon as they became operational, and nine of them were transferred in mid-1966. Toward the end of 1970 the ANG inventory still counted 26 RF-101Gs.

Item of Special Interest **January 1968**

The *Pueblo* crisis led the President to activate three RF-101 squadrons from the Air National Guard. Each of the squadrons served a rotational tour in Japan and compiled impressive records. Combined, they flew 19,715 tactical flying hours in 11,561 sorties and processed 841,601 feet of aerial film and 318,856 prints.

RF-101C

Manufacturer's Model 36X
Weapon System WS-105L

New Features

The single-place, supersonic RF-101C differed from the RF-101A in two respects. It had the strengthened internal structure of the F-101C, and had retained that aircraft's capability for delivering nuclear weapons. In terms of operational service, the RF-101C also followed the F-101C's pattern. Both quickly outclassed their A counterparts, with the RF-101C soon establishing itself as the Air Force's reconnaissance workhorse.

Production Contract **March 1956**

The contract called for procurement of 70 RF-101Cs.

Additional Procurement **December 1956**

The Air Force decided to reduce production of the F-101 and to convert to the reconnaissance configuration the last 96 aircraft under contract. Being late F-101 productions built to the 7.33-g specification of GOR 101 and singled out by the C suffix since September 1956, the converted aircraft entered the inventory as RC-101Cs.

First Flight **12 July 1957**

First Acceptance (Production Aircraft) **September 1957**

Enters Operational Service **1957**

The aircraft became operational at Shaw AFB, with the 20th and 29th Photo Jet squadrons of the 432d TRW.

Subsequent Model Series

None

Other Configurations **1966**

RF-101H—an F-101C, converted to the reconnaissance configuration. Like the RF-101Gs, the RF-101Hs were transferred to the ANG as soon as operational, the first transfer of 10 aircraft occurring in late 1966. In June 1970, 30 RF-101Hs were in the Guard's inventory.

End of Production **1959**

The last six RF-101Cs were accepted by the Air Force in March.

Total RF-101Cs Accepted

166

Acceptance Rates

Eighty RF-101Cs were accepted in FY 58, and 86 in FY 59.

Flyaway Cost Per Production Aircraft[4]

$1,276,145.00—airframe, $803,022; engines (installed), $287,764; electronics, $61,079; ordnance, $441; armament, $123,839.

Flyaway Cost Per Modified Aircraft (RF-101H)[5]

$2,979,745.00—airframe, $2,387,899; engines (installed), $429,016; electronics, $106,630; armament, $56,200; ordnance, none.

Average Cost Per Flying Hour

$853.00

Average Maintenance Cost Per Flying Hour

$322.00

Oversea Deployments **1958**

The new aircraft reached the oversea commands almost as soon as operational. By the end of 1958, 30 RF-101Cs had already joined the USAFE. They were stationed at Nouasseur AB, Morocco, and Laon and Phalsbourg Air Bases in France. In May 1959, following TAC inactivation of the 17th and 18th Photo Reconnaissance Squadrons, another contingent of 36 RF-101s came under USAFE's control. Deployment of the RF-101C to the Pacific Air Forces (PACAF) also took place in early 1958, but it was preceded by that of a few RF-101As. In December PACAF's 40 RF-101A/C aircraft, four more than first authorized, were located at Kadena AB, Okinawa and Misawa AB, Japan.

Initial Operational Problems **1958-1959**

Both the RF-101A and RF-101C were beset with excessive maintenance difficulties and poor supply support. Premature failure of components, due to design deficiencies, aggravated the initial operational problems. In January 1959 all RF-101s were grounded for 1 week because of the collapse of main landing gears. In

---

[4] Excluding $277,658 in Class V modification costs for each RF-101C.

[5] Also omitting Class V modification costs of $416,718 per RF-101H.

August of the same year, the aircraft were again temporarily grounded because of deficient hydraulic systems. The hydraulic problems, first experienced by the USAFE and PACAF aircraft, were not limited to the F/RF–101A and C model series; early F–101B productions were also grounded for the same reasons. Urgent modifications, accomplished by McDonnell teams and Air Force depot personnel, while helpful did not immediately eliminate the landing gears and hydraulic system malfunctions. In the latter case, some 500 manhours per aircraft—depending upon date of manufacture—were needed to solve the problem completely.

Other Significant Problems **1960**

The Air Force quickly improved maintenance and supply support of the Voodoos. By 1960 the squadrons so equipped were highly operational. Yet, no easy solution had been found for the skin crack and corrosion problems that plagued all model series of the F–101 since their service introduction. Cracks in fairing doors, wheel wells, ailerons, trailing edges and speed brakes were discovered during each periodic inspection, and contractor teams had to be hired to assist Air Force sheet metal specialists in the repair of affected areas. A main wing carry through spar also had to be perfected to correct suspected cases of wing fatigue. The corrosion problems, which later equally affected the USAFE F–101Cs of Bentwaters, first reached alarming proportions in PACAF. Although some repairs were made at the operating bases by depot field teams, many of the PACAF RF–101s had to be returned to the United States for reskinning of the wings, shingle, and fuselage at a cost of 8,400 manhours per aircraft. To alleviate the problem, the Air Force in June 1963 awarded a $1.5 million contract for the construction of a corrosion control facility at Kadena AB in Okinawa.

Modernization **1962**

The Air Force continuously strove to improve the RF–101's reconnaissance capability and gave the aircraft better photographic and electronic components as soon as they became available. However, the first major modernization program did not take place until 1962. New high resolution cameras were then installed in most RF–101s. A special modification allowed the aircraft to fly at lower altitudes and the installation of flash cartridge pods gave them a limited night capability. McDonnell's Voodoos were air refuelable. A simple modification, accomplished also in 1962, gave all RF–101 aircraft the added capability of air refueling one another. The modification consisted essentially of installing a buddy refueling tank in place of the external tank of the aircraft's left wing.

Special Assignment **23 October 1962**

Following confirmation on 14 October of the presence of missile sites in Cuba, USAF RF–101Cs were directed to fly at low level over the island. The occasion accented the RF–101C's shortcomings and the aircraft's continued lack of a satisfactory reconnaissance system.

New Improvements 1962–1967

The Air Force decided that the Hycon KS–72A framing camera being developed for the RF–4C—another McDonnell production, under contract since May 1962—also would be installed on the RF–101s. The decision in effect endorsed a whole new modernization program, first suggested by TAC in early 1960. Numerous modifications were grouped under Modification 1181, as the modernization was known, and estimated costs were high. They ran over $180,000.00 per aircraft, in addition to some $3 million of basic expenditures. Modification 1181 involved the installation of several new components, and anticipated technical difficulties were soon confirmed. Initial flight tests in July 1963 revealed major deficiencies in the KS–72A prototype. Testing of the camera's low-altitude reliability in late 1964 also was disappointing. Modification 1181, including the night capability expected of it, ran into further difficulties as testing was delayed because of the limitations of the RF–101 navigation system. Finally started in the fall of 1964 and first applied to the PACAF and USAFE aircraft, the new modernization program did not end until 1967. However, when completed, Modification 1181 and the KS–72A camera gave the RF–101C an improved low-altitude photographic capability that permitted taking full advantage of the aircraft's speed performance. Other accrued advantages were a high-altitude true vertical photographic capability, and an increase in sensor reliability through the use of automatic exposure control and an improved camera control system.

Interim and Other Modifications 1963–1965

Pending availability of the KS–72 cameras to supplement the KA–2s, faster KA–45 cameras were installed in some RF–101Cs during 1963. In the following 2 years, the Air Force also improved the flight safety and maintainability of the aircraft. New main landing gear struts were installed. The RF–101C's fire warning system was modified, and the main fuel lines, fuel filters, and air ducts of the aircraft were overhauled.

SEA Deployments 1961–1970

The RF–101s, the only Voodoos in the Vietnam War, performed reconnaissance and strike evaluations from 1961 through 1970. RF–101s were pathfinders for F–100s in the first USAF strike against North Vietnam on 8 February 1965. Operating originally out of South Vietnam, the RF–101s later flew most of their missions over North Vietnam from Thailand.

Attrition **1958-1970**

More than 30 RF–101Cs were lost during the early years of the aircraft's service life, often because of pilot inexperience. The first RF–101C combat loss occurred in late 1964. Highly sophisticated enemy defenses in North Vietnam accounted for most of the later losses.

Revised Training **October 1966**

The RF–101 pilots in Southeast Asia were still accident prone and not proficient in aerial refueling. Hence, despite acute shortages in aircraft and instructors, the Air Force extended RF–101 flying training to 94 hours.

Program Changes **1967-1969**

The RF–101s were earmarked to equip the Air National Guard. The RF–101Cs were to be supplemented beginning in 1965, and soon thereafter entirely replaced by the new RF–4C Phantoms. Continued increases both in war toll and reconnaissance requirements altered USAF plans. The older aircraft did not possess the speed and radar-homing and warning devices of the RF–4C, but its cameras could obtain broad and detailed coverage of the kind of targets encountered in the war and in 1967 all but one of TAC's RF–101C squadrons were dispatched to SEA. In October of the same year, following the arrival of an additional squadron of RF–4Cs, one squadron of RF–101s at Udorn AB, Thailand, was inactivated, but this was as far as earlier RF–101 planning could be carried. The RF–101s rendered surplus were distributed to depleted SEA units instead of being transferred to the ANG. At year end, and also contrary to plans, the Air Force decided to convert to reconnaissance configuration 29 F–101B interceptors in late 1968 and nine more in early 1969.

Other Reversals **1969**

With the RF–101 weapon system in SEA, the Air Force in late 1965 decided to accelerate the installation of long-range navigation (LORAN) D avionics in the aircraft. Delivery postponements and funding difficulties were to cause another change of plans. The project was cancelled in early 1969.

Phaseout **1969-1971**

A first contingent of five RF–101Cs was transferred to the Air National Guard in early 1969. Concurrently, in consonance with Vietnamization and force modernization programs, the RF–101Cs departed SEA, and the sole RF–101C squadron remaining in Europe converted to the RF–4C. The Air Force transferred its last RF–101Cs to the Guard during 1971. In October, upon completion of the final transaction and including earlier RF–101A and RF–101G and H allocations, the ANG inventory counted 131 RF–101s, 116 of which were fully operational.

Milestones **15 April 1959**

A new world speed record of 816.279 mph was set by an RF–101C Voodoo on a 500-kilometer closed circuit course without payload at Edwards AFB.

F-101B

Manufacturer's Model 36 AT
Weapon System 217A

Previous Model Series

F–101A and C

New Features

Elongated cockpit, permitting sitting of observer behind pilot; different armament (missiles and rockets carried by and launched from a hydraulically actuated rotary armament door); and a fire control system providing automatic search and track. The engines of the F–101B interceptor—two J–57–P–55 turbojets—also differed from those of both the F–101A and F–101C tactical fighter bombers by being fitted with longer afterburners.

Program Development

Development of the F–101B program was generated by a combination of factors. First, by Convair's failure to satisfy quickly the Air Force's "ultimate" interceptor requirements. Secondly, by the difficulties encountered with the same contractor's interim F–102, yet to be delivered in August 1953, when Russia exploded a thermonuclear bomb—less than a year after the United States first successfully demonstrated one. Finally, by ADC's insistence for the greater security that two new interceptors would provide pending availability of Convair's "ultimate" F–106.

Initial Requirements **October 1952**

Impressed by McDonnell's revised version of the F–88 Voodoo (rechristened F–101 in November 1951), ADC in October 1952 suggested the possibility of modifying the aircraft to serve as an interceptor. Headquarters USAF, mainly because of the Voodoo's high cost, rejected the plan and decided to attempt solving the interceptor problem by increasing the numbers of F–86Ds and "putting the heat" on the F–102. The suggestion was revived, however, with ADC's proposal in April 1953 to use the long range F–101 as an interceptor on the perimeter of the United States and in areas where ground radar was inadequate. The Air Force Council late in 1953 directed that the aircraft industry be invited to compete in determining the characteristics required by an interceptor other than the F–102—that would help fill the gap between the F–89 and F–106.

Competition's Results **June 1954**

ADC announced that of the three aircraft proposals that might meet its requirements—an advanced F–89, offered by Northrop, and interceptor versions of North American F–100 and McDonnell F–101—the F–101 was the best. Soon afterwards, the Air Force decided that the aircraft (titled F–101B in mid-1955), if produced, would include the MG–13 fire control system of the F–102 and would carry Falcon missiles.

Go-Ahead Decision **25 February 1955**

Almost 6 months elapsed between the F–101's first flight and the Air Force official endorsement of the F–101 interceptor program. Interim predictions that the interceptor, equipped with the advanced J–67 engine, would be ready to fly by the middle of 1956, that production could begin in 1957, and that the aircraft could be made available to active interceptor squadrons in early 1958 proved wrong or too optimistic. Nevertheless, later events wholly vindicated the production decision.

Contractual Arrangements **March 1955**

Just as with other F–101s, procurement was initiated by letter contracts, the first of which, issued in March 1955, covered 28 aircraft. Four months later, a formal contract, released on 12 July, increased the fiscal year 1956 program to a total of 96 interceptors. However, in December 1956 the Air Force curtailed the peak monthly production rate originally projected for the aircraft and significantly reduced future procurement.

Official Designation **August 1955**

The Air Force officially designated the interceptor version of the F–101 as the F–101B.

Mockup Inspection **14–15 September 1955**

Two of the alterations requested were of particular import. The first involved the aircraft's armament rack. The second dealt with the replacement of the F–101B's initial engines—two advanced but unproven J–67 turbojets developed by Pratt and Whitney.

Production Hold Order **May 1956**

The production restrictions imposed on the F–101A were extended to the F–101B. In the latter case, however, the Air Force restrictions were more drastic. The hold order remained totally in force through the end of 1956, at which time the projected armada of 651 F–101Bs was reduced by almost one quarter.

First Flight **27 March 1957**

The flight took place at Lambert Municipal Airport at St. Louis, Mo., nearly a year later than predicted in early 1955.

Flight Testing **1957-1959**

The Air Force spent close to 2 years of extensive testing and accepted 50 F–101Bs before allowing the Voodoo interceptors to enter operational service. Category I flight tests, conducted at

Edwards AFB, started immediately upon delivery of the first F-101B—March 1957. Category II and Category III flight tests, conducted at Eglin and at Otis AFB, respectively, were completed on 15 March 1959.

Unsolved Problems **1958**

Despite modifications that resulted from the experience with the basic F-101A, two serious flaws surfaced during flight tests of the B model. Both were unique to the interceptor version. The radar observer's cockpit had been badly designed and little could be done except to make minor changes. Too, the MG-13 fire control system developed by the Hughes Aircraft Company was not as advanced as the airframe in which it was placed. The MG-13 was merely a refinement of the E-6 fire control system of the F-89D and could not control the weapons of an interceptor as fast as the F-101B. Headquarters USAF denied replacement of the MG-13 with the MA-1 system of the F-106 because of the cost involved. This left only one course of action: to improve the Central Air Data Computer that was the heart of the MG-13 system.

Enters Operational Service **5 January 1959**

This was a 6-month delay from latest estimates, 18 months later than first expected and almost 2 years after USAF acceptance of the first F-101B. On the other hand, the F-101B received by the 60th Fighter Interceptor Squadron at Otis AFB, the first ADC unit to be so equipped, was a thoroughly tested aircraft, capable of advanced performance.

Operational Readiness **1959-1960**

Although support of the F-101B had been initially handicapped by shortages of parts, it improved during the later part of 1959, and by mid-1960 supply and maintenance problems were well under control. Other difficulties remained, however, including all Voodoos' susceptibility to corrosion and the skin cracks discovered in the rudder area of the F-101B model series. All the same, in December 1960 nine of ADC's 17 squadrons of F-101Bs were rated C-1—the highest degree of combat readiness—and seven were C-2. Only one squadron was considered deficient, and this was due to a temporary shortage of qualified personnel. On the average, 70 percent of the 371 F-101Bs, then assigned to the combat forces, were operationally ready.

Additional Testing **1960**

Despite the extensive flight tests of the 1957-1959 period, two separate testing programs were conducted at the Air Force Missile Development Center at Holloman AFB. One of the test programs further investigated the F-101B compatibility with both Falcon-guided missiles and MB-1 nuclear Genies. The other was an overall review of the entire weapon system. Representatives of

McDonnell and Hughes as well as Douglas, the producer of the MB–1 unguided nuclear rockets, participated in the latter.

Subsequent Model Series

None

Other Configurations **1959-1961**

TF–101Bs—F–101Bs with dual controls for pilot training. Contrary to plans, and because McDonnell took longer than promised to install the dual control kits, only one out of every four F–101Bs produced was so equipped. When fitted out as a trainer, the F–101B retained its original operational capability. The trainer versions entered ADC service in 1959. In April 1960 several of them were allocated to TAC for the training of tactical reconnaissance aircrews. *F–101Fs*—these were late F–101B productions that included modifications accomplished on the production line. Technically referred to as block 115–120 configurations,[6] these aircraft were first identified as F–101Fs in 1961 as arrangements were made to transfer 66 of them to the Royal Canadian Air Force (RCAF), where they acquired still another designation and became CF–101Bs. The trainer version of the block 115–120 F–101B configuration, the TF–101F, was known in RCAF service as the CF–101F. Ten TF–101Fs were included in the 66 Voodoo interceptors transferred to Canada in exchange for that country's operation and maintenance of 14 radar sites.

End of Production **March 1961**

It ended with delivery of the last three aircraft.

Total F-101B/F Accepted

480

Acceptance Rates

One Voodoo interceptor was accepted in FY 57, 15 in FY 58, 133 in FY 59, 241 in FY 60, and 90 in FY 61.

Flyaway Cost Per Production Aircraft[7] (F/TF-101B/F/TF-101F)

$1,754,066.00—airframe, $1,105,034; engines (installed), $332,376; electronics, $52,770; ordnance, $1,001; armament, $262,885.

---

[6] Because of the increasing complexity of aircraft being developed, modifications no longer necessarily entailed a change of the letter suffix in the aircraft model series designation. Since 1941, the aircraft being built with the same specifications were grouped into blocks as they were assembled on the production lines. The blocks were numbered beginning with 1, 5, and subsequently with sequential multiples of five. The intermediate figures were reserved for the identification of aircraft modified after production at a modification center or in the field. In general, block numbers were only allocated to combat aircraft and transports. Exceptions occurred, however. F–4s and C–123s left their assembling plants with consecutive block numbers. On the other hand, T–33 and T–38 trainers received block numbers.

[7] Did not include $13,333 of RDT&E costs and $52,922 in Class V modifications, spent on every F–101 interceptor.

Average Cost Per Flying Hour

$1,004.00

Average Maintenance Cost Per Flying Hour

$501.00

Postproduction Modifications **1961**

As a result of the additional tests conducted at the Air Force Missile Development Center during 1960, the Air Force decided to equip the F–101B/F with the MB–1 Genies produced by Douglas. Necessary modifications were authorized in July 1961.

Subsequent Improvements **1963–1966**

Because of the threat from airbreathing aircraft and missiles, the Air Force began planning modernization of its aging interceptor systems. The Interceptor Improvement Program increased the ability of the F–101B/F to thwart electronic countermeasures and to employ radar to search for and track low-flying aircraft. The two-phase program initiated in early 1963 was completed in mid-1966.

Other Modifications **1964–1968**

The unreliability of the F–101 engine starter (unimproved despite all efforts until the end of 1964) caused a number of incidents and personnel injuries. The problem was finally solved by installing a separate pneumatic cartridge starter for each of the two engines. The Pitch Control System (PCS) of the MB–5 Automatic Flight Control System (AFCS) in the F–101B/F interceptors also had been a source of difficulties for many years. In April 1968 Headquarters USAF approved the installation of a modifying kit which had been thoroughly tested by Honeywell, builder of the AFCS. The new kit completely eliminated use of the poorly designed PCS.

Attrition

The Air Force lost about one fifth of its Voodoo interceptors in some 10 years of operation. Accounting for most of these losses—the majority of which occurred during the early years of the aircraft's operational use—was the F–101's addiction to spins, a definite hazard to inexperienced pilots.

Phaseout **1968–1971**

The Voodoo interceptors began leaving USAF operational inventory sooner than expected because of the economy-induced accelerated inactivation of seven ADC F–101 squadrons in 1968. This action produced a surplus of 163 aircraft, 30 of which were converted to the reconnaissance configuration and transferred to the Tactical Air Command. Another 66 of these Voodoos were allocated to Canada to replace the older F–101Bs, previously furnished to the northern partner in the North American Air Defense Command (NORAD). Such allocations left a residue of 67 aircraft for storage at Davis-Monthan AFB, Ariz. Because of continued budgetary restrictions, three of the last six F–101 squadrons in the regular interceptor force were inactivated in mid-1969. Phaseout of the entire F–101B/F fleet was concluded in the spring of 1971.

Other Uses **December 1969**

Aside from five TF–101B aircraft allocated in 1966 for training, the Voodoo interceptors did not reach the Air National Guard until December 1969. Once underway, however, the conversion of ANG F–102 fighter groups to more modern F–101Bs proceeded smoothly. The three units involved—the 101st, 119th, and 141st Fighter Groups—resumed their alert posture actually ahead of schedule. The Guard proved itself further in 1970 by taking first place in the William Tell F–101 competition. Three other ANG fighter groups (the 142d, 148th, and 107th) began converting to the F–101B/F aircraft in March and April 1971, also without trouble. The 147th Fighter Group (Training) received some F–101Fs in June 1971 but retained its F–102s to train crews for both the F–101B and the F–102—a task turned over to the Guard by ADC.

PROGRAM RECAP

The Air Force bought a grand total of 807 F–101s—2 experimental models (first known as XF–88s), 77 F–101As, 47 F–101Cs, 35 RF–101As, 166 RF–101Cs, and 480 F–101B and F–101F interceptors.

TECHNICAL DATA
F–101A/C and RF–101A/C

Manufacturer — McDonnell Aircraft Corporation, St. Louis, Mo.

Nomenclature — Supersonic Tactical Fighter-Bomber (F–101A/C). Reconnaissance Aircraft (RF–101A/C).

Popular Name — Voodoo

Characteristics	*F–101A*	*F–101C*	*RF–101A/C*
Length/Wing	67 ft/40 ft	67 ft/40 ft	69 ft/40 ft
Take Off Weight	48,000 lb	49,000 lb	48,100 lb
Takeoff Ground Run	4,600 ft	4,800 ft	3,380 ft
Cruise Speed	0.87 kn	0.87 kn	
Max. Speed at 35,000 ft	870 kn	870 kn	
Cruise/Max. Speed			480 kn/ 875 kn
Cruise Range/Endurance			NA/3.9 hr
Ferry Range			1,864 nm
Radius	690 nm	525 nm	
Engine, Number & Designation[8]	Two J57–F–13	Two J57–F–13	Two J57–P–13
Crew	1	1	1
Rate of Climb (sea level)	8,300 fpm	8,300 fpm	
Service Ceiling	50,300 ft	50,300 ft	45,200 ft
Ordnance[9]	4 M–39 20-mm guns	4 M–39 20-mm guns	NA

[8] Pratt & Whitney

[9] Bombs—One Mark 7, one Mark 28, and one Mark 43

TECHNICAL DATA

F-101B/F and TF-101B/F

Manufacturer	McDonnell Aircraft Corporation, St. Louis, Mo.
Nomenclature	Fighter Interceptor. Fighter Interceptor/Trainer.
Popular Name	Voodoo

Characteristics	*Point Interceptor*	*Area-Interceptor*
Length/Wing	71 ft/39 ft	71 ft/39 ft
Takeoff Weight	45,461 lb	51,724 lb (w/two 450 gallon drop tanks)
Takeoff Ground Run	2,600 ft	6,280 ft w/o afterburner
Max. Speed at 35,000 ft	950 kn	950 kn (drops external tanks)
Rate of Climb (sea level)	36,000 fpm	7,610 fpm (Mil. Pwr. climb to best cruise alt)
Combat Ceiling	51,000 ft	50,700 ft
Radius	NA	603 nm
Engine, Number & Designation	2 Pratt & Whitney J57-P-55	2 Pratt & Whitney J57-P-55
Crew	2	2
Armament	2 AIR-2A rockets 2 AIM-4C missiles	2 AIR-2A rockets 2 AIM-4C missiles

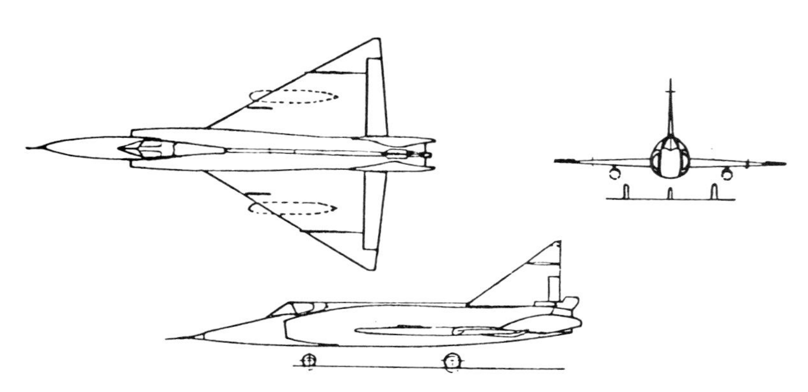

CONVAIR F–102 DELTA DAGGER

F–102A: Supersonic, all-weather, fighter-interceptor, and the Air Force's first operational delta-wing aircraft.

TF–102A: A two-seat combat proficiency trainer, identical to the single-seat F–102A from the wing leading-edge back.

CONVAIR F-102 DELTA DAGGER

Manufacturer's Model 8-10
Weapon System 201A

Basic Development

Convair F-102, like the subsequent F-106, grew out of the company's experimental XF-92A—the world's first delta wing airplane, originally known only as Model 7002, was successfully flown in September 1948.[1]

Advanced Development Objective **13 January 1949**

Called for an advanced, specially designed interceptor (dubbed the "1954 Interceptor"— for the year it was expected to become operational) that could surpass the estimated speed and altitude of Soviet intercontinental jet bombers. Recent intelligence warning and growth limits of the F-86, F-89, and F-94 interceptors spurred development of the Air Force ADO.

Concept Formulation **1948-1949**

The ADO of January 1949 also departed radically from past procedures. The Air Force recognized that the increasing complexity of weapons no longer permitted the isolated and compartmented development of equipment and components which, when put together in a structural shell, formed an aircraft or missile. It concluded that the new interceptor should be developed in conformity with the Weapon System Concept. This concept (yet to be tried) integrated the design of the entire weapon system, making each component compatible with the others.

Request for Proposals (RFPs) **18 June 1950**

As one of the coordinated steps toward development of the new interceptor (Project MX-1554), the Air Force requested an airframe structurally capable of withstanding a speed of more than Mach 1, at an altitude of 50,000+ ft. The 1954 operational date was included in the bidding announcement. In October 1950, 3 months before the MX-1554 bidding ended, the Hughes Aircraft Company was awarded a contract for Project MX-1179, the Electronic Control System (ECS), "around" which the MX-1554 airframe would be built. Hughes had been working on new radars, fire-control systems (beginning with the E-1, developed for the gunfir-

---

[1] Like many other aerodynamic innovations, the delta wing had its inception in the wind tunnels of wartime Germany, although low-aspect-ratio wing forms were also studied by the US National Advisory Committee for Aeronautics. Dr. Alexander M. Lippisch (leader of the German program) helped develop the spectacular Me-163 rocket-propelled interceptor for the Messerschmitt combine. Early design studies by NACA, captured reports of the Lippisch program, and later conferences with Lippisch himself convinced engineers of the Consolidated Vultee Aircraft Corporation (Convair) that the delta wing might be the answer to many of the problems of supersonic flight.

ing F–94A and F–86A aircraft) and related components since 1946. Production of the MX–1179 ECS was programmed for 1953.

Competitors and Selection **1951**

When the MX–1554 bidding closed in January 1951, six contractors had submitted nine proposals. Republic submitted three bids, North American two. Single proposals were made by Lockheed, Chance-Vought, Douglas and Convair. The Air Force on 2 July named three winners: Convair, Republic, and Lockheed, who were all to proceed with development through the mockup stage. At that time the firm providing the most promising design would be awarded a production contract. The MX–1554 three-pronged development was short-lived, however. The Air Force soon decided it was unwise to finance three concurrent Phase I development programs. It cancelled the Lockheed project in its entirety.

Letter Contract **11 September 1951**

The LC awarded Convair authorized use of the Westinghouse J–40 power plant for the MX–1554, pending availability of the much more powerful Wright J–67. Performance requirements for the MX–1554/J–40 prototype were set at Mach 1.88 with a 56,500-ft altitude. The J–67-equipped MX–1554 combination, officially designated by the Air Force as the F–102 and also referred to as the 1954 or Ultimate Interceptor, would include the Hughes MX–1179 ECS and was expected to reach Mach 1.93 at 62,000 feet. Production, if approved, was programmed for 1953 or early 1954 at the latest. Although development of one of the Republic proposals (the Air Force-designated XF–103) was still authorized, the LC of September 1951, in effect, declared Convair the undisputed winner of the design competition for the 1954 Interceptor.[2]

---

[2] The XF–103, one of the winning entries of the MX–1554 competition, was developed by the Republic Aviation Corporation from its AP–44A, a 1948 design for an all-weather, high-altitude defensive fighter. Like the AP–44A, the XF–103 (AP 57) presented numerous innovations, including all-titanium construction, dual-cycle propulsion, periscope for forward vision, and downward ejecting capsule for escape. The F–103 concept of a high-altitude (80,000 feet) Mach 3 interceptor was also far ahead of the state of the art. After a full-scale mockup inspection in March 1953, the Air Force decided to defer the XF–103 Phase II work and to extend for some 18 months the Republic Phase I development contract of September 1951. Republic finally received a contract for three experimental aircraft in June 1954 and the XF–103 (Weapon System 204A) Phase II program began 3 months later. In the following years, however, significant set-backs slowed the development pace of the new XF–103. Low titanium priority, difficulties encountered in the titanium alloy fabrication process, difficulties in engine development, funding problems—all had a hand in program slippage. After being reduced from three to one aircraft, the XF–103 program, still hampered by budgetary restrictions, was cancelled in September 1957—about 1 year before the aircraft's programmed first flight.

Production Decision **24 November 1951**

The Air Force decided to expedite the 1954 Interceptor program.[3] It confirmed that production of the new aircraft would follow the Cook-Craigie Plan for early tooling, limited production at first, elimination of faults by test flights, and accelerated production thereafter.[4] To permit full-scale testing prior to full-scale production, initial production would use the existing Westinghouse J–40 engine (previously earmarked for the MX–1554 F–102 prototype). As also called for by the LC of September 1951, Convair would equip the MX–1554 F–102 with the more powerful J–67, as soon as feasible.

Program Change **December 1951**

The November production go-ahead, while reflecting the Air Force's urgent need of the 1954 Interceptor, did not ignore the fact that the J–67 engine and the MX–1179 ECS were yet to be produced. In December 1951, convinced that the J–67 would not be ready on schedule, the MX–1179 ECS might also be late, and the so-called 1954 Interceptor would never meet its operational deadline, the Air Force changed plans. After surveying once again all existing fighter aircraft and future programmed designs that could be modified to an interceptor configuration, the Air Force gave Convair a new letter contract calling for the June 1953 production of an interim version of the MX–1554 interceptor. It decided to omit industrial competition, considering it time-consuming as well as useless so soon after the MX–1554 competition. Moreover (and of primary concern to the Air Force) use of the Convair MX–1554 airframe for the interim interceptor would allow a thorough, rational, carefully phased development of both the interim and ultimate interceptors. One would lead into the other—an arrangement very similar to that originally devised under the new weapon system concept and the Cook-Craigie production plan.

Operational Requirements **December 1951**

The Air Force in December 1951 drew no specific operational requirements for the interim interceptor. The only stipulation (and the basis for the Air Force decision to buy the Convair aircraft)

---

[3] The decision to accelerate Convair interceptor program halted further development of the Republic XF–91A, originally slated as an interim interceptor. Work stopped in October 1951, following the mockup inspection. The two experimental F–91s, already available, were modified to serve as high-speed armament test vehicles by augmenting their jet engines with rocket motors.

[4] The Cook-Craigie production plan was actually a mere concept, developed in the late forties by USAF Generals Laurence C. Craigie, DCS/Development, and Orval R. Cook, DCS/Materiel. This concept (closely related to the "fly-before-you-buy" concept of the late sixties) could be expensive. The generals both thought "it was only applicable where you had a high degree of confidence that you were going to go into production."

was that the interim interceptor be sufficiently advanced over North American forthcoming F–86D to warrant its procurement. Similarly, the single guideline for selection of components specified that the engine, armament, and, if need be, the electronic control system (while being as technically progressive as possible) would be available to meet the production of the MX–1554 airframe. In any case, the Air Force in late 1951 did not contemplate any large-scale production of the interim interceptor.

F–102A

Official Designation **1952**

The Air Force designated Convair interim interceptor the F–102A. The production-delayed, ultimate MX–1554, while retaining its original designation, would acquire a subsequent model letter series and become the F–102B. In 1956, after numerous engineering changes had further widened the two interceptors' dissimilarities, the Air Force redesignated the F–102B as the F–106.

Mockup Inspection **18 November 1952**

A number of design changes were requested. The Air Force decided the F–102A should be capable of carrying external stores (fuel tanks, armament, and the like). Also, cockpit components of the MX–1179 ECS (simultaneously inspected with the F–102A) had to be rearranged.

Second Program Change **1952–1953**

The Air Force, Convair, and Hughes agreed to equip the F–102A with an interim fire-control system, since it had become certain service-test quantities of the MX–1179 ECS would not be available prior to October 1955. Huges E–9, a modified E–4, was selected. The MX–1179 ECS and the MX–1554 airframe had been specifically designed to complement each other, and the MX–1179's temporary deletion from the F–102A proved to be an important decision. In effect, it marked the defeat of the weapon system concept's first application, for the MX–1179 never reached the F–102A. The E–9 (renamed MG–3 after a number of technical changes had substantially increased its overall capability) was eventually replaced by the MG–10. This system (itself a former MG–3 incorporating the AN/ARR–44 data link, the MG–1 automatic flight control system, and the AN/ARC–34 miniaturized communication set) became a permanent feature of the F–102A. Meanwhile, by almost imperceptible steps, the interim F–102A took on greater importance, and the quantities discussed grew larger. More emphasis on the F–102A meant less on the ultimate interceptor, leading to an insidious program change. The realities of the development situation, however, dictated this undesirable trend.

Development Problems **1952–1953**

The F–102A's development problems first centered on its weight, which was increasing continuously. The Westinghouse J–40 (the most powerful US turbojet engine qualifed for production in early 1951) lacked the thrust to give the F–102A the minimum requisite speed and altitude. Its replacement, the Pratt and Whitney J–57–P–11, officially rated as being in the 10,000-lb class and due to enter production in February 1953, was heavier. The post-mockup inspection requirements for additional armament also generated extra weight, as did the aircraft's new fire-control system, heavier than the future MX–1179. Meanwhile, a much more serious problem loomed.

Other Initial Problems **1953**

NACA wind tunnel tests in early 1953 showed that the maximum altitude of 57,000 feet and combat radius of 350 miles (304.3 nm) predicted for the F–102A were too optimistic. The designers of the original Convair proposal (MX–1554) had failed to make proper allowance for a delta-wing aircraft's aero-dynamic drag.[5] Convair drag estimates of the F–102A in its bulky amidship configuration did not coincide with the data upon which they were based. The solution was to indent the fuselage to a "coke-bottle" or "wasp waist" configuration, but first the contractor had to be convinced that its original design was in error. However, it was not until mid-1953 that Convair accepted the implications of the "NACA ideal body theory" and joined in the recommendations that the F–102A's design conform to this theory's requirements.

Definitive Contract for Production **12 June 1953**

The LCs, previously awarded to Convair, were superseded by a definitive contract. This contract, still based on the Cook-Craigie production plan, did not affect the number of aircraft initially ordered. Out of the 42 aircraft under procurement, several were earmarked for testing and two (F–102A prototypes) were scheduled for flight in October and December 1953, respectively. Production dates were significantly changed, however. Limited production would not begin until April 1954—10 months later than programmed in December 1951. Accelerated production of a combat-ready, fully tested weapon system was planned for December 1955—almost 2 years later than first anticipated.

First Flight (Prototype) **24 October 1953**

The first YF–102A, flown from Edwards AFB in October 1953,

---

[5] The area-rule concept of aircraft design (that interference drag at transonic speed depends almost entirely on the distribution of the aircraft's total cross-sectional area along the direction of flight) was verified during December 1952 by Richard T. Whitcomb in NACA's new transonic wind tunnels.

crashed on 2 November, but not before the aircraft's anticipated poor performance was fully demonstrated. The flight tests, resumed several months later with the second YF–102A (first flown on 11 January 1954), could only confirm that the F–102A in its present configuration was drag-limited to Mach .98 with a 48,000-ft ceiling—considerably below the required performance.[6]

Design Changes **1954**

While the MX–1179 deletion from the F–102A defeated the weapon system concept's first application, the aircraft's unavoidable redesign made havoc of the Cook-Craigie plan for early tooling. Of the 30,000 tools already purchased by Convair in October 1953 (when testing established unequivocally that important changes had to be made in the plane's design), 20,000 had to be discarded and new ones bought—a sizeable increase in production costs. Meanwhile, the April 1954 wind-tunnel and scale-model tests of a remodeled F–102A (that included cambered leading edges, reflex wing tips, rearward relocation of wing, relocation of vertical fin, 7-ft fuselage extension, and redesign of fuselage to incorporate the principles of the area-rule "coke-bottle" configuration) reflected continuing deficiency in performance. Moreover, airframe and component changes had added 3,500 pounds to the aircraft's weight.

Further Redesign **1954**

In May 1954 the Air Force approved further redesign of the first "coke-bottle" configuration. The new drag-reducing changes extended the fuselage another four feet and added: a new canopy (lighter and providing better visibility), new engine-intake ducts, an aft fuselage fairing, and wing-camber modifications. The J–57–P–23 engine (generating 16,000 pounds of thrust, or approximately 1,200 pounds more thrust than the -11) was to replace the -11 and the interim -41 (an -11 engine modified for new air bleed probes to eliminate cabin fumes). A major weight-reduction, likewise, was initiated.

New Procurement **1954**

Redesign of the F–102A, once agreed upon, was accompanied by new production decisions. The Air Force in March 1954 gave Convair a second production contract calling for delivery of 37 additional F–102As between February and July 1955. A third and larger order, placed in June 1954, scheduled the delivery of another 108 aircraft between August and December 1956.

General Operational Requirements **4 November 1954**

Convair's new production contracts were soon followed by definite

---

[6] The F–86D, that the F–102A was supposed to supplant, had a service ceiling of 49,600 feet and a maximum speed of 601.7 kn(Mach .9). It was fully operational in mid-1953, the initial production date originally set for the F–102A.

qualifications. In November 1954 the Air Force issued a set of general operational requirements that called for altitude performances up to 54,000 feet, a combat radius of 326 nautical miles, and speeds up to Mach 1.23 at 35,000 feet. The Air Force also placed an informal (but nevertheless meaningful) hold order on the FY 1955 funds for the 108 F–102As, recently ordered. This hold order would prevail until forthcoming flight tests of the new F–102A proved to be satisfactory.

First Flight (Revised Prototype) — 19 December 1954

A "synthetically modified" production F–102A made its initial flight and demonstrated substantial performance improvement over the original configuration, reaching Mach 1.22 and an altitude of 53,000 feet. This demonstration "coke-bottle" prototype (nick-named the Hot Rod to distinguish it from the two earlier YF–102As and the few initial straight-fuselage productions allocated to the testing program) was fitted with fillets designed to the latest, light-weight configuration that had been approved by the Air Force in May 1954. It was powered by an advanced production of the improved J–57–P–23 turbojet, due for delivery in June 1955.

Testing — 1955

Evaluation of the Hot Rod prototype's preliminary flight tests led the Air Force to rescind in early 1955 its administrative hold order of the previous year. Ensuing flight tests by Air Force pilots, while demonstrating that the aircraft's stability needed improving, were also satisfactory. They ended in June 1955, after the aircraft's initial high speed had been equaled and its original altitude performance actually exceeded. Ten months of structural integrity testing were initiated in July, when the Air Force concluded (after numerous airborne firing tests) that the F–102A would be able to launch the Falcon missile, as well as 2.75- and 2-inch rockets. A high point in the series of armament tests was reached on 8 July, when the YF–102A fired 6 Falcons and 24 rockets in less than 10 seconds.

First Flight (Production Aircraft) — 24 June 1955

This was the first production F–102A built to the Hot Rod, lightweight, "coke-bottle" configuration. The aircraft was accepted by the Air Force on 29 June, 5 days after its first flight.

Enters Operational Service — April 1956

The F–102A first entered service with the Air Defense Command's 327th FIS at George AFB. It became the Air Force's first delta-wing aircraft—almost 3 years past the June 1953 production date in the LC of December 1951, some 7 months beyond the revised delivery schedule of 1954, and nearly 10 years after the experimental, delta-wing F–92's first flight.

Production Modifications **1956**

One month before the F-102A entered operational service, the Air Force and Convair decided to give the F-102A a larger fin. This new design change, endorsed after a period of extensive testing, would alleviate the aircraft's instability, a remaining problem particularly acute at high speeds. The change became effective with the 26th F-102A, after Convair production schedule had been adjusted for this purpose. Enlarged fins were retrofitted on the 25 aircraft already off the production lines.

Armament Changes **1956**

As once planned and in order to simplify logistical support of the F-102A, the Air Force decided in mid-1956 that (beginning with all post-December productions) only the 2.75-inch Folding Fin Aerial Rocket would be used as backup to the Falcon (GAR-1 and infrared -1B) guided missiles—the aircraft's primary armament. Operational F-102As and those released from production before the decision could be implemented, would exchange their T-214 2-inch FFARs for the standard 2.75-inch rockets. Necessary modifications were subsequently made in the field by teams from the Air Force San Antonio Air Materiel Area, Tex. Some 170 F-102s were modified. In the meantime, after the first air-firing of an MB-1 rocket was accomplished from a YF-102 in May 1956, the Air Force again considered equipping the F-102A with Genie rockets, even though this would entail another production delay. This project, however, was given up in early 1957.

Additional Procurement **September 1956**

The Air Force gave Convair a fifth and final contract for 140 F-102As in September 1956, 10 months after the fourth and largest (562 aircraft) F-102A production contract had been placed.

Operational Problems **1957**

One year after becoming operational, the F-102A still harbored a number of deficiencies, but most defects were being corrected. By November, all F-102As had been retrofitted with serviceable struts and the incorporation of a new oleo strut metering pin and revision of the side brace boss bearing of the landing gear in all future F-102A productions gave assurance that the long-standing problem of landing gear failure (susceptible of affecting also the more advanced F-106 interceptor) was finally solved. Convair in addition had devised a fix for speed brake failures in flight, another critical problem which had dictated the reinspection of speed brake in each F-102A.

Other Production Modifications **1957**

While the F-102A's operational problems were being corrected, efforts to further improve the aircraft's performance did not slacken. After a successful prototype flight in May 1957, F–102As acquired a new wing. Referred to as the Case XX wing and phased into production after October 1957 (beginning approximately with the 550th F–102A), this final major structural change raised combat ceiling to 55,000 feet (a 5,000-ft increase), boosted maximum speed at 50,000 feet to Mach 1 (a Mach 0.06 gain), and substantially improved maneuverability. The F–102A's stability at low speeds, still marginal despite the previous in-production incorporation of a larger fin, also improved vastly.

Modernization **1957–1963**

Modernization of the F–102A, undertaken almost concurrently with the aircraft's final production change, lasted several years.[7] First involved were the addition of data link[8] and replacement of the MG–3 fire-control system by the improved MG–10. There followed the substitution of more sophisticated and less troublesome GAR missiles (as they became available) and the addition of the nuclear Falcon Model Y52A. This atomic missile, first known as the GAR–11 and subsequently redesignated the AIM–26A, had been designed by Hughes specifically for the F–102A. In 1963, after more than 450 aircraft had been modified and provided the necessary kits (one kit per aircraft, at an initial cost of $10,000 per kit), half of the F–102 interceptors (trainers included) could carry the AIM–26A. Ensuing modifications eventually provided interchangeable utilization of AIM–26 and AIM–4 (GAR–1 through 4 series of Falcons in post-1962 nomenclature) missiles in the center missile bay of a number of F–102As. Under project Big Eight (and still as part of the F–102A modernization), incorporation of an Infrared Search and Track System into the F–102 fleet also began in 1963.

Oversea Deployments **1958**

The F–102As were first deployed oversea in June 1958, when ADC's 327th FIS—the Air Force's first F–102A unit—moved to Thule, Greenland. The F–102As reached Europe and Alaska early in 1960, after some of the aircraft (due for deployment to oversea bases which only had tactical air navigation ground stations) were engineered to provide for the installation of AN/ARN–21 airborne TACAN equipment. The F–102As also joined the Pacific Air Forces early in 1960. They were to remain in both the European and Pacific theaters for nearly 10 years.

---

[7] The F–102A was still being modernized long after some of the aircraft had already begun to leave the regular forces. This took care of the air defense needs, increasingly provided by the Air National Guard, and of important oversea requirements.

[8] Data link furnished the pilot information electronically rather than by voice.

War Commitments **1962-1969**

Four F–102s were sent from Clark AB, P. I., to South Vietnam in March 1962, after radars had detected low-flying, unidentified aircraft along the Cambodian border. This started a series of rotations every 6 weeks by Navy EA–1F all-weather fighters and USAF F–102s to Tan Son Nhut. The rotation ended in May 1963 due to base overcrowding. Nonetheless, from the summer of 1963 to mid-1964, Thirteenth Air Force conducted no-notice deployments of F–102s to South Vietnam and brief training flights to Tan Son Nhut and Da Nang. The small number of aircraft committed to SEA air defense before 1965 tripled by the end of 1966. At that time 12 F–102s stood alert in South Vietnam (6 at Bien Hoa and 6 at Da Nang) and another 10 in Thailand (6 at Udorn[9] and 4 at Don Muang). Little change occurred in 1967 and 1968, the Air Force keeping a minimum of 14 F–102s on 5-minute alert with the remainder of the force on 1-hour call. F–102 operations in SEA ended in December 1969[10] with a remarkable safety record. In almost 10 years of flying air defense and a few combat air patrols for SAC B–52s, just 15 F–102s were lost.

Attrition **1956-1971**

The F–102A's overall safety record (including all SEA losses) was also impressive. In more than 14 years of operation, only 16 percent of the F–102A total force, or less than 140 aircraft were lost in flying accidents.[11]

Subsequent Model Series

None—the TF–102 (trainer variant of the F–102A) entered production almost concurrently with the Hot Rod, light-weight, F–102A.

Other Configurations

None, besides the TF–102A. The F–102C, an F–102A that would use an advanced engine (the J–57–P–47 with titanium compressor), never came into being. The Convair F–102C proposal of 1956, then referred to as the F–102X, also included a tail cone extension of 7 inches and an armament load of one MB–1 Genie rocket and four Falcon missiles. The contractor expected that these changes (estimated to result in a speed increase to Mach 1.33 and a 3,000-ft altitude gain over existing F–102As) would qualify the new model to fill a possible gap between the end of the service life of the F–102A and the introduction of the F–106. The Air Force in April

---

[9] More than a dozen F–104s based at Udorn also had air defense duties as a secondary mission.

[10] The last F–102 squadron at Clark was inactivated. However, a few F–102s remained at the Royal Thai Air Base of Don Muang until the summer of 1970.

[11] A minimal number of ground accidents occurred, bringing total F–102A operational losses to 141 as of 30 June 1971.

1957 decided to refuse the Convair proposal and to rely rather on the F–106 being ready for tactical inventory starting in mid-1958. Throughout the years the Air Force used a number of F–102As for special tests. As required by the testing programs in which they were used, these aircraft were sometimes stripped of their original components or fitted with additional equipment. They appeared on Air Force rolls on and off as JF–102As, but this was only a temporary designation. The Air Force used the J prefix to identify every tactical aircraft diverted to special test programs and later returned to their original or standard operational configuration.

End of Production **September 1958**

With delivery of five last aircraft.

Total F-102As Accepted

Of 889 accepted, 875 were assigned to the operational inventory and 14 were set aside for the testing program (2 YF–102As, 8 other early straight-fuselage aircraft, and 4 F–102As, built to the first major redesign configuration without intention of modification to a tactical configuration).

Acceptance Rates

One F–102A was accepted for the operational forces in FY 55, 45 in FY 56, 372 in FY 57, 427 in FY 58, and 30 in the first 3 months of FY 59. The highest production delivery was made in June 1956, when the Air Force accepted 51 aircraft. The Air Force accepted five straight-fuselage F–102As (including two prototypes) in FY 54 and five more in FY 55. The four redesigned, nontactical F–102As were accepted in FY 55.

Total RDT&E Costs

$101.92 million—prorated, it came to $101,921 and was included in every F–102's unit cost.

Flyaway Cost Per Production Aircraft[12]

$1.2 million—airframe, $744,258; engine (installed), $210,308; electronics, $9,208; armament, $219,876; ordnance, $525.

Average Cost Per Flying Hour

$611.00

Phaseout **1961-1973**

The F–102A replaced the F–86D as the most numerous interceptor and by the end of 1958 they numbered 627, or about half the total number of interceptors controlled by ADC. The F–102A began to leave the air defense system with the receipt of the F–101B and F–106A, but in mid-1961 there were still 221 of these aircraft

[12] Excluding $137,947 in prorated Class V modification costs and $11,612 spent on each F–102A for specific modifications.

available within ADC. Toward the end of 1969, when except for one squadron maintained in Iceland, all F–102s of the Air Defense Command had been transferred to the Air National Guard, the Air Force still retained a few oversea F–102 squadrons. Two were in the Pacific theater, three in Germany and one in the Netherlands. However, the F–102 squadrons stationed in Europe were being re-equipped with newer, more versatile F–4s and the F–102A's Pacific commitments were coming to an end. In mid-1972, only 17 F–102s (15 F–102As and 2 TF–102As) remained in the operational inventory of the Air Force and 69 F–102s were surplus. By 30 June 1973 the number of active USAF F–102s had been reduced to 10. Meanwhile, the F–102A had become an important asset of the Air National Guard. After receiving in 1960 an initial contingent of seven F–102As, the ANG's operational inventory of F–102As grew quickly. It jumped to 130 F–102s in 1961 and in mid-1966 reached 339 (311 F–102As and 28 TF–102As), a total that remained fairly constant in the ensuing years. In mid-1972, the ANG operational inventory of F–102s was down to 206 (181 F–102As and 25 TF-102As), but a USAF allocation of surplus F–102s had boosted this total to 224 by 30 June 1973.

Other Uses

The Air Force decided to convert aging F–102s into target drones. They would be used in Pave Deuce, an Eglin AFB program calling for low-cost, full-size, supersonic targets, representative of enemy aircraft (MIG–21s) in aerial combat. The Sperry Rand Corporation was selected for the conversion over Lear Siegler, Northrop, Celesco Industries, Lockheed Aircraft and Hughes Aircraft teamed with Honeywell. The $5.5 million Air Force contract awarded in April 1973 called for the modification of six F–102s into two different drone configurations. Two aircraft would be converted into QF–102A versions, retaining pilot controls for use in contractor-operated flights. The remaining four would be turned into "de-man-rated" afterburning targets, designated PQM–102As. The Pave Deuce PQM–102As would only be flown as drones, using less costly "de-man-rated" parts and checkout procedures. Sperry Flight Systems Divisions, Phoenix, Ariz., would handle the conversion, to be completed within 16 months. Ultimately, as many as 200 surplus F–102s might be modified.

TF-102A

Manufacturer's Model 8-12
Weapon System 201L

Previous Model Series

None. This was the trainer variant of the F–102A.

New Features

Wider forward fuselage providing side-by-side cockpit seating for student and instructor.

General Operational Requirements **April 1952**

For a dual-controlled trainer version of the F–102A interceptor to transition jet pilots to the intricately different delta-wing airplane. Neither ADC nor the Air Training Command believed that this training could be provided with conventional type jet trainers.[13]

Go-Ahead Decision **16 September 1953**

The Air Force authorized production of the TF–102A. However, because of the problems encountered with the basic F–102A design, initial procurement was delayed and further production postponed until the fate of the tactical program was determined.

Contractual Arrangements **July 1954**

A firm order for 20 TF–102As was placed on contract, with first delivery due in July 1955. This initial procurement followed approval by the TF–102A Mockup Board of the side-by-side trainer nose configuration, presented by the Convair Fort Worth plant in January 1954. It was endorsed (in preference to the conventional tandem configuration) to simplify training, realizing that the extra weight of the new forward fuselage would probably hinder trainer performance.

Mockup Inspection **September 1954**

The two-place TF–102A was identical to the F–102A aft of the cockpit section. It would also retain the F–102A's weapon capability.

Additional Procurement **1955**

In early 1955, following the December 1954 successful flight of the revised YF–102A, 28 additional trainers were ordered. The Air Force gave Convair a letter contract for 150 other TF–102As in December—1 month after the trainer's first flight. These planes were to be delivered between March and December 1957.

First Flight (Production Aircraft) **8 November 1955**

The Air Force accepted the first TF–102A during the month it first flew and took delivery of a second production in December 1955—several months past the original deadline.

Initial Problems **1955–1956**

Extensive operational testing soon revealed that the TF–102A's large cockpit and canopy created a serious buffeting problem at high speed. A new cockpit configuration with a cut-down canopy and revised windshield, flight-tested in April 1956, did not prove to

[13] Shortcomings of the then available T–33 and radar-equipped B–25 trainers had been confirmed by the F–86D and F–94 transition training programs.

be the answer. Buffeting was somewhat reduced but at the expense of landing visibility, which had become less than marginal. The simplest solution was to revert to the trainer's original cockpit. The buffeting problems would be eliminated by adding vortex generators and an increased area vertical stabilizer to the aircraft fuselage. These structural modifications, successfully tested with the third TF–102A accepted by the Air Force in June 1956, were introduced in all subsequent productions.

Production Hold Order **January/June 1956**

The TF–102A's initial buffeting problem caused the Air Force to stop Convair production. The Air Force released its hold order late in June 1956, after successful testing of the third TF–102A—a modified article, representative of subsequent productions. During the same period the Air Force also decided to reduce its TF–102A procurement and cut Convair's last order almost by half. Despite the reduction, Convair did not make up for the time lost. Final deliveries to the Air Force still lagged 6 months behind the original schedule.

End of Production **July 1958**

With delivery of the last five TF–102As.

Total TF-102As Accepted

111 (68 less than once programmed), bringing total F/TF–102A procurement to 1,000 aircraft.

Acceptance Rates

Three TF–102As were accepted in FY 56, 27 in FY 57, 76 in FY 58, and 5 in FY 59.

Flyaway Cost Per Production Aircraft[14]

$1.5 million—airframe, $1,135,018; engine (installed), $144,474; electronics, $11,365; armament, $173,777; ordnance, $1,192.

Average Cost Per Flying Hour

$611.00

Phaseout

The TF–102A's phase out and operational life followed the F–102A's pattern. As a rule, two TF–102As accompanied each F–102A squadron.

PROGRAM RECAP

The Air Force accepted a grand total of 1,000 F–102s. Of these, 889 were listed as F–102As, even though they included 2 prototypes, 8 early straight-fuselage, and 4 F–102A test aircraft. The remaining 111 were TF–102As.

---

[14] Excluding $137,947 in prorated Class V modification costs and $11,182 spent on each TF–102A for specific modifications.

TECHNICAL DATA

F/TF-102A

Manufacturer	Convair Division of General Dynamics Corporation, San Diego, Calif.	
Nomenclature	Supersonic, all-weather, fighter-interceptor.	
Popular Name	Delta Dagger	
Characteristics	*Point Interceptor*	*Area Interceptor*
Takeoff Weight	28,150 lb	31,276 lbs (w/two 215 gallon extra tanks)
Length Fuselage/Wing	68."3'/38."1'	68."3'/38."1'
Max. Speed at 35,000 ft	677 kn	677 kn
Radius		566 nm (w/two 215 gallon extra tanks)
Engine, Number & Designation	1J57-P-23A	1J57-P-23A
Takeoff Ground Run	2,290 ft	2,800 ft
Rate of Climb (sea level)	17,400 fpm	4,500 fpm (Mil. power climb)
Combat Ceiling	51,800 ft	51,400 ft
Crew[15]	1	1
Armament[16]	12 2.75" FFAR rockets	12 2.75" FFAR rockets
Ordnance	2 AIM-26/26A or 1 AIM-26/26A + 2 AIM-4A or 1 AIM-26/26A + 2 AIM-4C/D or 6 AIM-4A or 6 AIM-4C/D	2 AIM-26/26A or 1 AIM-26/26A + 2 AIM-4A or 1 AIM-26/26A + 2 AIM-4C/D 6 AIM-4A or 6 AIM-4C/D

[15] TF-102A, when used as trainer, provided accommodation for a two-man crew (student and instructor).

[16] FFAR rockets capability removed from aircraft modified to provide interchangeable utilization of Falcon AIM-26 and Falcon AIM-4 missiles in the center missile bay.

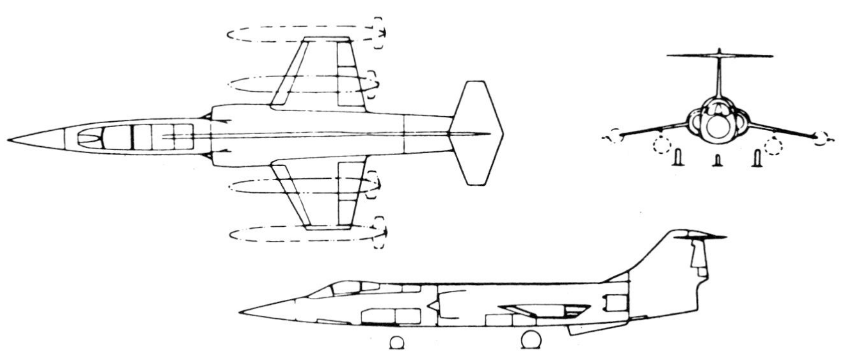

LOCKHEED F–104 STARFIGHTER

F–104A: One of the Air Force's smallest and lightest planes. The tiny F–104A, with its long-nosed fuselage and razor-thin trapezoid wings, had never been intended as an interceptor, but the Air Defense Command liked its performance.

F–104B: Second cockpit aft of the F–104A's single seat—in the space otherwise designed for the M–61 Vulcan gun. The F–104B trainer retained the Sidewinder air-to-air missiles of the F–104A.

F–104C: The slightly heavier F–104C served as a tactical fighter with the Tactical Air Command. It featured a more powerful engine, a probe-drogue air refueling system, and could carry nuclear stores. Several F–104Cs were used in Southeast Asia.

F–104D: The two-seater training version of the F–104C was eventually fitted with 2.75 inch rockets for air-ground support.

F–104G: This all-weather fighter-bomber had a stronger structure. It was produced under patent by Europe and Canada in various configurations. Japanese-made F–104s were interceptors, designated F–104Js.

LOCKHEED F-104 STARFIGHTER

Manufacturer's Model 183-93-02
Weapon System 303A

Basic Development **1949-1952**

Lockheed developed the F-104 from its F-90—flight tested in 1949 but never produced. The F-104 also benefited from Douglas work on the X-3—an experiment flown in October 1952 that did not meet expectations because of the lack of an adequate engine.[1]

Unsolicited Proposal **November 1952**

Lockheed knew[2] the Air Force (based on its Korean experience) needed a new air superiority fighter, capable of operating from forward air fields, accelerating rapidly from the ground, and fighting at high altitudes. Lockheed proposed a light-weight, straight-wing design, when the Air Force had in mind a relatively heavy delta-wing aircraft. Yet Lockheed's small, "Gee Whizzer" day-fighter (later dubbed Starfighter) was tempting for it would be cheaper.[3]

General Operational Requirements **12 December 1952**

Called for development of a light-weight air superiority day fighter to replace TAC's F-100s in 1956. The formal USAF requirement of December 1952 (finalized 1 month after Lockheed's unsolicited proposal) soon entered competitive bidding.

Contractor Selection **January 1953**

After considering entries from Republic and North American Aviation, the Air Force endorsed Lockheed's official bid. Circumstances had favored Lockheed from the outset. The relative merits

---

[1] To recoup its losses on the X-3 program, the Air Force insisted that Douglas deliver the aircraft plans to Lockheed.

[2] In fact, Lockheed had rejected in May 1952 a letter contract covering the construction of flying prototypes because of a clause forfeiting all patent features to, and permitting, the government to assign the new airplane's production to others. Similar provisions, initially included in the North American F-100, Convair F-102, and McDonnell F-101 production contracts, were also turned down by the contractors. In all these cases, the government eventually gave in.

[3] Moreover, in late 1952 all criteria in the world of aviation were subordinated to flight performance. The weight controversy born of the Korean air battles was unsettled. Despite its kill superiority over the MIG, the heavier F-86 (with its sometimes superfluous gadgets) was criticized for complexity and extra weight. Notwithstanding, Clarence L. (Kelly) Johnson, Lockheed's chief engineer, said in 1954: "This [the XF-104] is still a highly complex airplane. You simply don't fly around at 40,000 feet at those kinds of speeds just by throwing a saddle over the thing and riding it. But what we have done is bring an end to the trend toward constantly bigger, constantly more complicated, constantly more expensive airplanes."

of each proposal were of primary importance. Nevertheless, the Air Force wanted to prevent Republic and North American from monopolizing the development and production of new fighters.[4]

Letter Contract **11 March 1953**

Selection of the Lockheed proposal was not a blanket endorsement of the F–104 design. The Air Force moved cautiously. Lockheed was awarded a development LC for two XF–104s and 1 year of flight testing. An early 1954 first flight was scheduled.

Mockup Inspection **30 April 1953**

This initial inspection led to replacement of two 30–mm guns with one 20–mm GE Gatling gun-type M–61 Vulcan cannon (under development and then known as the T–171 gun) for a net weight decrease of 80 pounds. The F–104 cockpit's final inspection did not take place until 29 January 1955—almost 2 years later. Still, the F–104's early development stages were unusually rapid.[5]

First Flight (XF–104) **28 February 1954**

The aircraft featured a Buick-built J–65 engine,[6] far less powerful than the General Electric J–79,[7] intended for any F–104 productions. Lockheed flew its second XF–104 on 5 October, after fitting the J–65 engine with an afterburner. This raised the aircraft performance significantly.

F-104A

Go-Ahead Decision **July 1954**

Still cautious, the Air Force programmed only 17 aircraft under "fly-before-you-buy." This meant more development tests before any large-scale production.

Initial Procurement **October 1954**

One month after the first XF–104 successfully completed Phase I

---

[4] Republic was already committed to the XF–105, the XF–103, and the F–84 program; North American, to the F–86 and F–100.

[5] Less than a year separated the development LC of March 1953 and the XF–104's first flight. Nevertheless, Lockheed had turned down 1 year before a contract calling for similar prototypes. In effect, the same 1951 design competition which resulted in the so-called 1954 Ultimate Interceptor (F–102 and F–106) also, in a sense, spawned the F–104. The Air Force removed Lockheed from consideration as regards the Ultimate Interceptor in September 1951, but soon went back for development of a very advanced day fighter. Nonetheless, the F–104 was unique—experiencing few serious problems during development, perhaps due to its derivation from earlier (F–90 and X–3) developments.

[6] An adaptation of the British Sapphire, the J–65 was first built by Curtiss-Wright for the F–84F.

[7] The static thrust of the GE–J–79 engine (developed for the B–58 bomber and first tested in June 1954), with afterburner, exceeded 14,000 pounds. The XF–104's J–65 had only an 11,500–lb thrust, counting the 3,500 pounds added by its afterburner.

testing. Yet as programmed, Lockheed's first production contract covered only 17 F–104s[8] (closely resembling their experimental predecessors). The Air Force planned to refurbish these aircraft for normal employment, after completion of scheduled suitability tests.

Initial Testing (XF-104) 1954-1956

Scheduled XF–104 flight tests ended in August 1956, marred by the April 1955 crash of one of the two aircraft.[9] In March 1955 an XF–104, still powered by the interim J–65 had attained Mach 1.7 and an altitude of 60,000 feet. Lockheed designers had predicted a speed around Mach 2 and a combat ceiling of 53,000 feet for the aircraft.

First Flight (Production Aircraft) 17 February 1956

The flight was conducted at the Air Force Flight Test Center, Edwards AFB, Calif. A second aircraft, accepted in March, entered flight testing on 15 June.[10]

Other Flight Tests 1956-1958

The F–104 evaluation and suitability test program uncovered all sorts of unexpected problems. This stretched testing to 52 F–104s—35 more than the 17 test productions originally forecasted.

Engine Problems 1955-1958

Fearing the General Electric J–79 turbojet might not be ready in time, the Air Force (until 1955) thought of using the J–65 for initial F–104s. J–65's new malfunctions took care of this temporary planning, however. Since no F–104 airframes were available in 1955 the Air Force then flight-tested the experimental J–79 in a borrowed Navy XF–4D. This worked. The December 1955 testing of the XJ–79–GE–3 and production of the J–79–GE–3A enabled the F–104 2 years later to approach Mach 2. Notwithstanding, flameouts, ignition failures, and oil depletions caused several crashes and in-flight emergencies during testing and after the aircraft had become operational. General Electric came up with a better engine (the J–79–GE–3B), but not before the F–104s were repeatedly grounded. Retrofit of the –3B in early F–104s began in April 1958.

---

[8] The Air Force ordered 209 additional F–104s the following year and 480 more (including 106 earmarked for training) in late 1956. By 1957, 722 F–104s of one kind or another were programmed for production. This number was drastically reduced in December 1958—the entire USAF F–104 program never went past 294.

[9] Testing of the armament and fire-control system in this aircraft was then switched to a Lockheed F–94C, because none of the 17 aircraft ordered in October 1954 were yet available.

[10] First of the F–104s ordered in October 1954. Primarily earmarked for testing, these aircraft were immediately accounted for as production models.

Structural Deficiencies **1956-1957**

Lockheed reduced the F-104's pitchup to an acceptable USAF level in December 1956 and continued improvement. It corrected an aerodynamic weakness in 1957 by redesigning the tail section.

Other Problems **1956-1957**

The 20-mm, M-61 Vulcan cannon was selected for the F-104 in 1953. However, repeated flight-testing of the gun led the Air Force in November 1957 to consider it too unreliable for the early aircraft. (It was retrofitted in 1964.) The F-104's high speed rendered its downward ejection seat unsatisfactory despite safety improvements. Lockheed was perfecting a replacement upward ejection system, but progress was slow. Even so, retrofitting of all F-104s with the new seat got under way in the early 60's.

Enters Operational Service **26 January 1958**

The F-104A entered service 2 years late and not with TAC (as originally planned), but with ADC's 83d Fighter Interceptor Squadron at Hamilton AFB. This April 1956[11] shift rested on two factors: slippage of the F-104 operational due-date (causing TAC to make other arrangements) and ADC's urgent need of a fighter to fill the gap between the F-102 and F-106. The tiny F-104,[12] with its longnosed fuselage and razor-thin trapezoid wings, had never been intended as an interceptor. But ADC believed it could use it, due to its impressive performance.

Oversea Deployments **October 1958**

Twelve F-104As from the 83d FIS were disassembled and flown by C-124s to beef up Taiwan's air defense during the Quemoy crisis of 1958. This took place less than a year after the F-104 became operational.

Total F-104As Accepted

170 (excluding the two XF-104 s ordered in March 1953)—against the 610 programmed in 1957. Fund shortages accounted for most of the cut; TAC revised requirements, the remainder.

Acceptance Rates

The Air Force accepted 7 F-104As in FY 56, 28 in FY 57, 94 in FY 58, and 41 in FY 59.[13]

---

[11] The Air Force also decided at this time to give the aircraft Philco air-to-air, heat-seeking Sidewinder missiles—developed by the US Navy in 1947 and first carried by TAC's F-100Ds. The timing of the two decisions was coincidental. All F-104s were equipped with Sidewinders and a final decision on each model's allocation (F-104As and Bs to ADC, and F-104Cs and Ds to TAC) was not reached until January 1958.

[12] One of the Air Force's smallest, with a 21.9-ft wing span; lightest too, with maximum takeoff weight below 28,000 pounds for most models.

[13] Extensive F-104 testing and the problems uncovered resulted in only one or two F-104As being accepted each month until May 1957. Thereafter, monthly acceptance rates increased several fold.

End of Production **December 1958**

In that month, the last eight F–104As were received and the entire F–104 program was slashed.

Flyaway Cost Per Production Aircraft

$1.7 million—airframe, $1,026,859; engine (installed), $624,727; electronics, $3,419; ordnance, $29,517; armament, $19,706.

Average Cost Per Flying Hour

$655.00

Average Maintenance Cost Per Flying Hour

$395.00

Subsequent Model Series

F–104B

Other Configurations

None. In 1956 the Air Force approved a November 1954 TAC proposal of a preliminary design for a reconnaissance version of the F–104. The Air Force, however, cancelled all RF–104 work in January 1957, believing that forthcoming RF–101s (RF–101Cs in particular) would satisfy TAC requirements.[14]

Initial Phaseout **1960**

Longer-range all-weather F–101 and F–106 interceptors,[15] operational malfunctions and shortages of spare parts prompted ADC to quickly get rid of its four F–104 squadrons (B trainers included). Too small to carry the data link equipment called for by ADC's new SAGE control-system, the F–104 would be a windfall for the Air National Guard and the Military Assistance Program.

Reactivation **1961-1963**

The Berlin Crisis of 1961 embarked the F–104 on a new tour of active service. In October three federalized ANG squadrons of F–104s went to Europe and stayed until the summer of 1962. Then, one squadron converted to C–97 transports to support active military airlift requirements. The other two wound up their federalized duty with ADC. The Cuban Missile Crisis of October 1962 rekindled USAF interest in the F–104. This quick-reacting aircraft could challenge most hostile aircraft that might attack the United States from Cuba. So, upon return to state control, the two ANG F–104 squadrons surrendered their aircraft[16] to ADC's 331st

[14] TAC considered the earlier RF–101A (operational in May 1957) as a sort of consolation prize for the RF–104 and RF–105, both deleted from future reconnaissance forces for lack of money. TAC at one point had envisioned four RF–104 squadrons.

[15] Both the F–101B and F–106 entered operational service in 1959—the F–101B in January; the F–106, in May.

[16] Receiving F–102A interceptors in return.

FIS at Webb AFB, Tex., and to the 319th FIS at Homestead AFB, Fla.[17] Reactivated F-104s were retrofitted with M-61 Vulcans.

Final Phaseout **1967-1969**

A general reduction in active ADC fighter-interceptor squadrons brought the F-104A's final phaseout—the 331st was inactivated in February 1967; the Homestead-based 319th, in December 1969.

Other Countries

A number of F-104As relinquished by the Air Force in 1960 were transferred to the Chinese Nationalist Air Force and to the Pakistan Air Force.

Other Uses **1960-1963**

The Air Force converted 24 F-104As into target drones[18] soon after ADC first declared the aircraft surplus. In October 1963 one F-104A was delivered to Edwards AFB's Flight Test Center to test a liquid-fueled rocket that would add 6,640 pounds to the engine thrust. This test aircraft (NF-104A) set on 6 December 1963 an unofficial world altitude record by reaching 120,000 feet.

Milestones **1958**

The F-104 was the first USAF combat aircraft to sustain a speed faster than Mach 2. In May 1958 an F-104A at Edwards AFB set a world speed record of 1,404.19 miles per hour and a 91,249-foot altitude record for ground-launched planes. The following December, F-104A aircraft at Pt. Mugu, Calif., set three time-to-climb records: 3,000 meters in 41.35 seconds, 15,000 meters in 131.1 seconds; and 25,000 meters in 266.03 seconds.

F-104B

Manufacturer's Model Series 283-93-03

Previous Model Series

F-104A

New Features

Second cockpit aft of the F-104A's single seat—in the space otherwise designed for the M-61 Vulcan gun.[19]

Basic Development

Lockheed developed the F-104B purely as a two-seat training version (TF-104) of the F-104A. The Air Force's December 1955

[17] The 319th was purposefully relocated to Homestead during the Cuban Crisis.

[18] Flyaway cost per drone (QF-104) reached $1.7 million—airframe, $1,010,830; engine (installed), $628,551; electronics, $3,419; ordnance, $29,517; armament, $19,706.

[19] In contrast to the F-104A (retrofitted with the M-61 in 1964), the F-104B's armament never exceeded two AIM-9B (originally designated GAR-8) Sidewinders.

decision to equip operational F–104A squadrons with the two-seater brought about its redesignation (all possible F–104A armament was retained—usual in such cases). The Air Force earlier in the year also thought of using the F–104 trainer for suitability, high-altitude, and physiological research tests.

Initial Procurement **April 1956**

Procurement started slowly, as it had for the F–104A. The Air Force first ordered six F–104Bs; 106 more in 1957.

First Flight (Production Aircraft) **16 January 1957**

The flight took place less than a year after the two-seater's first mockup inspection—an uneventful flight over California, from the Lockheed Palmdale plant to the nearby USAF Flight Test Center. The Air Force took official delivery of the aircraft in the same month.

Flight Testing **1957**

The first 30 days of flight tests showed F–104A and F–104B performance to be similar. This was expected. The Air Force did not plan to accept any more F–104Bs until the fall of 1957, when extensive F–104A flight tests would be completed. Meanwhile, it needed the first F–104B to test the downward ejection seat that first equipped most F–104s. The Air Force took official delivery of a second F–104B in September—1 month ahead of schedule.

Enters Operational Service **1958**

With the 83d FIS (the first F–104A recipient) at Hamilton AFB. ADC's three other F–104A squadrons shared later F–104Bs.

Total F–104Bs Accepted

26—against 112 ordered in 1957.

Acceptance Rates

The Air Force accepted one F–104B in FY 57, 14 in FY 58, and 11 in FY 59.

End of Production **November 1958**

With delivery of the last 4 F–104Bs.

Subsequent Model Series

F–104C

Other Configurations

None

Flyaway Cost Per Production Aircraft

$2.4 million—airframe, $1,756,388; engine (installed), $336,015; electronics, $13,258; ordnance, $59,473; armament, $231,996.

Average Maintenance Cost Per Flying Hour

$544.00

Phaseout **1960–1969**

Transferred to the ANG in 1960, the F–104B returned to ADC's active inventory in 1962–1963. It phased out again in 1967–1969, along with and in the same manner as the F–104A.

F-104C

Manufacturer's Model 583-04-05

Previous Model Series

F–104B

New Features

J–79–GE–7A engine (15,000–lb static thrust with afterburner) having 1,000 pounds more thrust than the J–GE–3B (with afterburner) in F–104Bs, late F–104As, and retrofitted in early F–104As. The F–104C also featured an improved fire-control system (AN/ASG–14T–2, replacing the F–104A's–1) for day and clear-night operations; a probe-drogue air refueling system; and external nuclear stores.[20]

First Flight Production Aircraft **July 1958**

First Acceptance **September 1958**

The Air Force accepted four F–104Cs, then seven or more each month, beginning in October.

Enters Operational Service **September 1958**[21]

The 476th Tactical Fighter Squadron at George AFB, along with three other squadrons of the 479th Tactical Fighter Wing, became TAC's only F–104 combat units. All four squadrons at George converted from F–100s, the last in 1959.

Total F-104Cs Accepted

77

Acceptance Rates

All F–104Cs were accepted in FY 59—seven to nine each month from October 1958 through June 1959.

End of Production **June 1959**

It ended with delivery of the last seven F–104Cs.

Subsequent Model Series

F–104D

Other Configurations

None

---

[20] Previous F–104s carried only conventional ordnance and extended their range with external fuel tanks (suspended from a centerline fuselage rack, in place of additional Sidewinders).

[21] TAC officially accepted the F–104C in mid-October during the USAF annual fighter weapons meet at Nellis AFB.

Flyaway Cost Per Production Aircraft[22]

$1.5 million—airframe, $863,235; engine (installed), $473,729; electronics, $5,219; ordnance, $44,684; armament, $91,535.

Average Maintenance Cost Per Flying Hour

$395.00

Operational Problems **1959-1964**

Shortages of engines, components, and supplies plagued TAC's F–104Cs and their few accompanying trainers (F–104Ds). Even worse was the unreliability of components—the new J–79–GE–7A engine a major culprit. In less than 5 years, 40 major accidents occurred claiming nine lives and destroying 24 aircraft. This paved the way for Project Seven Up, a General Electric modification that started in May 1963 and ended in June 1964.

Modernization **1961-1963**

In October 1961,[23] the Air Force had launched Project Grindstone by which Lockheed modernized the F–104 air superiority fighter. Completed by early 1963, Grindstone gave the F–104C four Sidewinders (all other F–104s carried only two), plus a variety of airground weapons—2.75–inch rockets, napalm and gravity bombs.

Special Deployments **1962-1964**

The Cuban Missile Crisis of 1962 saw the unexpected deployment of F–104Cs to Key West, Fla. As a result of the same crisis, F–104Cs in 1964 were also called upon to fulfill some F–104As air defense commitments. They moved to Homestead AFB, while F–104A interceptors were retrofitted with M–61 Vulcans.

Oversea Deployments **1965-1967**

F–104Cs went first to Southeast Asia on a temporary basis. In 1965 one squadron stood alert at Kung Kuan, Taiwan, and Da Nang, South Vietnam. From Da Nang, the aircraft soon struck targets in both South and North Vietnam—enemy ground fire taking its toll. A new contingent of F–104Cs returned to SEA in mid–1966, this time permanently. F–104Cs of TAC's 479th Tactical Fighter Wing were then assigned to the 435th TFS at Udorn, resuming their attacks until they were replaced by more efficient F–4Ds in July 1967.

Phaseout **1966-1967**

The F–4D program slippage and the war's impact on USAF resources postponed the aircraft phaseout. In 1962 one of TAC's four squadrons of F–104 tactical fighters equipped a combat crew training squadron, the other three did not begin converting to F–

[22] Plus cumulative R&D and Class V modification costs of $189,473 and $198,348 per aircraft.

[23] Almost 2 years before implementing the upcoming Seven Up modification.

4Ds until 1966. For all practical purposes, phaseout wound up in 1967—almost 5 years later than planned—with redeployment of the last F–104s left in Thailand. The aircraft joined the ANG in time for the 198th Tactical Fighter Squadron in Puerto Rico to convert in August from the elderly F–86H.[24]

Milestones **14 December 1959**

An F–104C reached 103,389 feet, breaking the world altitude records set by the Soviets and the US Navy (who had broken records set by an F–104A in May 1958).

F-104D

Manufacturer's Model 583-04-06

Previous Model Series

F–104C

New Features

A rear cockpit, basic to most trainers. (To make room, the M–61 Vulcan had to be removed.)

First Flight **October 1958**

Enters Operational Service **November 1958**

First, the 476th Tactical Fighter Squadron at George AFB, and later TAC's three other F–104C squadrons were equipped with the F–104D.

Total F-104Ds Accepted

21

Acceptance Rates

The Air Force accepted 16 in FY 59 and 5 in FY 60 (2 monthly from November 1958 through August 1959).

End of Production **September 1959**

With the delivery of the last F–104D.

Flyaway Cost Per Production Aircraft[25]

$1.5 million—airframe, $873,952; engine (installed), $271,148; electronics, $16,210; ordnance, $70,067; armament, $269,014.

Average Maintenance Cost Per Flying Hour

$395.00

Modernization **1961**

Under Project Grindstone's F–104C modernization, Lockheed fitted the F–104D with 2.75–inch rockets for air-ground support.

---

[24] By mid–1972, the Air Force had only 18 F–104s (6 F–104Cs and 12 F–104Ds) in active service; the Guard, 6 (2 F–104Cs and 4 F–104Ds).

[25] Excluding cumulative R&D and Class V modification costs of $189,473 and $196,396 for each F–104D.

Subsequent Model Series

F-104G—mostly foreign-made.

Other Configurations

F-104F. Built in the United States for MAP, the F-104F was accepted by the Air Force (20 in FY 60 and 10 in FY 61) for West German pilot training in Europe. The F-104F closely resembled the F-104D but featured upward ejection seats. Until retrofitted, most USAF F-104s (D models included) had the troublesome downward ejection seat.

Phaseout **1966-1967**

F-104Ds phased out of TAC's active inventory along with and in the same manner as the F-104Cs. In 1967, the D model, as well as the C, equipped the ANG 198th Tactical Fighter Squadron in Puerto Rico.

F-104G

Manufacturer's Model 863-10-19

New Features

Stronger structure (through extensive internal redesign) for performing many roles in any weather.[26] Had four Sidewinders for interceptor duty. Carried air-to-surface missiles,[27] rockets, and gravity bombs for attack. Featured the J-79-GE-11A engine—with the -7's thrust, but more reliable—and F-15AM-11 fire-control system.

Production Decision **December 1960**

The Office of the Secretary of Defense, based the decision on West Germany interest in 1958 and the growing obsolescence of allied forces' F-84s and F-86s.[28]

Production Policy **December 1960**

US agreements with West Germany, Belgium, the Netherlands, and Italy authorized these countries to produce F-104s. The United States subsequently signed similar agreements with Canada and Japan. In keeping with political restraints on offensive

[26] The F-104G retained the 20-mm M-61 Vulcan of other F-104s and, in addition, the nuclear-conventional ordnance of the F-104C.

[27] Two nuclear warhead AGM-12Bs, an improved version of the Martin air-to-surface Bullpup missile developed in 1954 by the US Navy. Then known as the GAM-83B, the AGM-12B first equipped TAC's F-100s in November 1960.

[28] F-84/F-86 shortcomings had long been known. USAF as early as 1953 needed a lightweight, high-performance fighter to satisfy the requirements of the North Atlantic Treaty Organization standing group. The Lockheed F-104 was then the leading American contender; the British pushed their Folland Knat (FO-141) small jet fighter. As a ground-support fighter, the French SNCASE (*Société Nationale de Constructions Aéronautiques du Sud-Est*) SE-5000 Baroudeur transonic jet was highly favored by the Western European powers.

operations, Japanese production was limited to an interceptor version of the F–104.

First Production Order **February 1961**

The order was placed by the United States with the Lockheed California plant (with MAP funds) for TAC training of allied pilots.

Other US Procurement

F–104G components, paid for by MAP, would also be manufactured in the United States to support allied F–104 production. Moreover, MAP-funded F–104Gs would be fabricated by Canadair (a Lockheed subsidiary in Ontario, Canada) and handed out to Denmark, Norway, Greece, and Turkey.

First Acceptance **July 1962**

The Air Force accepted the first American-made MAP F–104G earmarked for TAC. The Air Force then accepted the first Canadair-built F–104G in September 1963.

Enters Operational Service **10 October 1962**

With a TAC combat crew training unit at George AFB. MAP F–104 training began at George and Luke AFB, Arizona. It was later consolidated at Luke, where West German pilots had been the first students.

Total MAP F–104Gs Accepted

Of 192 accepted, 52 came from California (for TAC allied training) and 140 from Canadair (for designated allies).

Acceptance Rates

From California, 23 in FY 63 and 29 in FY 64; from Canadair, 40 in FY 64, 74 in FY 65, 25 in FY 66, and 1 in FY 67.

End of Production **June 1964**

Production first ended in California. Canadair F–104G production extended to September 1966.

Subsequent Model Series

None

Other Configurations

RF–104G. A MAP, California-produced, F–104G was equipped with three KS–67A cameras to demonstrate its reconnaissance potential. The Air Force accepted 24 RF–104Gs between March and September 1963 (14 in FY 63 and 10 in FY 64), but quickly returned 5 to their basic F–104G configuration.

TF–104G. A two-cockpit F–104G built in California for MAP and Military Assistance Sales (MAS). The Air Force accepted 29 MAP TF–104Gs—28 for TAC allied training (the first in September 1962, the last in December 1964) and 1 for Spain in October 1965. The Air Force also accepted 87 MAS TF–104Gs between October 1962 and February 1965 (40 in FY 63, 35 in FY 64, and 12 in FY 65). West Germany bought 72; Italy, 12; and Belgium, 3.

F–104J. Produced by Mitsubishi Heavy Industries, under license from Lockheed. Japan also manufactured a two-cockpit F–104J interceptor—the TF–104J trainer.

CF–104. Produced by Canadair for air support of Canadian ground troops. For better ground-attack performance it sacrificed versatility—an F–104G strong point. A two-crew CF–104D accompanied the Canadian CF–104.

Flyaway Cost Per Production Aircraft[29]

F–104G. $1.42 million—airframe (including electronics, ordnance, and armament), $1,251,000; engine (installed), $169,000.

TF–104G. $1.26 million.

Items of Special Interest

More than 1,400 F–104Gs of one configuration or another were produced during the 1960's by Europe, Japan, Canada, or the United States. This bore out Lockheed's financial foresight in retaining all F–104 patent rights.

PROGRAM RECAP

The Air Force accepted a grand total of 663 F–104s—296 for its own use, the rest for MAP and MAS. The USAF lot counted 2 XF–104s, 170 F–104As, 26 F–104Bs, 77 F–104Cs, and 21 F–104Ds. The 280 MAP F–104s consisted of 30 F–104Fs, 197 F–104Gs (some of them accepted as RF–104Gs but quickly stripped of recon equipment and returned to F–104G configuration), 24 RF–104Gs, and 29 TF–104Gs. All 87 MAS F–104s were TF–104Gs.

---

[29] Applied to both the California and Canadair-built F–104Gs and TF–104Gs, accepted by the Air Force for MAP.

TECHNICAL DATA

F–104A and F–104B

Manufacturer		Lockheed Aircraft Corporation, Burbank, Calif.
Nomenclature	XF–104	Air Superiority Jet Fighter.
	F–104A	Lightweight Fighter (served as a day-night interceptor).
	F–104B	Lightweight Fighter/Trainer (served as a day-night interceptor and trainer).
Popular Name		Starfighter

Characteristics	*F–104A*	*F–104B*
Length/Span	54.8/21.9 ft	54.8/21.9 ft
Engine, Number & Designation	1J79–GE–3	1J79–GE–3
Max. Takeoff Weight	24,804 lb	24,294 lb
Takeoff Ground Run	6,190 ft	5,870 ft
Average Cruise Speed	520 kn	515 kn
Max. Speed	2 Mach	2 Mach
Ferry Range	1,376 nm	1,210 nm
Combat Ceiling	55,200 ft	48,600 ft
Rate of Climb (max.)	36,000 fpm	37,000 fpm
Combat Radius	350 nm	188 nm
Crew	1	2
Ordnance Max. lb[30]	930 lb	420 lb
Guns (internal)	1 M–61[31]	None

---

[30] Ordnance included combinations of Sidewinder (AIM–9B) air-to-air missiles, 2.75-inch (FFAR) rockets, and gravity bombs (MK–117, MK–84, MK–83, MK–28 and MK–43) and ammunition for the M–61 gun.

[31] Five years after its production, the F–104A received the M–61 Vulcan cannon.

TECHNICAL DATA

F–104C, F–104D, and F–104G

Nomenclature		
	F–104C	Lightweight Fighter (served as a tactical fighter).
	F–104D	Lightweight Fighter/Trainer (served as a tactical fighter and trainer).
	F–104G	All Weather Fighter Bomber.[32]

Characteristics	*F–104C*	*F–104D*	*F–104G*
Length/Span	54.8/21.9 ft	54.8/21.9 ft	54.8/21.9 ft
Engine, Number & Designation	1J79–GE–7	1J79–GE–7	1J79–GE–11A
Max. Takeoff Weight	27,853 lb	23,725 lb	29,038 lb
Takeoff Ground Run	5,880 ft	5,400 ft	6,000 ft
Average Cruise Speed	507 kn	500 kn	509 kn
Max. Speed	2 Mach plus	2 Mach plus	2 Mach plus
Ferry Range	1,500 nm	1,195 nm	1,628 nm
Combat Ceiling	58,000 ft	53,000 ft	46,500 ft
Rate of Climb (max.)	45,000 fpm	45,000 fpm	41,000 fpm
Combat Radius	306	157	538
Crew	1	2	1
Ordnance Max. lb[33]	930 lb	420 lb	2,510 lb[34]
Guns (internal)	1 M–61	none	1 M–61

[32] The F–104G version used by Japan (the F–104J) was fabricated as in interceptor.

[33] Ordnance included combinations of Sidewinder (AIM–9B) air-to-air missiles, 2.75-inch (FFAR) rockets, and gravity bombs (MK–117, MK–84, MK–83, MK–28 and MK–43) and ammunition for the M–61 gun.

[34] On a LO-LO-LO bombing mission, maximum ordnance 4,000 lb.

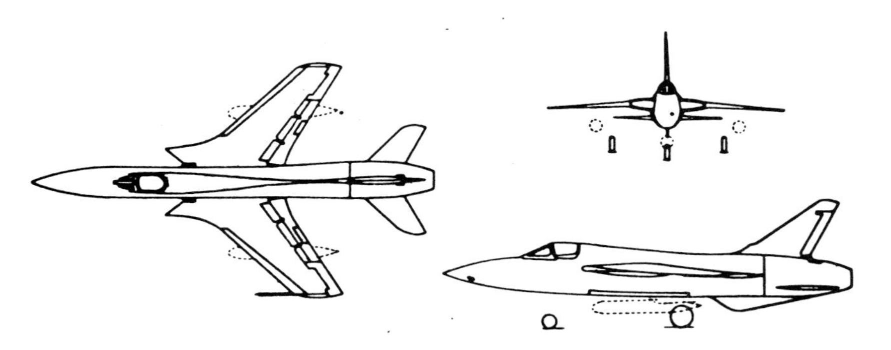

REPUBLIC F–105 THUNDERCHIEF

F–105D: Supersonic, long-range, thin mid-wing F–105D fighter-bomber. Most produced of the F–105 model series.

F–105F: A higher tail fin and a longer fuselage, to accommodate second cockpit, set the F–105F apart from the F–105D.

REPUBLIC F-105 THUNDERCHIEF

Manufacturer's Model AP 63-31

Weapon System 306A

Basic Development **1951**

Developing this aircraft on its own, Republic envisioned it as the Mach 1.5 successor to the F–84F Thunderstreak (before the latter entered the USAF tactical inventory in 1954). Republic studied many configurations (all labeled AP–63) before settling on a single-seat, single-engine aircraft, meant for a nuclear role but also having an air-to-air capability.

Contractor's Proposal **April 1952**

Republic's proposed Model AP–63 contained most of the features which the Air Force would have liked to have added to the F–84F had it been technically possible.

Go-Ahead Decision **May 1952**

As recommended by the Aircraft and Weapon Board, the Air Staff endorsed the F–105's development in lieu of creating an improved F–84F. No general operational requirements were issued at that time.

Letter Contract **September 1952**

This contract covered preproduced engineering, tooling design and fabrication, and fabrication and material procurement as called for by the Air Force's original planning which envisaged the acquisition of 199 aircraft, the first of which to be operationally ready by 1955. In March 1953 a change of plan reduced the program to 37 F–105s and nine RF–105s.

Mockup Inspection **October 1953**

No sweeping changes were recommended. Interim use of the Pratt & Whitney J–57 engine was discussed upon confirmation that the J–71 engine, earmarked for installation into the F–105, might not meet thrust requirements. Delivery of the first aircraft was still scheduled for the spring of 1955.

Development Slippages **December 1953**

The Air Force suspended procurement of the F–105, marking the beginning of a period of uncertainty because of excessive delays at Republic. Procurement was reinstated in February 1954 but reduced to 15 aircraft. At the same time, decision was made to equip the test aircraft with the proven, 16,000–lb thrust, J–75 engine and to incorporate the J–75 engine into the production aircraft. Further development slippages led the Air Force in September 1954 to reduce the program to three aircraft. An October revision of the month-old stop order restored the number of aircraft to six.

General Operational Requirements **1 December 1954**

Based on the Fighter Bomber Weapon System's Military Characteristics of January 1951, as revised in January 1952 but published some 18 months after development of the F–84F successor had been approved. GOR 49, three times amended between December 1954 and April 1955, called for an inflight refueling capability, a more complex fire-control system, and improved performance. The GOR also dictated the installation of the higher-thrust J–75 engine to qualify the fighter-bomber for first-line service from 1958 through 1960.

F-105A

New Procurement **February 1955**

The Air Force again authorized acquisition of the 15 test aircraft funded in February 1954—2 As, 10 Bs, and 3 RFs.

First Flight (YF-105A Prototype) **22 October 1955**

After 22 hours of flight time, the first YF–105 was returned to the factory because of major damage sustained in flight and on landing. The second YF–105A, still powered with the J–57 engine, flew for the first time on 28 January 1956. These were the only F–105As built. The other test aircraft were designated YF–105Bs (except for three, finally accounted for as TF–105Bs) and equipped with the production type J–75 engine. All 15 test F–105s had been built by April 1958.

F-105B

First Flight (YF-105B) **26 May 1956**

The aircraft flew for 1 hour but was damaged on landing. Necessary repairs delayed the flight test program.

Significant Problems **1955-1957**

Further development slippages and excessive costs plagued the F–105 program, in turn generating numerous changes in Air Force procurement planning. In March 1956 the Air Force released $10 million of FY 57 funds for the acquisition of 65 F–105Bs and 17 RF–105s. In June five F–105Cs were added to the program. This was the first of several two-seat versions of the F–105 considered at one time or the other. In July 1956 procurement of the RF–105 was cancelled as was that of the F–105C in 1957.

Preproduction Modification **22 January 1957**

A major preproduction modification of the F–105 was directed. The modification called for incorporating the APN–105 all-weather navigation system into the new tactical aircraft.

Revised General Operational Requirements **22 November 1957**

A complete revision of GOR 49 was published, consolidating all F-105 requirements in one document. Installation of an inertial navigation system was deleted in favor of the projected AN/APN 105 system. Several requirements were added. Namely, a new cockpit instrument display, a tow target subsystem, and a TX-43 nuclear weapon capability were required.

Production Slippages **1958**

The Air Force plans of May 1958 called for a 4-year production of 472 F-105D and E aircraft, but the added requirements of November 1957 and the complexities of the F-105 subsystems compounded the contractor's difficulties. Republic again requested new production schedules. In March 1959 the Air Force cancelled production of the F-105E, a second two-seat version of the F-105.

First Acceptance (Production Aircraft) **27 May 1958**

The Air Force accepted the first production model of the F-105 at the Republic's Farmingdale plant in Long Island, N. Y. This F-105B was the first aircraft specifically designed as a fighter-bomber and developed under the integrated or weapon system concept.

Enters Operational Service **August 1958**

It was delivered 3 years later than originally planned, to the 335th Tactical Fighter Squadron of the Tactical Air Command's 4th Fighter Wing, first at Eglin and subsequently at Seymour-Johnson AFB, the squadron's permanent station. Production slippages still occurred, however, and TAC did not have a complete squadron of F-105Bs until mid-1959.

Flight Testing **1957-1960**

Category I, II, and III flight tests either were delayed or interrupted because of the difficulties encountered with the pioneer F-105. Special tests of the new weapon system's unproven components were conducted. Their results, often calling for engineering changes or the incorporation of "fixes" in the aircraft, contributed to the delays. Category II testing, a joint contractor-USAF effort started on 8 January 1957, was extended beyond the 30 November 1959 deadline, officially ending 30 March 1960. Four additional tests, properly part of Category II, were conducted subsequently under an amended test directive. To speed transition of the new F-105B jet from test to squadron use, operational testing at Eglin AFB was accomplished by the 335th TFS. Category III testing, postponed until modification of the aircraft's fire-control system was completed, started in late July 1960. It was conducted by both the 334th and 335th TFS at Williams AFB, Ariz., and Nellis AFB, respectively. The Category III tests were completed on 15 August, after being handicapped by a severe shortage of parts. During the tests, the poor reliability of the MA–8 fire control system placed doubt on the success of the modification recently accomplished.

Modifications **1959**

The first F–105B productions, designated F–105B–10s and F–105B–15s, were essentially similar and were equipped with the J–75–P–5 engine. A third F–105B version, the F–105B–20, featuring changes in electronic equipment and powered by a J–75–P–19 engine, was flown successfully in June 1959. The gas turbine J–75–P–19 engine, providing an additional 1,000–lb thrust, substantially improved the aircraft's performance, and replacement of the J–75–P–5 engines in the earlier F–105Bs was directed. The Air Force also approved a new antiskid brake system developed by Goodyear, directed installation of the system on all future F–105s, and retrofitting of the aircraft already manufactured. Other modifications were directed toward the end of 1959 as Category II tests brought to light deficiencies of the MA–8 fire control system, central air data computer (CADC), and autopilot of the F–105B. The modifications, referred to as Project Optimize, eventually involved 26 engineering changes requiring on occasions that components be returned to the factories for rework. Scheduled for completion in April 1960, Project Optimize also slipped several months because of the lack of spares and repair money. In any case, there was still no guarantee that the modifications would eliminate most of the problems.

Operational Readiness **1960**

During the first 3 months of the year, none of the 56 aircraft possessed by TAC were operationally ready. The unreliability of the MA–8 system, CADC, and autopilot remained the principal deterrents. However, the average number of aircraft out of commission for lack of parts and repairs also was abnormally high.

Significant Operational Problems **1961**

The difficulties inherent to the increased complexity of the F–105 weapon system did not subside. The aircraft in-commission rates remained low. It required 150 maintenance manhours for each hour of flying. Moreover, problems stemming from a shortage of spare parts and maintenance skills were not solved. Temporary groundings were frequent.

Subsequent Model Series

F–105D

Other Configurations

None

End of Production **1959**

With the December delivery of six aircraft.

Total F-105Bs Accepted

Seventy-five, 13 of which were former test aircraft—the other test aircraft, 2 YF–105s and 3 TF–105Bs—were accepted by the Air Force in FY 56 and FY 58, respectively. The 3 TF–105Bs were used for development of the proposed RF–105 aircraft.

Acceptance Rates

Three F–105Bs were accepted in FY 57, 6 in FY 58, 28 in FY 59, and 38 in FY 60.

Flyaway Cost Per Production Aircraft[1]

$5,649,543.00—airframe, $4,914,016; engine (installed), $328,797; electronics, $141,796; ordnance, $32,021; armament, $232,913.

Average Maintenance Cost Per Flying Hour

$718.00

Item of Special Interest **May 1963**

Modernization of the F–100C–equipped "Thunderbirds," the Air Force Aerial Demonstration Team, was decided. Flight-testing of the first of the nine F–105Bs, to be modified for team use, ensued a few months later. The last modified aircraft was delivered to the "Thunderbirds" on 16 April 1964, 10 days before the first scheduled performance with the new plane. A serious accident in May of the same year, as well as the modifications directed as a result of this accident, prevented the "Thunderbirds" from using the aircraft. Because of its heavy schedule, the team was re-equipped with eight F–100Ds, urgently modified for demonstration purposes. The exchange, considered temporary at the time, was extended until 1969, when the "Thunderbirds" began flying F–4Es.

Phaseout **1964-1967**

TAC's two squadrons of F–105Bs were re-equipped with F–105Ds and most B model series were phased out of the active inventory during 1964. The first excess F–105Bs reached the ANG's 108th Wing on 16 April 1964. The F–105Bs, including those modified for the "Thunderbirds," were so different from the D and F model series that their training value was limited. Nonetheless, the Air Force utilized a few of them for training at McConnell AFB, Kans., until late 1969—2 years after disposing of all other F–105Bs.

Record Flight **11 December 1959**

An F–105B, without payload, set world speed record of 1,216.48 mph over a 100–kilometer closed course at Edwards AFB. Previous record was set in June 1959 at 1,100.42 mph by a French Nord-Griffon II aircraft.

---

[1] Excluding $2,716 of prorated RDT&E cost. Cumulative modification costs (differing according to model) were also excluded. By 30 June 1973, $261,793 had been spent on each F–105B; $282,687 on each F–105D; $701,645 on each F–105F, and an additional $1,803 on the F–105G—a reconfigured F–105F.

F-105D

Manufacturer's Model AP-63-31
Weapon System 306A

Previous Model Series

F–105B

New Features

Higher thrust J–75–P–19W engine with water injection, cockpit with vertical instrument panel, bad-weather navigation system, attack equipment, and integrated instruments. The last Ds off the line could refuel from either the flying boom or hose-drogue type tanker.

Configuration Planning **Mid-1957**

Configuration of the D cockpit was finalized by a Mockup Board on 11 December.

Preproduction Slippages **1958**

Republic requested new production schedules. The contractor claimed that the F–105D, although similar in appearance to the F–105B would be different enough to make it difficult to use the B production line, even with many modifications. The higher gross weight of the new model series would require stronger main gear, wheels, and brakes. The F–105D's improved engine would necessitate changes in the fuselage and intake ducts. Fabrication time, Republic stated, would be raised from 144 to 214 workdays.

General Operational Requirements 49-1 **16 May 1958**

GOR 49, as revised 22 November 1957, was amended. The amendment required that the F–105 be capable of delivering at least two of the air-to-surface missiles specified in GOR 166 of October 1957.

Program Change **18 March 1959**

Production of an increased number of F–105Ds was programmed at the expense of the two-place F–105E. The Air Force hoped that cancellation of the high cost F–105E and replacement by the cheaper F–105D, on a one-for-one basis, also would enable Republic to speed production.

First Flight **9 June 1959**

From Farmingdale. Republic reported that the vertical instrument panel and nose wheel steering of the aircraft worked well.

First Acceptance **28 September 1960**

TAC formally accepted the first F–105D at Nellis AFB.

Modifications **1960-1961**

Despite the efforts expanded on the aircraft and its components, the F–105B was still not fully proven when the first F–105D was accepted by the Air Force. The engineering changes made on the

F–105B under Project Optimize and the subsequent Prove Out testing of the MA–8 fire control system were but one example of the difficulties experienced with the new components and their integration into the weapon system. Other modifications were either established or proposed for both the production-completed F–105Bs and the incoming F–105Ds. To avoid a variety of aircraft configurations, the Air Force decided to process these modifications as a single package. The first production black box aircraft, received at Eglin AFB on 27 October 1960, upon evaluation proved to be adequate and the F–105D's operational capability in all visual and blind bombing was recognized. The black box modification of all F–105 aircraft was confirmed in November. Republic's lack of experience in delivering aircraft with the modification affected production schedules and delayed various phases of the F–105D flight testing program.

Flight Testing **1959–1962**

During tests, the F–105D encountered problems similar to those that had plagued the F–105B. Category I flight tests were delayed because of difficulties with the J–75 engine and speed restrictions placed on the aircraft. Category II testing, scheduled to start in May 1960, did not begin until 26 December because of the black box modification and other production slippages. The F–105D's airframe and engine had undergone evaluation either on the F–105B or during the D model's Category I tests. This let the Air Force cut short the delayed Category II tests that centered on the instrument display as well as the fire-control and navigation systems. Conducted by the 335th TFS at Eglin AFB, these tests ended on 31 October 1961. Category III flight tests were also reduced and conducted by the 335th but took place at Seymour Johnson AFB, which became the collecting point for all specialized test equipment and spare parts prior to TAC acceptance of the first F–105D. Most of the support problems encountered during the Category III testing of the F–105B were eliminated.

Enters Operational Service **1961**[2]

TAC's 4th Fighter Wing was first to receive the aircraft.

Oversea Deployments **1961–1962**

F–105Ds began reaching USAFE's 36th Tactical Fighter Wing in May 1961. Deliveries to PACAF started in October 1962.

Grounding **December 1961**

All F–105Ds were grounded for inspection after the aircraft's main fuselage frame failed during a routine laboratory fatigue test at Wright-Patterson AFB. Ensuing tests confirmed that the frame

[2] TAC formally accepted the F–105D at Nellis AFB on 28 September 1960, but the aircraft did not enter operational service until the following year.

retained considerable strength after cracking. Republic had suitable adapters and tools to do the corrective work required.

Production Slippages **1962**

Production again slipped because of a labor strike started at Republic on 2 April. A Taft-Hartley injunction ended the strike on 18 June, but production was delayed sufficiently to disrupt concurrent USAF plans.

Significant Operational Problems **1962-1964**

In June 1962, following two major accidents at Nellis AFB, all F–105B and D aircraft were grounded for correction of chafing and flight control deficiencies. The project, referred to as Look Alike and started in July, was expected to be done quickly, but continuous operational difficulties caused it soon to grow into an extensive, $51 million modification program. The 2–year spanned modifications, grouped under Look Alike, were accomplished in two phases, the first of which was completed in November 1962 by the Air Force with the assistance of several technicians from Republic. The second phase, extended to include a dual in-flight refueling capability for the last 20 F–105Ds produced, was done entirely by Republic and did not end until mid–1964.

Support Problems **1962-1964**

Look Alike created a new supply problem. The modifications eliminated the use of many of the items only recently stocked in sufficient quantities.

Continued Operational Problems **1964-1967**

Despite the successful completion of Look Alike, the efficiency of the F–105Ds had not peaked. At the time production ended in early 1964, they experienced a series of accidents due to engine failures, fuel leaks, and malfunctions of the fuel venting systems. This in turn added a shortage of J–75 engines to the similar problems hampering F–105D operations from 1964 through 1967.

SEA Losses **1965-1968**

F–105Ds, flying from Korat AB, began striking carefully selected targets north of the 17th parallel in early 1965. While participating in tactical air strikes over South Vietnam, in 1966 and subsequent years they carried out more strikes against the North than any other USAF aircraft. Operating against ever stiffening defenses, the F–105Ds also led in SEA battle losses. The steady loss of F–105 aircraft to enemy action, accidents, and normal attrition necessitated urgent repairs, cannibalization of the more badly damaged aircraft, and depletion of USAFE and TAC inventories. TAC's resources for training and support of the combat effort were also reduced.

Special SEA Modifications **1965-1971**

The F–105Ds were repeatedly modified to meet changing SEA combat requirements. They were equipped with armor plates, backup flight control systems, X-band beacons, new radar altimeters and ASG–19 gun bombsights. Primarily designed to carry nuclear bombs, their conventional bombing capability was increased. The pilot ejection seat of all F–105 aircraft was improved as were the refueling probes of the early F–105Ds. Modifications, first impeded by sparse funds often were delayed by technical difficulties. A most important and complex modification (putting ECM pods on the aircraft's wings) began in 1966 and consumed several years. Another crucial modification, started in 1966 and hindered by numerous problems, would give 30 F–105Ds improved visual bombing accuracy, a more precise navigation system, and a better blind bombing capability. An overriding problem was the poor reliability and rising cost of the AN/ARN–85 LORAN system first considered. This problem persisted until new testing began at Eglin AFB in September 1969. The T–Stick II/Loran prototype aircraft was then equipped with the AN/ARN–92 (produced by International Telephone and Telegraph) and successfully flight-tested. Still, modification of the 30 aircraft was not completed until late July 1971.

Subsequent Model Series

F–105F

Other Configurations

None. Production of a reconnaissance version of the F–105, after progressing through a February 1954 mockup inspection, was cancelled on 20 July 1956. Amendment No. 2 to the revised GOR of November 1957, published on 7 December 1960, reinstated as well as enlarged the project by calling for a reconnaissance version of the F–105 model series D. The new reconnaissance aircraft, while retaining the strike capability of the F–105D, would be equipped with a podcontaining side-looking radar, infrared sensors and a variety of cameras. In-flight development of films and ejection of film casettes were included in the specific operational requirements issued in December 1960. Revival of the project, however, was of short duration. One year later, on 23 December, the new RF–105 contract was terminated in favor of a reconnaissance version of the F–4C Phantom II, soon to be produced by the McDonnell Aircraft Corporation. SOR 49–2 was cancelled on 30 April 1962, its requirements being transferred to SOR 196, issued for the RF–4C in the spring of 1962.

Acceptance Rates

The Air Force accepted 17 F–105Ds in FY 60, 149 in FY 61, 171 in FY 62, 198 in FY 63, and 75 in FY 64.

Last Acceptance **January 1964**

The F–105Ds began to see action in Southeast Asia 1 year later. Ensuing battle losses were considerable, and reopening of the production line was considered in mid–1967. The project, however, did not materialize.

Total F-105Ds Accepted

610

Flyaway Cost Per Production Aircraft

$2.14 million—airframe, $1,472,145; engine (installed), $244,412; electronics, $19,346; armament, $167,621; ordnance, $19,346.

Average Cost Per Flying Hour

$1,020.00

Average Maintenance Cost Per Flying Hour

$809.00

Phaseout **1971-1973**

Phasing out of remaining F–105Ds (roughly one fourth of some 600 productions) took shape in November 1970, when two ANG units were alerted to their impending conversion. F–105Ds began reaching the 184th Tactical Fighter Training Group, McConnell AFB, and the 192d Tactical Fighter Group (TFG), Byrd Field, Va., in January 1971.[3] Conversion of a third ANG unit, the 113th TFG, Andrews AFB, Md., swiftly followed. By mid–1973 USAF active rolls showed 6 F–105Ds left—two were used for special tests, the other four for training.

Items of Special Interest **1968**

As war losses foretold its gradual removal, the F–105 was increasingly praised for its payload, range, and exceptional speed at low altitudes. It was praised as the "hardest worker" of the Vietnam War by pilots who regretted that the planes were not being replaced.

1970

Loaded with twelve 750–lb bombs, the F–105D was faster than any other available USAF aircraft flying under the same conditions.

---

[3] Air Force Reserve units, strictly concerned with the airlift business since 1958, resumed a tactical role in 1972. The 507th TFG at Tinker AFB and the 301st TFW at Carswell AFB acquired F–105Ds in June and August, respectively. In January 1973, the 508th TFG at Hill AFB gave up its C–124As for F–105Bs. This time the aircraft came from the Air National Guard (the 177th TFG, a New Jersey unit converting to F–106s).

F-105F

Manufacturer's Model AP-63-31
Weapon System 306-A

Previous Model Series

F-105D

New Features

Higher tail fin and a 31-inch longer fuselage to accommodate second cockpit. The heavier (by 2,000 lb) F-105F retained many features of the D, including the air refueling probe-drogue and boom receptacle of later ones. A transfer system in the F-105F allowed each crew member to monitor or control all or any of the aircraft's subsystems.

Go-Ahead Decision **May 1962**

The Secretary of Defense decided to go ahead on the basis of the cancellation of the two-place F-105E in 1959 which had left a vacuum in the advanced bombing and navigational training programs. Use of the F-100F for combat proficiency evaluation and transition training of future F-105 pilots, once considered, was impractical because of the cost involved and the scarcity of F-100F aircraft. As an interim expedient, TAC utilized six modified T-39s.

Contractual Arrangements

Republic received $8 million to convert the last 143 single place F-105Ds in production to dual place F-105Fs. No additional aircraft were procured.

Development Engineering Inspection (DEI) **2-5 January 1963**

First Flight **11 June 1963**

The flight took place earlier than expected, and the aircraft reached a speed of 1.15 Mach.

First Acceptance (Production Aircraft) **7 December 1963**

The first production aircraft was assigned to the 4520th Combat Crew Training Wing at Nellis AFB.

Enters Operational Service **23 December 1963**

The F-105F entered operational service with TAC's 4th Tactical Fighter Wing at Seymour-Johnson AFB.

Flight Testing **1963-1964**

As a development of the F-105D, the F-105F did not require an extensive testing program. Category I tests, initiated in mid-1963, were completed in July 1964; Category II tests, 1 month later.

Operational Problems and Modifications **1964-1968**

Because of similarity between the two aircraft, the F-105F experienced all of the F-105D's problems. Both received the safety modifications and improvements dictated by their common SEA mission. In addition, like the F–105D and several other tactical aircraft, the F–105F was modified to increase its capability to attack as well as avoid the North Vietnamese SAM and AAD radar sites.[4] The radar homing and warning modification, started in late 1965, primarily involved the replacement of the AN/APS–107 with the improved AN/APR–25–26.

Special Modifications **1966–1973**

Eighty-six of the RHAW-equipped F–105F aircraft were included in the Wild Weasel program initiated in 1965 to improve the Air Force's electronic warfare capability. The modification, first applied to the F–100F, was extended to the F–105F in January 1966, because of the appearance of a growing number of Russian-built SA–2 Guideline missiles in North Vietnam. Thirteen modified F–105Fs, deployed to SEA in the summer of 1966, were joined by 10 others in the ensuing 3 months. The Wild Weasel III modification (F–105 aircraft, only) was completed in March 1968, 1 month after completion of an additional modification which enabled 14 of the 86 aircraft to launch Standard Arm Mod 0 missiles.[5] Almost concurrently, a new modification was directed, which at first only involved 16 other Wild Weasel F–105Fs. Beginning in November 1968 these aircraft were modified so they could fire the new AGM–78B missile, an improved version of the Standard Arm. In spite of engineering difficulties, the modification of the 16 aircraft was completed in June 1969. In September of the same year this modification (plus other improvements) was programmed for 60 Wild Weasel F–105Fs that would be redesignated F–105Gs.

Oversea Deployments **1966–1972**

The aircraft did extensive and diversified work overseas. For example, five of the first 16 Wild Weasel F–105Fs, scheduled for SEA in the summer of 1966, arrived there in mid-April. Another six (from the 4525th Fighter Weapons Wing) left Nellis AFB for

---

[4] A few F–105Fs (dubbed Combat Martins) received unique modifications. They were equipped with QRC–128 VHF jammers to block communications between the MIGs and their ground-control intercept centers. Other F–105s saw modification of their R–14A radars (to expand presentation for sharper target definition) and a rearrangement of the pilot's weapon release switch (enabling the rear seat pilot to control bomb release). These Commando Nail F–105Fs carried out extremely hazardous, night, all-weather, radar low-level bombing missions, the first two flown over North Vietnam on 26 April 1967. Six Combat Martin and six Commando Nail F–105Fs were returned to their previous configuration in mid-1971 to help fill the quota of Wild Weasel F–105Fs—that had or were being modified into Gs.

[5] AGM–78A/B antiradiation missiles manufactured by General Dynamics for the Navy. The Standard Arm missiles require that the carrying aircraft (Navy A–6Bs and USAF F–105Fs) have a sophisticated avionics system to sort and select the signals encountered.

Osan AB, Korea, on 28 January 1968, following North Korean seizure of the USS *Pueblo*. Again, 12 F–105Gs (modified F–105F Wild Weasels from TAC's 23d TFW) joined in Constant Guard I, the first of several USAF deployments to SEA in the spring of 1972. These aircraft left McConnell AFB for Korat in April.

Subsequent Model Series

None. The F–105G, at times considered a separate model, actually came off the production line as an F–105F.

Other Configurations—F-105G

F–105G—a modified Wild Weasel F–105F. This aircraft featured an internally mounted jamming system, an AGM–78 Standard antiradiation capability, a new combat-event recorder, and other improvements (not all expected to be completed before the end of 1973). The Air Force planned an F–105G fleet of 60 but missed its goal by several aircraft.

End of Production **December 1964**

The Air Force took delivery of the last F–105F in January 1965.

Total F-105Fs Accepted

The Air Force accepted 143. More than one-third of this total was brought up to the F–105G configuration.

Acceptance Rates

One F–105F was accepted in FY 63, 83 in FY 64, and 59 in FY 65.

Flyaway Cost Per Production Aircraft[6]

$2.2 million—airframe, $1,524,000; engine (installed), $290,000; electronics, $251,000; armament, $154,000; ordnance, $21,000.

Average Cost Per Flying Hour

$1,020.00 (F and G models)

Average Maintenance Cost Per Flying Hour

$808.00 (F and G models)

Operational Status **Mid-1973**

The Air Force lost many of its F–105Fs. The modification and redesignation of about 60 others nearly exhausted the entire inventory.[7] In mid–1973, only 17 F–105Fs still flew—5 with the Air Force, 12 with the Guard.[8] Forty-eight F–105Gs (reconfigured F–105Fs) were in the active inventory. The Air Force intended to transfer these aircraft to the Reserve Forces beginning in mid–1975—if F–4Ds were available for replacement.

---

[6] Applied to both the F–105F and F–105G and did not include development as well as cumulative modification costs.

[7] At the close of FY 1970, 33 F–105Gs were on USAF rolls.

[8] The Air National Guard received its first 8 F–105Fs in FY 1971.

PROGRAM RECAP

The Air Force bought a grand total of 833 F–105 aircraft—355 less than authorized by Congress. Specifically, the F–105 program consisted of 2 YF–105As, 75 F–105Bs, 3 TF–105Bs, 610 F–105Ds, and 143 F–105Fs. F–105Gs were modified F–105Fs.

TECHNICAL DATA

F-105B/D and F-105F

Manufacturer	Republic Aviation Corporation, Farmingdale, N. Y.
Nomenclature	Supersonic Long Range Tactical Fighter-Bomber. F-105F—Supersonic Long Range Tactical Fighter-Bomber/Trainer.
Popular Name	Thunderchief

Characteristics	*F-105B*	*F-105D*	*F-105F*
Length/Wing	64.4/34.9 ft	64.4/34.9 ft	67.0/34.9 ft
Takeoff Weight[9]	52,500 lb	52,500 lb	54,300 lb
Takeoff Ground Run	5,920 ft	5,920 ft	6,356 ft
Average Cruise Speed	726 kn	726 kn	726 kn
Max. Speed	2.08 Mach	2.08 Mach	2.04 Mach
Ferry Range	1,917 nm	1,917 nm	1,623 nm
Engine, Number & Designation	1J-75P-19W with a/b	1J-75P-19W with a/b	1J-75P-19W with a/b
Crew	1	1	1
Combat Ceiling	49,000 ft	49,000 ft	49,000 ft
Radius/Loiter Time	200 nm/15 min	200 nm/15 min	200 nm/15 min
Rate of Climb	34,000 fpm	34,000 fpm	34,000 fpm
Ordnance, No/Bomb	16/750 lb[10]	16/750 lb[11]	16/750 lb[11]
Close Air Support Characteristics		*F-105D*	*F-105F*
Guns & Type		1 M-61 20-mm	1 M-61 20-mm
Ammo (rds)		1,029	1,029
Weapon Load		6/8 CBU-24	6/8 CBU-24
Loiter Time at 100 nm		1.8/1.6 hr	1.8/1.6 hr

---

[9] Carrying Bomb Load

[10] or 1 MK-28 or MK-43

[11] or 1 MK-28 or MK-43 (internal), 2 MK-28s or MK-43s (external), or 4 AGM-12Bs.

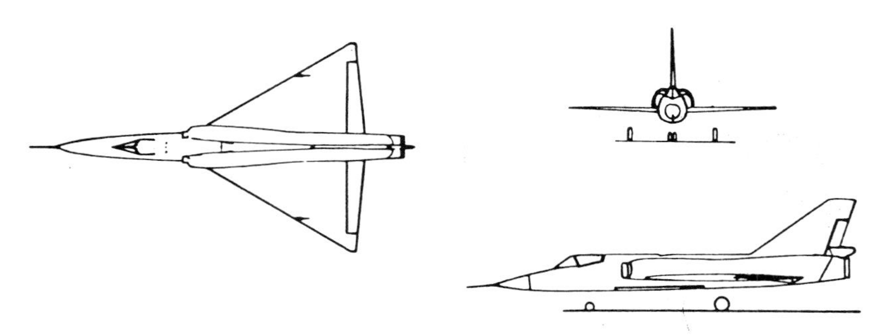

CONVAIR F–106 DELTA DART

F–106A: After many years of duty, the supersonic delta wing F–106A remained a most competent all-weather interceptor.

F–106B: Aside from the second seat, that took the place of one of the fuel cells of the single-seat F–106A, the two were practically identical.

CONVAIR F-106 DELTA DART

Manufacturer's Model 8-24
Weapon System 201B

Basic Development

Convair F-106, like the preceding F-102, grew out of the company's delta-wing XF-92A—an American application of Germany's wartime theories and preliminary testing. The F-106 and F-102 in fact originated as only one aircraft, the so-called "1954 Ultimate Interceptor."

Advanced Development Objective **13 January 1949**

The ADO of early 1949 called for an advanced, specially designed interceptor that would be operational in 1954—a project which soon became one of the most complicated undertakings in the history of the Air Force.

Production Decision **24 November 1951**

After the customary call on industry and the September 1951 selection of Convair competitive entry, the Air Force decided in November 1951 to expedite production of the 1954 Ultimate Interceptor. The decision did not affect the weapon system concept and Cook-Craigie production outlined in the ADO of January 1949.[1]

Program Change **December 1951**

The production decision of November 1951 also did not ignore the fact that the state of the art would probably preclude the 1954 Interceptor from meeting its operational deadline. Hence, since some sort of advanced interceptor was needed as soon as possible, the Air Force in December 1951 authorized a two-step production of the aircraft. First would come the F-102A, an interim, less ambitious version that would be produced in limited quantity. The Ultimate Interceptor, no longer referred to as the 1954 Interceptor, would follow as the F-102B. The two models would have the same airframe that was to be produced by Convair, as the winner of the MX-1554 airframe competition initially held for the so-called 1954 Interceptor. They would have different engines, however, with the F-102B retaining the high thrust J-67, an American version of the British Bristol Olympus turbojet to be produced under license by the Wright Aeronautical Corporation of America. Finally, only the F-102B would be equipped from the outset with the highly sophisticated electronic control system being developed

[1] The weapon system concept, introduced in the late forties, integrated from the start the design of the entire weapon system to make each component compatible with the other. The offshoot of this concept's failure when first applied was the F-102. The Cook-Craigie production policy called for early tooling, limited production at first, elimination of faults by test flights, and accelerated production thereafter. The F-102 also bared some of this production plan's pitfalls.

by the Hughes Aircraft Company under project MX–1179, a project around which the MX–1554 airframe specifications had actually been drawn.

Program Slippage **1952-1955**

The F–102's two-step development plan, despite its blueprint logic, did not work as anticipated. The decision to produce an interim version of the interceptor (F–102A), with an interim engine and interim fire-control system, devolved from delays in the development of important subsystems. Yet, concentration on new requirements lessened the attention that could be given to these subsystems and to the F–102B as a whole. Another unfortunate consequence of the two-step development plan was that components for the F–102A could be financed from production funds, while development of the F–102B J–67 engine and MX–1179 ECS had to come from less plentiful research money. Meanwhile, problems with the original configuration of the Convair airframe almost obliterated the entire F–102 program. By the end of 1954, when the F–102 fuselage problems were solved, the production-delayed F–102A, after losing its interim status, had acquired further importance at the F–102B's expense.

Development Problems **1952-1955**

While airframe deficiencies hampered the F–102A, technical difficulties and a basic funding problem retarded the F–102B's progress. In mid–1953 development of the MX–1179 ECS (later the MA–1 Automatic Weapon Control System)[2] was slipping badly, and it took another year before a nearly completed experimental sample of the system could be installed in a T–29B for testing. Similarly, although the J–67 showed early promise, in August 1953 Wright was almost a year behind schedule in adapting the engine to the future F–102B, and the Air Force had begun to consider use of another engine. As Wright's trouble with the J–67 did not subside, the Pratt and Whitney J–75 engine (an advanced model of the J–57 eventually used in the F–102A) gained added favor. Its substitution for the J–67 was approved in early 1955.

Initial Procurement **November 1955**

Satisfied with the F–102's new airframe configuration (extensively tested since the successful Hot Rod flight of December 1954), the Air Force awarded Convair new production contracts. One covered 562 F–102As, pushing to 749 the F–102As thus far on order. Another, first of its kind, was for 17 F–102Bs—a far cry from the December 1951 USAF plans, calling for few interim F–102As and large-scale F–102B production.

---

[2] The MA–1 Automatic Weapon Control System (AWCS)—until 1960 more often referred to as the MA–1 fire-control system or MA–1 ECS—was first used by an F–106A on 18 March 1958.

Mockup Inspection **December 1955**

Of primary interest was the proposed cockpit arrangement for the Hughes MA–1 fire control system (the former MX–1179), a radical deviation from standard cockpits and instrument displays. A recently approved armament change (with more to come) was also discussed.

First Definitive Contract **18 April 1956**

The Air Force finalized the F–102B production contract of November 1955, earmarking the 17 aircraft for testing. Although the aircraft's redesignation was not yet official, this production document basically became the first F–106 research and development contract. One prototype was to be delivered in December 1956, the other in January 1957. Other deliveries would begin in July 1957.

Redesignation **17 June 1956**

The F–102B designation of the ultimate interceptor was changed to F–106. The redesignation symbolized the past technical differences that had distorted the original F–102 program. It also recognized that further changes could be forthcoming.

Production Policy **August 1956**

Two months after the F–102B's redesignation, the Air Force practically re-endorsed the production policy originally outlined for the "1954 ultimate interceptor." On 18 August 1956 it issued a system development directive calling for concurrent development and production of the new F–106—a procedure responsible for several later problems.

Initial Requirements (F–106) **28 September 1956**

As stated in a system development directive, issued by the Air Force on 28 September 1956, the new F–106 would be capable of intercepting and destroying hostile vehicles under all weather conditions, at all altitudes up to 70,000 feet, and within a radius of 375 nautical miles. Interceptions would be accomplished at speeds up to Mach 2 at 35,000 feet. Flight would be "under automatic guidance provided by the ground environment and the aircraft's fire-control system." The F–106 would carry guided missiles and rockets with atomic warheads. It would be available in August 1958—some 4 years past the original deadline of the Mach 1.93, 60,200–ft altitude "ultimate interceptor."

First Flight (Prototype) **26 December 1956**

Convair test flew the F–106 for the first time on 26 December 1956, 38 months after the F–102A (the Air Force's first supersonic delta-wing interceptor) made its first flight. The second F–106 prototype, after being also transported from its San Diego plant to Edwards AFB, was initially flown on 26 February 1957.

Initial Shortcomings **1957**

The first USAF F–106 test flight, made from Edwards AFB on 29 April 1957, showed deceptive results. The F–106 reached a speed of Mach 1.9 and an altitude of 57,000 feet. However, upon completion of the Category II flight tests (started in May 1957 and purposefully accelerated to end in July of the same year), the first F–106 prototype's overall performance (after more than 70 flights) was much less impressive. The F–106's acceleration and maximum speed were both below Convair's estimates and a September preliminary Category II end-report on the second F–106 prototype proved equally discouraging. Mach numbers above 1.7 were not considered tactically usable because of the aircraft's poor acceleration. Under standard conditions, the airplane took almost 4½ minutes to accelerate from Mach 1 to Mach 1.7 and another 2½ minutes to accelerate to Mach 1.8—eating up 2,000 pounds of fuel in the process.

General Operational Requirements **19 June 1957**

The F–106 requirements, underlined in the system development directive of September 1956, were finalized in June 1957. Maximum speed (at least, Mach 2.0) and combat radius (375 nautical miles or better) were unchanged, but the aircraft's required combat ceiling was reduced from 70,000 feet to a minimum of 55,000 feet.[3] The F–106's required capability of operating on 6,000–ft runways was defined as well as its armament. The F–106 would carry one MB–1 air-to-air atomic rocket and four GAR–3/GAR–4 Falcons, launchable in salvo or in pairs. The new interceptor would be provided with TAGAN (tactical air navigation), BROFICON (broadcast fighter control), and an AMTI (airborne moving target indicator) unit that would assure an interception capability at any altitudes between sea level and the aircraft's maximum combat ceiling.

Early Modifications **1957**

The F–106 deficiencies, pinpointed by the first Category II flight tests, although disappointing, came as no great surprise. The Air Force (after reviewing the flight test data obtained during Convair Category I testing of the first F–106 prototype) had already decided that modification of the aircraft's inlet duct cowling and charging ejectors would probably increase speed and acceleration. It planned to modify the aircraft upon completion of the Category II tests and to evaluate the results of these changes during the Category III testing. The Air Force made every effort to hasten the F–106 development/production cycle. In April 1957 it author-

[3] By way of comparison, the performance required of the F–102A called for a speed of Mach 1.2 and a 54,000–ft combat ceiling. The F–102 and F–106 combat radius was later stretched to 566 nautical miles and 633 nautical miles, respectively, by adding external fuel tanks to the aircraft.

ized the conditional acceptance of several aircraft from the Convair flight-test inventory. In September, it quickly approved a Convair engineering proposal to enlarge the capture area of the F–106 ducts and to thin down the duct lips in order to satisfy the J–75–P–9 engine's airflow requirements, higher than anticipated. Hopefully, these changes would reduce drag, raise the aircraft's ceiling by 5,000 feet, and increase maximum speed. Acceleration time (from cruise speed to maximum Mach conditions) would be shortened by perhaps as much as 3 minutes. Meanwhile, there were other problems.

Other Problems **1957**

While airframe modifications were being worked out to satisfy the requirements of the F–106's engine, all was not well with the engine itself. The Pratt and Whitney J–75–P–9 turbojet, substituted for the Wright J–67 in 1955 because of rapid development progress, had also become a source of delay. In June 1957 production was still behind schedule, and upon availability the J–75–P–9 (later replaced by the more powerful 17,000 lb s.t. –P–17) proved to be less reliable than the Air Force would have liked. Another problem of long standing, which reached a climax in 1957, pertained to the F–106 cockpit. After endorsing relocation of the F–106 center-mounted control stick to the side of the pilot to assure his unrestricted view of Hughes proposed-Horizontal Situation Indicator (HSI), the Air Force reversed its decision. It confirmed that both the USAF vertical instrument flight panel and the HSI would be incorporated in the F–106 but announced that the pilot's control stick would be returned to its original center position. This final change proved to be sound, but its delayed approval precluded it from being incorporated in any of the F–106 test aircraft. Altogether, the Air Force's late decision of 1957 concerning the cockpit foretold a $10 million cost increase that could not have been more ill-timed.

Program Reappraisal **1957**

A severe fund shortage caused the Air Force to reappraise many of its plans. While the F–106 program came to the fore because of its great cost, other factors singled it out for reappraisal. Besides the aircraft's disappointing overall performance, its J–75 engine and MA–1 ECS still did not function properly by the spring of 1957. Moreover, as a result of the numerous development delays since the ADO of 1949, other weapon systems—such as the McDonnell F–101B interceptor—had been partially substituted for the F–106, which had long lost the high priority initially afforded to the Ultimate Interceptor. Hence, the Air Force considered giving up the entire F–106 program, or redesigning the aircraft as a long-range interceptor. In its financial dilemma, the Air Force finally raised the possibility that the F–101B might have to be dropped if the F–106 was retained. The Air Defense Command liked none of these alternatives. It believed redesign as a long-range interceptor would take so long that it would mean the end of the F–106. If a shortage of funds required buying fewer interceptors, even though the F–101B was cheaper than the F–106, ADC wanted to spread the reduction over each kind, since the two aircraft were complementary.[4] ADC won its case and the F–106 program did survive. However, not without drastic changes.

F-106A

Program Change and Final Procurement **1957-1958**

In mid–1957, when only 120 F–106As had been funded for procurement and Headquarters USAF thought of liquidating the entire program, ADC plans called for an F–106 buildup of 40 squadrons (more than 1,000 aircraft). This total was reduced to 26 squadrons by the end of the year, and another cut took place in September 1958. This last reduction finalized the F–106 force level at little more than one-third of the 1,000 aircraft originally sought by ADC.[5] The decrease was so sharp that the Air Force, despite the extra expense, decided in August 1959 to convert the F–106 test aircraft (35 in all by that time) to operational status.

Enters Operational Service **May 1959**

ADC's 498th Fighter Interceptor Squadron at Geiger AFB, Wash., reached an initial operational capability in October 1959 (5 years later than originally planned). Notwithstanding, the 498th on 21st July scrambled five F–106s on a simulated combat mission with remarkable success. All targets were found and destroyed within 10 minutes after takeoff.

Operational Problems **1959-1960**

In spite of the initial achievements of the first F–106s, ADC was not fully convinced that it was getting a combat-ready aircraft.

---

[4] At the time, the F–101B had a maximum speed (at 35,000 feet) of about Mach 1.7, a combat ceiling of 50,000 feet, and a combat radius of about 600 nm, compared respectively with the F–106 tentative figures of Mach 1.8+, 53,000 ft, and 350 nm.

[5] Another casualty of the late fifties' financial crisis was the F–108 Rapier, cancelled by the Air Force on 23 September 1959. The F–108, formerly referred to as the LRIX (long-range interceptor, experimental) and officially named the Rapier on 15 May 1959, was being developed by North American Aviation since 1957. As called for by USAF GOR 114 (6 October 1955), the stainless steel, two-place, two-engine, Mach 3, 70,000–ft altitude weapon system for use during the 1963–1970 time period, was designed to launch an atomic missile 1,000 miles from home base and return to base within 30 minutes. Despite encouraging development progress and a satisfactory mockup inspection in January 1959, the Rapier was cancelled before production of the first prototype.

Generator defects, fuel-flow difficulties (particularly acute in cold weather), and fuel-combustion-starter malfunctions were only a few of the frequent problems. In December 1959, after a canopy had been accidentally jettisoned in flight, all F–106s were temporarily grounded. Some of these early problems persisted a year later.

Flight Testing **1957–1961**

Testing of the F–106 was extensive. The Category II flight tests conducted at Edwards AFB, after being first accelerated, were extended and did not end until June 1959. Because of a shortage of aircraft, the Category III tests did not begin until July 1959 (a few months after the F–106 entered operational service with ADC's 498th FIS). They were conducted by another ADC unit, the 539th FIS at McGuire AFB, N. J., with the assistance of that command's interceptor and missile school at Tyndall AFB, Fla., where the ADC pilots learned to fire the new interceptor's armament. Category III testing ended in early 1961, after being somewhat hampered by logistical shortages.[6] Meanwhile, justifying ADC suspicion of the F–106's initial combat readiness, each phase of the test programs gave way to important engineering changes. Yet, each change had to be "defined, engineered, reviewed, and approved for production" before modification of aircraft off the assembly line could begin. Hence, by 1960 ADC possessed so many divergent F–106 configurations that maintenance support was almost impossible—a problem partially due to the Cook-Craigie production policy re-endorsed in August 1956. Moreover, in spite of successive production-line improvements (and an advanced Category III end-report in late 1960 declaring the F–106 operationally suitable) the Air Force still sought ways to enhance the aircraft.

Necessary Retrofit **September 1960**

Two major modification projects were undertaken. Wild Goose (started in September 1960 and completed in exactly 1 year), was designed to standardize the F–106 fleet.[7] It was largely retrofit work, mostly done at ADC bases by roving AMC field assistance teams supported by ADC maintenance personnel. Broad Jump (also initiated in late 1960) was a long-term program to improve the new interceptor. It took the Sacramento Air Materiel Area an

---

[6] Despite fire-control problems and a lack of scoring equipment and targets, MB–1 atomic warhead rocket and radar-guided GAR–3 Falcon firing missions of the Category III tests ended at Tyndall AFB in May 1960. The entire Category III testing was completed with a series of GAR–3A and infrared GAR–4A tests.

[7] Early in 1960 ADC could list 63 changes in the F–106's fire-control system and 67 changes in the airframe that would be necessary to give early F–106 productions the same configuration as the most recent aircraft off the assembly line.

average of 60 days per aircraft to apply Broad Jump, which extended through early 1963.[8]

Other Improvements **1960**

Endorsement of the Wild Goose and Broad Jump modifications in the summer of 1960 did not deter the Air Force from seeking further F-106 improvements. Devices for long-range detection and electronic counter-counter measures (CCM), parametric amplifiers, along with angle chaff, silent lobing, and pulse-to-pulse frequency shift techniques were among those recommended and, for the most part, eventually approved. Meanwhile, Convair's struggle to provide the F-106 with a better supersonic ejection seat (one that would also work safely at low speed) had sufficiently progressed to warrant installing the new seat in the last 37 F-106A productions and its future retrofit in all others.[9] In 1960 Hughes flight-tested an infrared search-and-track sight that could operate at low altitudes and against varied backgrounds.[10] Tests were so encouraging that the infrared unit was included in the F-106 program of possible improvements, some of which were developed soon enough to become part of the Broad Jump program.

Other Postproduction Modifications **1961-1964**

In face of Wild Goose and Broad Jump changes—and Dart Board, another retrofit/modification program (August 1961-April 1962)—the F-106 weapon system still had problems. Dart Board had given the aircraft a thermal flash blindness protection hood, provided it with Convair's new Upward Rotational Ejection Seat, and added devices to help correct flameout from fuel starvation (one of the F-106's first deficiencies). But a lot more remained to be done. The MA-1 AWCS, "the most complex, sophisticated and completely integrated automatic weapon control system" designed for an all-weather fighter-interceptor aircraft, remained unrelia-

---

[8] Not more than half of any squadron's F-106As were released to Wild Goose and Broad Jump at one time, so as to preserve a measure of combat capability during the $15 million, 800,000-manhour modification period.

[9] Development of the supersonic ejection seats (two-stage boom seats) required by the F-106B, the two-seater trainer variant of the F-106A, took longer, and sled tests did not start until mid-1960. As in the case of the F-106A, the F-106B's ejection seats featured a dual timing system, one for high-altitude/low-speed ejection and one for high-altitude/high-speed ejection. At sufficient flying speed, either seat enabled pilots to escape safely at low altitude.

[10] Hughes infrared search and track sight was an outgrowth of the ASG-18 pulse-doppler fire-control system developed by the same firm for the F-108 interceptor. The F-108 program was no longer in existence, but development of the ASG-18 and its accompanying GAR-9 missile (later designated AIM-47A) continued. The Hughes ASG-18/AIM-47A combination became part of the Lockheed YF-12A interceptor, first publicly displayed on 30 September 1964.

ble.[11] Correction efforts unabated, the Air Force embarked in two new modification programs. One involved the installation of parametric amplifiers in the MA–1 AWCS to up the system's detection and lock-on range by about 30 percent. The other also dealt with the MA–1, mainly to add anti-chaff devices. The two new in-house modification programs, involving 314 F–106s, were to be completed by the end of 1963.[12]

Initial Modernization **1965–1967**

After divers modification programs, the F–106, the Air Force's first-line interceptor since 1959, entered its modernization phase. In 1965 the Air Force awarded a $6.2 million contract for producing new tactical air navigation systems for its best interceptor. The new TACAN, the first to use microelectronic circuits, would be one-third the size and weight of the current F–106 navigation system and would provide 450 hours of maintenance-free operation. The Air Force in addition approved in-house modifications that would give the F–106 an in-flight refueling capability for long-range ferrying. The installation of new external wing-mounted supersonic fuel tanks, also authorized, would increase the F–106's radius of operation. These modifications would allow F–106 deployment for air defense of US forces overseas in an emergency. They had been applied to two squadrons of F–106s by the end of 1967—just a few months before the North Korean seizure of the USS *Pueblo*. Modification of the entire F–106 fleet was scheduled for completion by the fall of 1969.

Modernization Planning **1967–1968**

The F–106 modernization, begun in 1965, would satisfy neither long-term air defense requirements[13] nor potential short-term ones. The F–106 needed a 20–mm gun (for close-in attack against hostile fighter aircraft). It required a new canopy (for better observation of the air battle), radar homing and warning equipment (to warn the pilot of enemy air/ground radar and missile

---

[11] The MA–1 AWCS was made up of 170 "black boxes" and weighed about 1,800 pounds. Practically all the F–106's electronic equipment, including the communication receiver and transmitter, the gyro compass, automatic direction finding and certain electronic counter-counter-measure (ECCM) elements, were part of the MA–1 complex. The nine subsystems of the MA–1 contained about 200 major components.

[12] During the same period, similar modifications were programmed for the MG–13 fire-control system of 431 F–101Bs.

[13] The Air Force directed upgrading of the existing manned interceptor force in the mid–1960's as a stop-gap measure, pending outcome of advanced manned interceptor (AMI) studies such as operational versions of the YF–12A and F–111. Other candidates for the AMI role later included the F–14 (a proposed Navy aircraft), possibly a new interceptor, and the proposed F–106X, a drastically modified F–106.

launches), and a device to show when maximum turn angle of attack had been reached. In addition, the F–106 could fire its air-to-air missiles in salvo or in pairs, but not singly, and missile preparation took too long. The F–106 weapon system nonetheless remained the best interceptor available, and ADC (still intent upon making it more reliable and easier to maintain) readied for USAF approval a program which was called Simplified Logistics and Improved Maintenance (SLIM). This original SLIM improvement package carried in September 1967 a price tag of $120 million. The Secretary of Defense's decision on 23 November 1967 to discontinue F–12 development and to select the F–106X as the future interceptor to complement a new airborne warning and control system (AWACS)[14] altered ADC planning.[15] The SLIM program was put aside in favor of a more costly one—nearly $1 billion—for the so-called (but as it proved out, never-to-be) F–106X.

Oversea Deployments **March 1968**

As part of the Korean buildup stemming from the *Pueblo* crisis, a series of F–106 deployments to Korea began. The first F–106s deployed from McChord AFB and conducted in-flight refueling en route—the first such refueling of F–106s.

Other Modernization **1969–1973**

When it appeared in late 1968 that the F–106X would not materialize,[16] ADC renewed its efforts to modernize the entire F–106 weapon system which, it believed, had become one of the Air Force's most competent fighters. The original $120 million SLIM program of September 1967 was revived and further simplified. It eventually emerged in mid–1969 as the cheaper Minimum Essential Improvement in System Reliability (MEISR) program ($91 million for 250 F–106A/B aircraft). MEISR would still significantly improve the radar, automatic flight control and DC power system of the F–106[17] and it was quickly approved by the Air Force. Though MEISR modifications were to be done by AFLC[18] person-

[14] Approved for development in November 1967.

[15] On 15 January 1968 the Air Defense Command became the Aerospace Defense Command.

[16] As estimated in mid–1969, the F–106X would require the expenditure of more than half a billion dollars ($626.2 million), but money alone probably did not decide its fate. The impasse between the Department of Defense (pro–F–106X) and Congress (supporting the Air Force-preferred F–12) most likely also contributed to the demise of the F–106X program.

[17] Overall weapon control system mean time between failures (MTBF) would be increased by 80%, and annual maintenance would be reduced by more than 50%. Intercept success rates would increase from 75% to 87% with primary armament; from 58% to 85% with secondary armament.

[18] The Air Force Logistics Command (the former Air Materiel Command) came into being on 1 April 1961.

nel at Hamilton AFB (where ADC's F–106s would be rotated through the 4661st Air Base Group), budgetary constrictions would probably delay completion until sometime in 1973. Despite austere funding, the Air Force in 1969 also endorsed most of Sixshooter—an ADC project outlined in February 1967, after the F–106 had shown the speed and maneuverability for a fighter-to-fighter role. Foremost among the Sixshooter F–106 modernization projects were addition of a 20–mm. gun (M–61), a lead-computing gunsight, a clear cockpit canopy, electronic countermeasures gear, and a RHAW device. The Air Force spent $1.5 million for a Sixshooter "feasibility demonstration" with generally satisfactory results, but eliminated the ECCM improvements recommended by ADC. All other Sixshooter modernization projects were approved, but technical as well as financial difficulties slowed their progress. The Air Force decided in October 1969 that something better than the current (and, in any case, extremely scarce) RHAW equipment would have to be developed to cope with increasingly sophisticated enemy radars. Similarly, installation of the clear-top canopy was not expected to begin until January 1972, and testing of the new gunsight, not before mid–1972.[19]

Special Testing **1972-1974**

In June 1972 one F–106 entered a Convair flight-and-fatigue test program to recertify the aircraft for longer service life—8,000 flight hours instead of the current 4,000. This program, expected to run through mid–1974, would also further evaluate the F–106's new stretched-acrylic, clear top canopy.

Subsequent Model Series

F–106B

Other Configurations

None. Production of two other F–106 model series, the F–106C and F–106D, was first considered, then dropped. The proposed F–106C would have featured a new engine (JT4B–22), a new fuselage structure, and a variety of technical changes. For example, a new 40–inch radar that would only slightly decrease the aircraft's absolute altitude and combat radius, but would appreciably increase its "kill" probability by extending search range a minimum of 50 percent. While the F–106D never went past the planning stage, the Air Force in mid–1957 anticipated the production of at least 350 F–106Cs. Two F–106C prototypes were built and accepted by the Air Force in December 1958—a few months after cancella-

[19] The Air Force approved on 27 January 1972 Air Force Academy development of the new gunsight that would complement the F–106's forthcoming M–61. While contractor gunsight engineering costs were estimated at something over $6 million, the Academy required only an initial $100,000 to get its work under way.

tion of the F–106C program.[20] Some 10 years later a third configuration, the so-called F–106X,[21] received considerable attention. The F–106X was a basic F–106 that would feature a new radome and a larger radar antenna. It would also receive, among other things, a modified fire-control system (providing "look-down" capability) and a new air-to-air missile with "shoot-down" capability. Like the superior Lockheed F–12,[22] the so-called F–106X did not materialize.

End of Production **December 1960**

With delivery of the last eight F–106As.

Total F-106As Accepted

The Air Force accepted 275 F–106As, including the first production aircraft earmarked for testing (later modified for tactical use) and the two F–106s used as prototypes.

Acceptance Rates

Two F–106As (designated YF–106As) were accepted in FY 57, 16 in FY 58, 45 in FY 59, 150 in FY 60, and 62 in FY 61 (during the second half of 1960).

Total RDT&E Costs[23]

$1.0 million

Flyaway Cost Per Production Aircraft

$4.7 million—airframe, $2,090,000; engine (installed), $274,000; electronics, $1,300,000; armament, $950,000; ordnance, $102,000.

Average Cost Per Flying Hour

$1,600.00 (maintenance included)

Operational Status **Mid-1973**

The Air Force in mid–1973 retained 174 of the 340 F–106s produced, the last of which had been delivered in December 1960. Seventy-three other F–106s were flown by the Air National Guard, ADC's increasingly close partner. Moreover, modernization of the versatile F–106 was in process. Obviously, the upgraded F–106 would be around for many years to come.

---

[20] F–106Cs and F–106Ds were deleted when Headquarters USAF limited on 23 September 1958 the F–106 production program to a total of 340 aircraft (F–106Bs, included). Two YF–106Cs, already funded, were accepted.

[21] A somewhat misleading designation. The "X" implied that a new model would be created, which was never intended to be the case.

[22] As demonstrated by available YF–12As, the F–12 could fly faster than Mach 3 and reach an altitude of 70,000 feet with ease. It was the most advanced aircraft during the late 1960's but fabulously expensive.

[23] Prorated, this amounted to $2,941 that were reflected in the flyaway cost of each F–106. By contrast, cumulative modification costs of $659,603 (spent on each F–106A by 30 June 1973) were excluded.

Record Flight **15 December 1959**

An F–106 jet interceptor at Edwards AFB set world speed record of 1,525.695 mph on 11–mile straightaway course, eclipsing the Russian mark of 1,483.84 mph set in an "E–66" delta-wing aircraft.[24]

Other Milestones **December 1967**

F–106s flew nonstop from McChord AFB to Tyndall AFB for the first extended-range interceptor flight marked by inflight refueling and missile firing. In early 1968, air-refueled F–106s flew from Richards-Gebaur AFB, Mo., to Elmendorf AFB, Alaska.

F-106B

Manufacturer's Model 8-27
Weapon System 201B

Previous Model Series

F–106A

New Features

Tandem two-seat cockpit, redesigned fuselage tank area, and Hughes AN–ASQ–25 fire-control system—equivalent to the F–106A's MA–1.

Go-Ahead Decision **3 August 1956**

The Air Force authorized production of a trainer version of the F–106A. A late August decision not to confine the aircraft to a trainer role prompted its redesignation. The future TF–106A became the F–106B, a two-seater packing the F–106A's tactical punch.

Development Engineering Inspection **13 September 1956**

One day after that of the F–106A.

Mockup Inspection **September 1956**

The first of several, chiefly concerned with the aircraft's cockpit. The second inspection of the F–106B's cockpit, also at the Convair Fort Worth plant, was conducted in mid-December.

Contractual Arrangements **April 1957**

Procurement of the F–106B was included in the third F–106A contract, but the F–106B definitive contract was not finalized until 3 June 1957.

First Flight (Prototype) **9 April 1958**

The Air Force accepted the aircraft during the same month.

[24] Design of the basic E–66 was attributed to Artem Mikoyan, who worked with Mikhail Gurevich in designing the MIG–15, the first really-modern Soviet jet-fighter. The delta-wing E–66, powered by a single turbojet engine, seemed a version of the MIG–21 Fishbed, one of the many configurations progressively developed from the MIG–15. The MIG–21 was first seen in the Soviet Aviation Day display at Tushino Airport, Moscow, on 24 June 1956.

First Flight (Production Aircraft) **October 1958**

Basically similar to the F–106A, the F–106B shared the former's development and production vicissitudes. The Air Force accepted nine F–106Bs between April and December 1958, but did not initially release any of them to the operational forces.

Initial Operational Capability **July 1960**

Eight months after ADC achieved an IOC with the A model. The first F–106B, earmarked from the onset for the operational inventory, was accepted from Convair in February 1959.

End of Production **December 1960**

Production ended with delivery of the last two F–106Bs.

Total F-106Bs Accepted

63

Acceptance Rates

One F–106B (prototype) was accepted in FY 58 (April 1958), 11 in FY 59, 36 in FY 60, and 15 in FY 61 (during the last 6 months of 1960).

Flyaway Cost Per Production Aircraft[25]

$4.9 million—airframe, $2,200,000; engine (installed), $274,000; electronics, $1,350,000; ordnance, $24,000; armament, $1,089,000.

Average Cost Per Flying Hour

$1,600.00 (maintenance included)

Modification/Modernization Programs **1960–on**

The F–106B, of necessity, participated in all F–106A modification and modernization programs. Like the 35 F–106As initially allocated to testing, the first 12 F–106B productions were eventually brought up to the tactical standards of the entire F–106 fleet. In the process, they exchanged their original J75–P–9 turbojet engine for the more powerful J75–P–17. All 64 F–106Bs received Convair's new ejection seats (two-stage boom seats) after production.

Operational Status **Mid-1973**

Each ADC and ANG F–106 squadron had several two seaters for normal intercept missions as well as combat proficiency training and checks. Hence, the F–106B's operational life was likely to last as long as that of the F–106A.

PROGRAM RECAP

The Air Force accepted a grand total of 340 F–106s—275 F–106As, 63 F–106Bs, and 2 YF–106Cs. Included in the F–106A total were the 2 prototypes, first referred to as YF–102Bs, and early productions marked for testing but later modified for operational use.

---

[25] Excluding modification costs totaling $59,251 by 30 June 1973.

TECHNICAL DATA

F–106A and F–106B

Manufacturer	Convair Division of General Dynamics Corporation, San Diego, Calif.
Nomenclature	Supersonic, all-weather, fighter-interceptor.
Popular Name	Delta Dart

Characteristics	*F–106A Point Interceptor*	*F–106A Area Interceptor*	*F–106B Point Interceptor*
Takeoff Weight	36,000 lb	38,700 lb	36,500 lb
Length Fuselage[26]/Wing	70.″7′/38.″3′	70.″7′/38.″3′	70.″7′/38.″3′
Max. Speed	1,100 kn	1,100 kn	1,100 kn
Radius (combat)	NA	633 nm (w/ external fuel tanks)	633 nm (w/ external fuel tanks)
Engine, Number & Designation[27]	1J75–P–17	1J75–P–17	1J75–P–17
Takeoff Ground Run	3,000 ft	3,600 ft	3,200 ft
Rate of Climb (sea level)	39,800 fpm	7,170 fpm	39,400 fpm
Combat Ceiling	52,000 ft	52,000 ft	51,400 ft
Crew	1	1	2
Ordnance/Armament	1 AIR–2A Genie, plus 4 AIM–4F Falcons, or 4 AIM–4Gs, or 2 AIM–4Fs & 2 AIM–4Gs	1 AIR–2A Genie, plus 4 AIM–4F Falcons, or 4 AIM–4Gs, or 2 AIM–4Fs & 2 AIM–4Gs	1 AIR–2A Genie, plus 4 AIM–4F Falcons, or 4 AIM–4Gs, or 2 AIM–4Fs & 2 AIM–4Gs

[26] Including nose boom

[27] Pratt & Whitney; 17,200 lb s.t. (24,000 lb with afterburner).

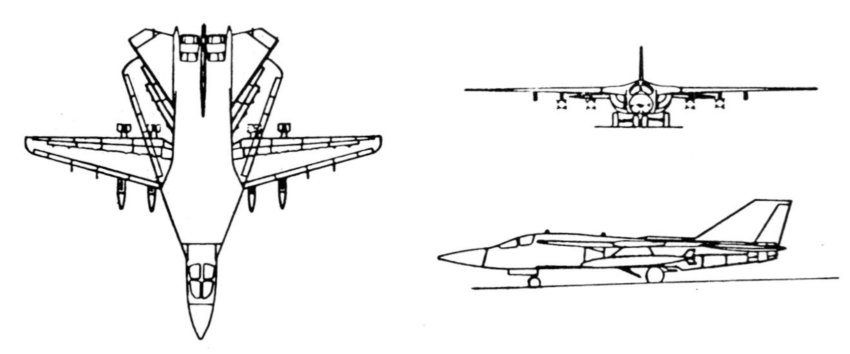

GENERAL DYNAMICS F–111

F–111A/B/D/E/F:	The variable-sweep wing could be positioned in flight at various angles between the full forward and aft positions—enabling all F–111 tactical fighters to operate from relatively short runways, fly at supersonic speeds at low altitudes, and reach Mach 2.5 above 60,000 feet.
FB–111A:	Longer fuselage, extended wing tip, stronger undercarriage and landing gear, extra and bigger fuel tanks, were some of the distinctive features of the FB–111A medium range strategic bomber.

GENERAL DYNAMICS F-111

Manufacturer's Model 12
Weapon System 324A

Basic Development

Much of the F-111 design technology evolved from Bell's potbellied X-5—America's first swingwing airplane—and US Navy's Grumman XF-10F. The F-111's two-pivot, variable-sweep wing, as opposed to the single-pivot used in previous experiments, spelled the success of the variable-wing idea.[1] It was discovered in 1959 by engineers at the Langley Research Center of the National Aeronautics and Space Administration.

General Operational Requirements — 27 March 1958

The GOR called for Weapon System 649C—a 1964 Tactical Air Command Mach 2 +, 60,000-ft altitude, all-weather fighter, capable of vertical and short takeoff and landing (V/STOL). The Air Force cancelled its March 1958 GOR (No. 169) on 29 March 1959, on the belief that, after all, vertical takeoff had not yet arrived.

System Development Requirement (SDR) — 5 February 1960

As issued by the Air Force, SDR No. 17 encompassed most of the cancelled GOR's requirements, except for vertical takeoff and landing (VTOL). Combined with TAC's revised specifications and a delayed operational due-date, it allowed the subsequent definition of specific requirements for a new weapon system—WS 324A.

Specific Operational Requirements (SOR) — 14 July 1960

This was SOR 183, a follow-on to the SDR of February 1960. It called for Weapon System 324A, an air superiority, Mach 2.5, 60,000-foot-plus altitude, all-weather, day and night, two-crew, STOL fighter (that could take off or land, even on sod fields, in less than 3,000 feet), with an 800-mile low-level radius (including 400 miles close to the terrain at Mach 1.2 speed), carrying either conventional or nuclear weapons. The unrefueled 3,300-nm ferry range and 1,000-lb internal payload (in addition to a lifting payload

---

[1] From the days of Leonardo Da Vinci men had dreamt of flying with flapping wings. Experiments with the variable-sweep wing began in France in 1911 and the practical idea of moveable wings was introduced at a Rome scientific convention by Dr. Adolf Busemann, a young German designer. The Busemann theory and ensuing research by Dr. Albert Betz of the Gottingen Aerodynamics Research Institute spurred Messerschmitt in 1942 to begin work on a sweep-wing design dubbed the P-1101. Perhaps because contemporary engines could not give fighters high-enough speed for the variable wing to make any appreciable difference, the war ended before Messerschmitt's completion of the first German swingwing aircraft. The captured prototype (transported intact to the United States and soon loaned to the Bell Aircraft Company) led to design studies in 1948 which gave way, 3 years later, to the X-5's first flight.

between 15,000 and 30,000 pounds), also required by SOR 183, put the so-called fighter[2] in the fighter-bomber class—like the TAC F–100Ds and F–105s that it was expected to begin replacing in 1966. The Air Force considered that a variable-sweep wing and a forthcoming, improved turbo-fan engine would satisfy SOR 183. A reconnaissance version (six squadrons) of Weapon System 324A (expected to equip a minimum of six tactical wings) was part of the Air Force requirements.

Requests for Proposals **October 1960**

The Air Force prepared to inform industry of its new fighter requirement, but the Office of the Secretary of Defense (OSD) asked in November 1960 that the October RFPs be withheld for further review of SOR 183. The deferred project acquired a new status in December, becoming the TFX (Tactical Fighter Experimental), a name later embroiled in controversy.

New Requirements **7 June 1961**

The October RFPs stayed in abeyance. Believing a triservice fighter would save money, Secretary of Defense Robert S. McNamara on 16 February 1961 asked the Air Force to determine with the Army and Navy if the TFX could provide close air support (CAS) to ground troops; air defense of the fleet; as well as interdiction of enemy logistics—the Air Force's primary objective. The Army and Navy wanted a simpler CAS airplane, preferably the Navy-sponsored VAX (attack aircraft, experimental). The Air Force did not go along with this thinking, but it did agree that the TFX was not the plane for close air support. Army and Navy CAS objections to the TFX finally prevailed in May. Notwithstanding, Secretary McNamara remained convinced that the TFX could satisfy other Navy and Air Force needs. In June he instructed the Air Force to "work closely" with the Navy in tying the two services' requirements into a new, cost-effective TFX configuration.

Go-Ahead Decision **8 September 1961**

The decision by OSD was accompanied by a revised SOR 183, reflecting Secretary McNamara's arbitration of Air Force and Navy unreconciled requirements.[3] The September 1961 SOR 183

---

[2] As a rule, fighters were designed to climb and maneuver rapidly, but they lacked payload and range. The weapon system called for by SOR 183 became the first aircraft specifically built to reverse the historic trend toward specialization. It achieved a versatility that justified reference as strike, attack, advanced tactical fighter, and the like.

[3] In spite of their unreconciled requirements, Admiral George Anderson, Chief of Naval Operations, and General Curtis LeMay, Air Force Chief of Staff, with the Secretary of Defense's approval, had publicly announced their endorsement of a new tactical fighter program on 1 September.

called for a wider fuselage (to satisfy Navy needs for more internal fuel and a panoramic nose antenna), with overall dimensions and weight kept to the maximum acceptable for carrier operation. The Air Force's TFX version could have a gross takeoff weight of 60,000 pounds (20,000 less than anticipated), compared to the Navy's 55,000. The airframe would not figure in the 5,000-lb difference in gross takeoff weight. Nor would heavier Navy avionics (offset by the weight of Air Force loads and armament).

New Requests for Proposals **29 September 1961**

These replaced the October 1960 RFPs and were sent to Boeing, Chance-Vought, Douglas, General Dynamics, Grumman, Lockheed, McDonnell, North American, Northrop, and Republic. Only Northrop turned down the USAF invitation, and nine responses were received in early December. The Air Force Selection Board and a Navy representative endorsed the Boeing proposal on 19 January 1962, but the Air Force Council rejected it. In late January Air Force and Navy agreed that none of the contractor proposals were acceptable, but that two—the Boeing and General Dynamics—deserved further study. A February, $1 million letter contract to each of the two solicited more design data. Meanwhile, the bi-service TFX was renamed.

Official Designation **December 1961**

The Air Force's future version of the TFX was designated F–111A; the Navy's, F–111B.

Contractor Selection **24 November 1962**

The LCs of February 1962 did not solve the competition problem. In May both the Air Force and Navy Secretaries disapproved the two contractors' second proposals for lack of sufficient data. Third proposals, appraised in late June, brought another impasse. The Air Force endorsed the Boeing input, but the Navy "refused to commit . . . unequivocally with this program until after the design had been defined." Secretary McNamara on 1 July ordered a final runoff on the basis of open "pay-off points" for performance, cost, and commonality. After receiving an additional $2.5 million apiece, Boeing and General Dynamics submitted in September their fourth and last proposals. The Air Force Selection Board as well as the Air Force Council again chose the Boeing design, but on 24 November the OSD publicly ruled in favor of General Dynamics.[4]

Initial Procurement **21 December 1962**

The Air Force initiated procurement of 23 RDT&E F–111s (18 F–

[4] The decision spurred a congressional investigation, the long-drawn TFX Hearings that required Secretary McNamara's written testimony. Justifying his contractor selection, the Secretary underscored the fact that the General Dynamics proposal was closer to a single design, required only minor modifications to fit Navy and Air Force requirements, and embodied a more realistic approach to the cost problem.

111As and 5 F–111Bs), without awaiting the time-consuming negotiation of a definitive contract, by amending the LC that initially covered General Dynamics' second competitive proposal. The $28 million amendment of December 1962[5] made possible urgent subcontracts[6] and a November 1963 agreement with Grumman (the number one subcontractor, actually part of the General Dynamics team) for development and production of the Navy F–111B.

Mockup Inspection **September 1963**

Following separate inspections of the engine in July, and of the airframe in August.

Definitized Contract (RDT&E Aircraft) **1 May 1964**

The amended LC of February 1962 was finalized as a fixed price incentive fee (FPIF) contract (AF 33–657–8260), with a 90/10 percent sharing arrangement. The ceiling price ($529 million) was based on 120 percent of the $480.4 million target cost for 23 RDT&E F–111s. This included flight testing, spares, ground equipment, training devices, static and fatigue test data. The FPIF development contract of May 1964 contained cost, schedule, performance, and operational clauses, plus a provision for the "correction of deficiencies."

F-111A

First Flight (RDT&E Aircraft) **21 December 1964**

The flight was made from Carswell AFB, Tex., by the first test F–111A that had rolled out of the General Dynamics' Fort Worth plant on 15 October—37 months after the OSD go-ahead decision, 22 months after the program's actual beginning, and 2 weeks ahead of schedule.[7] Although performance restrictions had been

---

[5] Plus $22 million obligated to the Navy for development and hardware of a Pratt and Whitney engine—the TF–30. The Air Force assumed this Navy responsibility in late 1967, after the TF–30 had undergone several transformations.

[6] By the spring of 1964 AiResearch, AVCO, Bendix, Collins Radio, Dalmo Victor, General Electric, Hamilton Standard, Litton Systems, McDonnell Aircraft, Texas Instruments, and seven other major subcontractors had become involved in the F–111 program and were doing business with 6,703 suppliers in 44 states. An associate prime contract for the F–111B's Phoenix missile system had also been signed by the Navy and the Hughes Aircraft Company.

[7] The 15 October roll-out ceremonies prompted Secretary McNamara to remark: ". . . the Air Force, the Navy, and General Dynamics and its subcontractors . . . have produced a plane which will fly faster at any altitude than our best current fighter—a plane with several times the payload and twice the range of any previous fighter-bomber. One F–111 will have the fire power of five World War II flying fortresses. . . . For the first time in aviation history, we have an airplane with the range of a transport, the carrying capacity and endurance of a bomber, and the agility of a fighter pursuit plane. . . ."

set before the flight (and the flight was shortened to 22 minutes because of flap malfunctions), overall results were satisfactory. The aircraft immediately entered Category I testing. During this early testing period, the F–111A achieved Mach 1.3, and maintenance proved comparatively simple. On its maiden flight (25 February 1965), a second F–111A swept its wings from a 16° to a 72.5° aft position (as designed). These were the only test F–111s accepted by the Air Force (each on its first flight's date) prior to the initial production agreement.

Program Change **1965**

A cost rise from an estimated $4.5 to $6.03 million per aircraft led the OSD in early 1965 to cut the F–111 program sharply. Accrued USAF requirements likewise shaped the program. These included improved avionics (formally directed by the OSD in January 1966) and a strategic F–111 bomber to replace B–52C through F aircraft (OSD-endorsed in June 1965 but not made official until December). Development of a reconnaissance F–111 (approved in October 1965, but eventually cancelled) was also a factor.

Letter Contract (Production Aircraft) **12 April 1965**

The Air Force started procurement of the F–111 productions as it had the RDT&E aircraft. As publicly announced by the OSD, it gave General Dynamics an April 1965 fixed price incentive fee LC, authorizing the production of 431 F–111s—a more than 50-percent reduction of the total aircraft initially planned. The production LC also authorized negotiation of an unusually large number of subcontracts—mostly with firms already involved in the F–111 development.

Flight Testing **1964–1973**

The 1965 program change added eleven F–111A productions to the already extensive F–111A RDT&E program and expanded it. The Category I flight tests (started in December 1964) did not end until 31 March 1972. At that time, Category II tests (begun in January 1966) were still going on. Several postponements slipped the Category III tests to 1969. They were finally cancelled as operationally unnecessary.

Initial Problems **1964–1967**

Engine malfunctions and weight increases were the main drawback.[8] The Pratt and Whitney P–1 (production version of the afterburning turbofan TF–30) was first flown in an F–111A on 20 July 1965. Despite thorough testing (like that for the experimental TF–30), problems soon arose. The first 30 F–111As (each equipped with two P–1s) had numerous engine stalls, particularly at high

[8] Not unusual during the development of high-performance aircraft, even less revolutionary than the F–111A.

Mach numbers and high angles of attack. Other F–111As received the P–3, an improved P–1 that became available in 1967. The new engine (later retrofitted in several of the first 30 F–111As) was accompanied by an air diverter (Triple Plow I). The P–3/Triple Plow I combination did not cure the stall problem. However, it helped enough, required little airframe modification, and led to further progress. Efforts to control the aircraft's weight were less successful. The F–111A's final takeoff weight for conventional missions (92,000 lb) exceeded the OSD September 1961 specification by 30,000 lb, but USAF expectations by only 10,000 lb.

First Flight (Production Aircraft) 12 February 1967

Two F–111A productions first flew on the 12th. By August the Air Force had accepted these two and nine others, sending them on to testing. All were part of the 30 productions, initially equipped with P–1 engines.[9]

Special Tests April-May 1967

Every facet of the F–111A's widened testing proved to be crucial. Yet, the Combat Bullseye I tests, conducted in the spring of 1967, had the greatest immediate impact. They confirmed the superior bombing accuracy of the aircraft's radar and prompted the F–111A's early deployment to Southeast Asia—a project that acquired overriding priority.

Definitized Contract (Production Aircraft) 10 May 1967

The production LC of 1965 was replaced by a multi-year, FPIF contract (AF 33–657–13403) in May 1967. Production was then raised to a total of 493 F–111s--24 Navy F–111Bs (later, practically cancelled); 24 F–111Cs for Australia; and 445 F–111s of one kind or another (including 50 first earmarked for the United Kingdom) for the Air Force. Unlike the development contract, the production contract of May 1967 (the only one through mid-1970) had an initial ceiling price based on 130 percent of the target cost. This percentage, however, was to be renegotiated for each engineering change. Initial contract profit was still set at 9 percent, but the cost sharing formulas (75/25 sharing to 107 percent and 85/15 from 107 to 130 percent of the ceiling cost) also differed.[10]

---

[9] Engine problems, notwithstanding, an RDT&E F–111A had reached top design speed of Mach 2.5 on 9 July 1966.

[10] By mid-1970 (after more than 2,000 engineering changes), overall ceiling was nearer 127 percent than 130. Profit for all follow-on work was also variable. Hence, overall profit rate "before" overtarget settlement was 8.06 percent; "after" overtarget settlement, only 4.46. On the other side of the ledger, the cost of the contract's first batch of aircraft (about one-third of the 493 on order) had almost doubled, with each F–111A priced at $11 million.

First Flight (31st Production Aircraft) — 24 September 1967

The first F–111A (31st production), featuring the P–3 engine/Triple Plow I air diverter combination successfully concluded the flight. This aircraft and subsequent F–111As were the only ones directly earmarked for the operational inventory.

Enters Operational Service — 16 October 1967

A handful of aircraft were assigned to the 428th, 429th, and 430th Tactical Fighter Squadrons of TAC's 474th Tactical Fighter Wing. The 474th, Cannon AFB, N. Mex., moved to Nellis in early 1968.

SEA Deployment — 15 March 1968

The Combat Bullseye I tests of early 1967 clinched the Air Force decision to rush a small detachment of F–111As to Southeast Asia (Combat Lancer). This would boost night and all-weather attacks while testing the aircraft's overall combat capability. Combat Lancer was preceded by Harvest Reaper, started in June 1967, to temper known F–111A shortcomings and prepare the aircraft for combat. The Harvest Reaper modifications (mainly more avionics and electronic countermeasures (ECM) equipment) would enter the F–111A production lines, if successfully combat proven. Combat Lancer looked to another precombat project (Combat Trident) for trained pilots, Trident running up 2,000 flying hours and 500 bombing sorties in the face of a critical aircraft shortage. Yet, despite engineering changes, perfected penetration aids, and Combat Trident (completed on 6 March, only 9 days before the Combat Lancer deployment), the F–111A's entry into combat was not a success.

Combat Lancer Attrition — March/April 1968

The six Combat Lancer F–111As departed Nellis AFB on 15 March and reached Takhli Royal Thai Air Base on the 17th. At month's end, after 55 missions that centered on North Vietnam targets, two aircraft had been lost. Replacements left Nellis, but the loss of a third Combat Lancer aircraft on 22 April halted F–111A operations.[11] However, the aircraft remained poised for combat despite the first two losses and the marginal success of sorties flown prior to the third combat loss. Even so, the Combat Lancer detachment (Det I of the 428th TFS) saw little action before its November return to the United States.

Initial Operational Capability — 28 April 1968

The 428th TFS of the 474th Tactical Fighter Wing reached an initial operational capability in the spring of 1968. There followed

[11] Keen interest of the nation's press in the controversial F–111 stepped up. In articles, the aircraft became McNamara's "Flying Edsels." Occasionally defended, it was also accused of being a potential "Technological Gold Mine for the Reds."

Harvest Reaper modifications (validated by the Combat Lancer testing operation), other modifications (mostly unexpected), plus a clutch of problems (technical and financial). The wing was therefore not operationally ready until July 1971.

Postproduction Modifications **1969**

The Harvest Reaper improvements (tailored to the Combat Lancer F–111As), although approved for production in April 1968, were delayed. The Air Force decided that the improvement program should include modifications possibly called for by Round Up—a 3-month evaluation of Combat Lancer. Round Up ended in August, but it took longer than expected to tie the Combat Lancer crashes to malfunction of the aircraft's tail servo actuator in one case, and poor mounting of the M–61 gun and pilot error in the two others. Similarly, F–111 testing and training incidents (including two crashes in early 1968) dictated a detailed evaluation that became quite involved. Moreover, on 27 August (1 day after the beginning of the F–111A's Category II fatigue tests)[12] an F–111 wing-carry-through-box failed during a ground fatigue test.[13] Hence, General Dynamics' overall improvement of the F–111 (particularly, additional Harvest Reaper avionics) did not go as planned. It started in January 1969 and required extensive retrofits because most F–111As had cleared the production lines. Still, where necessary, retrofit modifications were integrated into the production of later F–111s.

Grounding **1969–1970**

The Air Force lost its 15th F–111A on 22 December 1969,[14] due to

---

[12] The beginning of the F–111A's fatigue test program slipped from February 1965 to July 1968 because of design and weight reduction changes that had to be reflected by the test airframe to assure realistic testing; also, because of General Dynamics late submission of acceptable testing procedures. A final 3-month delay was due to late modifications, as called for by the new Triple Plow I air diverter, a deficient carry-through-box (that had failed during early static tests) and an unsatisfactory tail pivot shaft fitting.

[13] In early 1969 General Dynamics discovered that Selb Manufacturing, who made the defective steel boxes, was paying off inspectors for approving unauthorized weldings. An FBI investigation followed. A federal grand jury indicted General Dynamics in 1972 for destroying $114,000 worth of flawed boxes and filing a claim with the Air Force for repayment—instead of charging the loss to Selb. A trial jury acquitted General Dynamics in 1973.

[14] The accident triggered renewed criticism of the aircraft. In congressional testimony on 17 March 1970, the Secretary of the Air Force admitted difficulties but pointed out . . . "this plane per thousand hours flown, has fewer accidents than any other Century series aircraft . . ." In February 1972, after 150,000 hours, the F–111 still had the lowest accident rate of the nine most recent USAF/USN high-performance tactical aircraft, even though a large percentage of its work was on the deck (200′-to-500′ above the terrain), and much of it at night. The F–111 accident rate in early 1972 was 40% under that of the F–106—USAF's next safest aircraft.

failure of the forged wing pivot fitting (a part of the basic wing structure, sitting next to the wing-carry-through-box). It grounded all F–111s the next day, except for a few used in flight tests. The grounding was lifted on 31 July 1970.

Modernization **1970-On**

The December 1969 accident casted doubt on the F–111's structural integrity and compounded the aircraft's modernization. The January 1969 improvement program (and delayed addition of Harvest Reaper avionics) had already been expanded to include wing-carry-through-box structural modifications that would extend fatigue life to the 10-year contractual design requirement.[15] Investigation of the most recent F–111A crash now dictated a thorough structural inspection and proof testing program. This was Recovery, a $31.2 million,[16] non-destructive, cold-proof testing and modification effort, started in the spring of 1970. The Air Force believed that blending this project with the F–111's overall modernization, should restore the F–111s to operational status in early 1971. Little slippage occurred. TAC returned a first F–111A to General Dynamics in April 1970 and by December 1971 the last of 340 F–111s (counting 125 F–111As) had been processed. The Recovery testing of each F–111 covered more than a dozen structural components—4 of which required load-proof testing at a temperature of minus 40° F. A few bolts broke, which was not surprising, yet no forging defects appeared in more than 3,500 units inspected. But still cautious, the Air Force in August 1971 scheduled a further (Phase II) structural in-house inspection of every F–111 model. Each F–111A had to undergo Phase II processing before reaching 1,500 flying hours.[17] The first F–111A entered Phase II at the Sacramento Air Materiel Area on 16 May 1973.

Oversea Redeployment **27 September 1972**

F–111As were returned to SEA not long after a crash and another 8-day grounding. In fact, two F–111A squadrons (429th and 430th) were in combat 55 miles northwest of Hanoi—33 hours after

---

[15] Cyclic loads ground testing of a modified wing-carry-through-box were resumed in December 1969. They gave the box a test-life of 24,000 hours (equivalent to a safe service-life of 6,000 hours). Even so, the Air Force authorized General Dynamics on 18 May 1970 to give North American a development contract for a titanium box.

[16] This amount would cover nonrecurring costs for materials and equipment, plus the recurring costs for labor to see the aircraft through inspection and testing. The Air Force wanted General Dynamics to do this under the contract's correction of deficiencies clause. Approved aircraft procurement took care of inspection and proof testing funding (the Air Force covering it by dropping several F–111Fs from follow-on buy).

[17] F–111E and D aircraft fell under this criterion. The F–111F and FB–111A could pile up 2,000 and 2,500 hours, respectively, prior to Phase II.

leaving Nellis AFB. Flying again from Tahkli (the Combat Lancer deployment base of 1968), F–111As also attacked Laotian targets in the midst of the monsoon season. They fought without "Iron Hand" electronic countermeasure escort aircraft, EC–121s to vector them, or KC–135 tankers (as needed by the F–4s which they replaced). F–111As flew 20 strikes over North Vietnam on 8 November, in weather that grounded other aircraft.

SEA Operational Problems **1972–1973**

Four F–111As could deliver the bomb loads of 20 F–4s (an operating cost saving of no small significance). Yet, all was not well. Shortly after returning to SEA, an F–111A experienced double engine rollback after entering heavy rain, a critical problem since the aircraft were to serve as all-weather fighters. Crucial shortages of spares (such as brakes, wheels, and struts) arose. Added to this were continued problems with both the terrain-following radar (TFR) and attack radar sets. Malfunctions of the internal navigation and weapons release systems also cropped up. The loss of several F–111As brought about Constant Sweep, a team effort that found no single factor for the SEA losses but identified several real and potential deficiencies. Temporary Constant Sweep flying restrictions were removed in January 1973. There followed a 17 February midair collision of two F–111As near Udorn and the next day loss of a single F–111A.[18] The squadrons' maintenance and supply practices thereupon came under closer scrutiny. When seven of the 52 fully-equipped F–111As were lost in SEA, TAC had to remove penetration aids from later models (F–111Fs) to equip replacements. Still, more than 3,000 F–111 missions preceded the Paris peace accords of January 1973. Meanwhile, aircrew enthusiasm for the aircraft continued to grow.

Subsequent Model Series

F–111B (Navy's)

Other Configurations

RF–111A[19]—an F–111A equipped with a removable sensor pallet. Sensor imagery testing of the converted F–111A (between December 1967 and October 1968) achieved good results. However, it took days (not hours, as the OSD had hoped) to make the conversion. Return of the converted F–111A to its basic configuration proved equally impractical. Consequently, the Air Force again tried to obtain a separate, more sophisticated reconnaissance force of F–111s (RF–111Ds)—as long preferred, but much smaller than originally planned. Dearth of funds killed the high-cost RF–111D in

[18] A 20 March midair collision of two F–111Ds, near Holbrook, Arizona, brought several procedural changes. TAC prohibited formation flying until 4 April.

[19] The flyaway cost of the sole RF–111A was set at $12.1 million.

September 1969. This time the OSD decision was final. The Air Force's fall-back reconnaissance alternative (modification of 52 F–111As to an austere sensor configuration) fared no better and was dropped in March 1970.

F–111C—a modified F–111A, specifically designed for the Royal Australian Air Force (RAAF). Modifications included new, longer wings, and a heavier gear (similar to that of the FB–111A).

F–111K—an F–111A featuring more advanced avionics and the FB–111A's undercarriage. Two of 50 programmed F–111Ks came into being. Never flown, they were salvaged following Great Britain's cancellation of its order in January 1968.

EF–111A—modified F–111A featuring a version of the AN/ALQ–99 noise-jamming system employed on the EA–6B. The Air Force expected the EF–111A would have an on-station loiter time of 8 hours (when operating 100 miles from home base) compared with 2.5 hours for the Navy/Grumman EA–6B. This added endurance would make the EF–111A available for successive strikes. Improved survivability, due to the EF–111A's Mach 2.2 speed, was another plus. Two EF–111A prototypes were under contract in mid-1973, General Dynamics and Grumman each having received one F–111A for modification.

End of Production **30 August 1969**

With delivery of the last F–111A.

Total F–111As Accepted

The 158 aircraft accepted included 17 of the 18 RDT&E F–111As ordered in December 1962. The 18th test F–111A was used as bomber prototype and charged to the FB–111A program.

Acceptance Rates

Four RDT&E F–111As were accepted in FY 65, 8 in FY 66, and 5 in FY 67. The Air Force accepted 5 F–111A productions in FY 67, 36 in FY 68, 86 in FY 69, and 14 in FY 70. Monthly acceptances averaged 3 F–111A productions until July 1968, when they rose to 7.

RDT&E Total Cost **Mid-1973**

$1.657 billion—$200,000 more than concurrently estimated by General Dynamics, but $1.176 billion over the target cost of May 1964.

Procurement Costs **Mid-1973**

$5.479 billion for 541 F–111s[20] (excluding the 23 RDT&E F–111s—18 for the Air Force and 5 for the Navy). The contractor's lower

[20] In late 1973, it seemed the F–111 program would be held to 529 F–111s (plus the 23 RDT&E aircraft). After 1970 the Congress had insisted on funding 48 additional late models of the aircraft (F–111Fs). The Air Force, however, had bought just 36 and hoped to defer acquisition of the remaining 12 indefinitely.

figure ($5.431 billion) still represented an overall target cost increase of $3,228 billion.

Flyaway Cost Per Production Aircraft[21]

$8.2 million—airframe, $4,304,000; engines (installed), $1,354,000; electronics, $1,688,000; ordnance, $7,000; armament, $925,000.

Average Cost Per Flying Hour

$1,857.00

Operational Status **Mid-1973**

Though grounded often, the F–111A after 6 years showed an ever-increasing potential. In face of losses in SEA and elsewhere, the aircraft's rate of attrition remained low. The F–111A was assured of an important role in USAF long-range planning.

Other Uses **Mid-1971**

The Air Force awarded a $2.5 million letter contract to General Dynamics for design and fabrication of a "supercritical" variable-sweep wing. Total value of ensuing cost-plus-incentive fee contract, including F–111 airframe modification costs, was expected to reach $12.9 million. This decision followed NASA testing of supercritical wings up to low supersonic speeds, using a North American Rockwell T–2 trainer and an LTV Aerospace F–8 fighter. Flight tests of the modified F–111's new wings were set for mid-1973. They would be part of an Air Force/NASA program at Edwards AFB, run by NASA's Flight Research Center.

Other Countries **1973**

The last 6 of 24 F–111Cs, bought by Australia for some $250 million, left the United States on 26 November 1973. This was nearly 10 years after the two countries signed a June 1964 F–111 agreement, and more than 5 years since General Dynamics delivered the first F–111C on 6 September 1968. Engineering changes separating the F–111C from the basic aircraft did not get under way until August 1966, but this did not slow the program. What first delayed it was the F–111A's wing carry-through box failure. Incorporation of fixes on production aircraft slipped delivery of the remaining 23 F–111Cs to late 1969. The entire F–111 fleet was then grounded. In April 1970, a joint agreement deferred Australia's acceptance of the purchased F–111Cs pending vertification of their structural integrity. It specified that the RAAF lease F–4E aircraft; new wing carry-through boxes be installed on all F–111Cs; and the aircraft be delivered in mint condition. More than a million manhours went into the F–111C modification and refurbishment program started by General Dynamics on 1 April 1972.

---

[21] Excluding some $2.8 million spent for RDT&E and about $800,000 worth of modification, bringing the actual cost of each F–111A to more than $11.8 million.

As the aircraft were released, Australian crews flew them from the contractor's Convair Aerospace Division in Fort Worth. Tex., to McClellan AFB. Once at McClellan, each F–111C completed between 4 and 6 training missions before departure. The first F–111Cs reached Australia on 1 June 1973, replacing the RAAF's Canberra bombers in use since the early 1950's.

Milestones **May 1967**

An unrefueled F–111A set a flight record of 7 hours and 15 minutes on 1 May. On the 22d, two F–111As attained a fighter-type aircraft unofficial record for transatlantic flight without refueling and external tanks. The two (on their way to the Paris Air Show) flew from Loring AFB, Maine, to Le Bourget Airport in 5 hours and 54 minutes. They covered 2,800 nautical miles at an average speed of 540 mph, their wings extended most of the time in cruise position.

F-111B

Previous Model Series

F–111A

New Features

Shorter fuselage nose radome with retractable long-range panoramic radar for interceptor role. Longer wing tips for improved low-speed ferry and loiter performances.[22] Enlarged ventral fin, housing carrier arrester hook. P–12 engine (another version of the TF–30), carrying maximum thrust of 20,250 pounds with afterburner—1,700 pounds more than the F–111A's P–3. Six AIM–54A air-to-air Phoenix missiles, developed by Hughes specifically for the Navy.[23]

Basic Development **1961**

F–111B development, like that of the USAF F–111A, mirrored Secretary McNamara's September decision to meet each service's long-range requirements with one plane. The biservice F–111 would replace the F–105, as basically called for by the Air Force's SOR of July 1960. It would also succeed the carrier-based F–4H, eliminating the Navy's chances for getting the F–6D Missileer as the F–4H's replacement.[24]

---

[22] The F–111B's overall length of 66 feet and 9 inches was about 6 feet under the F–111A's; its 70-foot wing span was 7 feet longer than the F–111A's.

[23] The Phoenix's fire-control system owed much to the USAF ASG–18 system (developed in the early 1960's) for launching nuclear-tipped AIM–47A air-to-air missiles—then known as GAR–9 Falcons. Originally meant for the North American F–108 Rapier (cancelled by OSD in September 1959), the Hughes ASG–18/AIM–47A combination could fit later interceptors, including the YF–12A, ADC badly wanted.

[24] The F–4H, topping all Navy interceptors in speed, altitude, and range, was introduced into the Fleet in January 1961, only a few months before the OSD rejection of the single mission Missileer interceptor.

Contractual Arrangements **November 1963**

Design, development manufacturing, final assembly and delivery of the F–111B were delegated to the Grumman Aircraft Corporation. The Air Force authorized General Dynamics to negotiate the subcontract in September, 2 months before its official ratification.

First Flight (Prototype) **18 May 1965**

A modified RDT&E F–111A (powered by the initial TF–30–P–1 engine) flew for 1 hour and 18 minutes after taking off from Grumman's Peconic, N.Y., facility. It had rolled out of the subcontractor's Bethpage, N.Y., plant 7 days earlier. The Air Force immediately accepted for the Navy the first YF–111B, sending it to the Patuxent Naval Air Test Center in Maryland, where all F–111Bs would be tested.[25] The aircraft reached supersonic speed on 1 July.

First Flight (RDT&E F-111B) **May 1966**

F–111B's development took longer than the F–111A's mainly because of difficulty in integrating the Phoenix missile system with the aircraft.[26] The F–111B also shared the F–111A's engine problem. The Navy believed these would be solved with the P–12 (one more engine version of the TF–30), which would equip F–111B productions and retrofit RDT&E F–111Bs, beginning in late 1966.

Configuration Changes **11 March 1967**

The F–111's crew module lacked sufficient forward visibility for a carrier-based aircraft. The OSD, in March 1967, authorized a new module for the F–111B, even though this would mean aerodynamic changes and widen differences between the F–111A and F–111B.[27] Meanwhile, continued USAF and USN efforts to check F–111 weight increases proved futile. The first F–111B prototype flown (modified F–111A), weighed 69,000 pounds;[28] the first F–111B

---

[25] The F–111B's Phoenix missile system would undergo tests in California, at the Hughes Culver City Plant and at the Naval Point Mugu Missile Center.

[26] The F–111B's first successful launch of the AIM–54A Phoenix took another 6 months.

[27] Differences (first authorized in 1962 to meet the aircraft's operational needs) were few—the Navy accepting a heavier aircraft, with a longer fuselage and smaller panoramic radar than desired; the Air Force, a lighter, two-crew aircraft, with a Navy side-by-side sitting arrangement instead of the usual tandem configuration. Hence, commonality, a prime OSD requirement from the onset of the F–111 program was relatively high through January 1966. However, redesign of the F–111A's aft fuselage structure (to fit the new P–3 engines) and modification of the same section on the F–111B (to accommodate the P–12s) decreased commonality. The overall percentage of common parts, once around 80, fell below 70. Redesign of the F–111B's crew module (including pilot elevation and increased windshield slant) was another factor.

[28] Too much to permit the aircraft's operation from carriers smaller than the *Forrestal.*

production (due to fly in 1968), 75,000—about 20,000 pounds more than originally planned.

Definitized Contract (Production Aircraft) **10 May 1967**

It was signed by the Air Force—24 Navy F–111Bs were included in the 493 F–111s covered by the contract.

First Delivery (Production Aircraft) **30 June 1968**

Grumman delivered the first one to the Air Force, for the Navy.

Production Hold Order **9 July 1968**

The Air Force stopped work on the F–111B after the House Armed Services Committee joined the Senate in disapproving a $460 million appropriation requested by the Defense Department for further development and procurement of 30 aircraft.

Program Cancellation **August 1968**

Projected, but now cancelled, F–111Bs went to the USAF program.[29] Still, the Navy's withdrawal (on the heels of the British government's cancellation of its F–111K purchase) forced the Air Force to adjust its plans. For instance, by fiscal year 1970, the May 1967 contract's buy of 493 F–111s over 4 years had been stretched to 6 years.

End of Production **28 February 1969**

With delivery of the seventh and last F–111B.

Total F-111Bs Accepted

7—5 RDT&E F–111Bs and 2 productions.

Flyaway Cost Per Production Aircraft

$8.7 million—as estimated in early 1968. In light of later F–111 cost increases, this was probably far below the aircraft's potential cost.

Subsequent Model Series

F–111E—the F–111B should have been followed in the USAF inventory by the F–111C, but the latter was put aside for Australia. The F–111D, next in line, was preceded by the less-sophisticated F–111E and the strategic FB–111A bomber.

Other Configurations

None—the RF–111B, called for by Navy SOR TW–35–10 in August 1963, was abandoned 2 years later.

Other Uses

Two F–111Bs were lost in crashes and a third was severely damaged in landing. The Navy used the remaining 4 to continue testing the Phoenix missile system and P–12 engine. Both would

---

[29] Cancellation of the Navy F–111B led General Dynamics to sever its relationship with Grumman and Hughes. The latter, as associate contractor under Navy contract, developed the Phoenix missile system.

equip the F–111's successor—the VFX (Grumman F–14), authorized for development by Congress in July 1968.[30]

F-111E

Previous Model Series

Navy's F–111B[31]

New Features

Triple Plow II air inlets, improving engine operation at high speed and high altitude; stores management set, corresponding to the one planned for the F–111D and F–111F aircraft.[32]

Go-Ahead Decision — **27 February 1968**

The decision underscored the F–111's urgency. Since the sophisticated F–111D could not be had quickly, the Air Force had to approve a simpler configuration for its second tactical wing. Designated F–111E, the aircraft closely resembled the F–111A.

Program Slippage — **1969**

Triple Plow II (a development of the General Dynamics Triple Plow I air diverter that accompanied the F–111A's P–3 engines) spelled the main difference between the E and A models. Still, F–111E production was postponed for 6 months at the outset. This afforded time for F–111A modifications[33] (begun in January 1969) to become part of the General Dynamics F–111E production line.

First Flight (Production Aircraft) — **20 August 1969**

Concurrent with delivery of the last F–111A.

Enters Operational Service — **30 September 1969**

TAC's 27th Tactical Fighter Wing at Cannon AFB reached initial operational capability in the fall of 1969. The wing had 29 F–111Es by December, but these flew under restrictions until the Air Force was convinced the longerons were perfectly safe.

---

[30] The Navy planned to utilize the F–4J while awaiting its new interceptor.

[31] The F–111E, authorized for production after the F–111C, F–111D, and FB–111A, was the first of the three to reach an operational capability, beating the FB–111A by 1 month.

[32] All F–111s shared similar air-to-ground radios, intercommunication systems, navigational radios, instrument lending systems, and central air data computers. They also had like identification equipment, flight control, and radar altimeter subsystems, as well as extensive electronic countermeasure and penetration aid equipment. Remaining avionics were quite different. For instance, the Mark I system (consisting of attack radar, navigation-attack system, and a lead computing optical sight), common to the F–111A, C, and E models, could not be compared to the Mark II that was being developed.

[33] These included Harvest Reaper, Round-Up, and wing-carry-through box improvements.

Testing **1969–1972**

Special tests (requiring additional equipment on two of the 5 first F–111Es, reserved for testing) delayed the program, already affected by production slippages. The Category I and II flight tests, started in October 1969, extended through July 1971; others,[34] through 1972.

Second Program Slippage **1970**

The F–111E program slipped another 6 months, following the December 1969 loss of the 15th F–111A. The Air Force refused to accept any F–111 delivery until the end of July 1970, when the fleet grounding was lifted. All F–111Es (accepted before and after the grounding) went through the Recovery Program and other structural inspections stemming from the December 1969 accident.

Oversea Deployments **September 1970**

The F–111E had an integral radar homing and warning and electronic countermeasures capability.[35] It was greatly needed overseas. The United States Air Forces in Europe counted on the F–111E for the all-weather and night work its F–4s were not equipped to do. Despite the program's initial slippage, the first two of the 79 F–111Es,[36] slated for USAFE's 20th Tactical Fighter Wing, arrived in England on 11 September. The 79th, one of the wing's three squadrons, reached an IOC in December. The wing became fully operational in November 1971.

Operational Problems **1969–1973**

The F–111E shared most of the operational and support deficiencies of the F–111A—the Air Force learning much from F–111E accidents. A 23 April 1971 F–111E crash, during a Category II flight test, uncovered a malfunction of the recovery parachute (part of the excellent escape module[37] that kept down the F–111

[34] F–111E category II system evaluation tests were concluded on 23 July 1971, after showing that the aircraft's major subsystems worked well. Category I separation testing for nuclear weapons was completed in April 1972; stability and control tests, in June.

[35] The F–111A was the Air Force's first tactical weapon system to have this equipment built in from the start.

[36] Out of the total 90 aircraft (counting the five productions allocated to the testing program). Remaining F–111Es stayed with TAC. The 442d squadron at Nellis used them to train F–111 pilots, including USAFE pilots.

[37] General Dynamics believed the F–111's crew module (first known as "boiler plate" crew escape capsule) ranked alongside the F–111's variable-sweep wing and fan-afterburning engine as major advancements in aircraft design. Developed by the McDonnell Aircraft Corporation and initially tested in February 1966, the F–111's crew module was fully automated. When forced to abandon his aircraft, the pilot only had to "press, squeeze, or pull" one lever. This caused an explosive cutting cord to shear the module from the fuselage; a rocket motor ejected the module upward and it parachuted to the ground or sea. There it could serve as a survival shelter, like the Mercury and Gemini capsules of the US early space programs.

accident's death rate). Another F–111E crashlanded in Scotland on 18 January 1972. This accident pointed out the need for an audio and visual stall warning system.[38]

Other Problems **1969–1973**

Early F–111A and F–111E aircraft had deficient windshields. On 29 May 1969, an F–111 on a training flight at Nellis crashed at low altitude when the windshield bulged down from the top of the canopy bow and instantly crazed. TAC replaced 50 F–111 windshields in 1969; 93, the following year. However, this did not solve the bird-strike problem, shared by all F–111s and older high-speed aircraft. By September 1971, 52 F–111s suffered damage from bird strikes—2 F–111s being lost.[39] This reaffirmed the urgent need for a stronger windshield. TAC wanted one that could withstand the impact of a 4-lb bird at 500-knot airspeed, but exorbitant costs killed this proposal. In mid-1973, development of an improved, reasonably priced windshield still showed scant progress.[40] Meantime, the Air Force tested a Navy helmet that promised some windblast protection because of its polycarbonate faceplate—possibly more than the current Air Force acrylic faceplate. Individual helmet liners (foamed-fitted to the pilot's head) were obtained. They helped considerably in preventing crews from losing their helmets when their windshield broke. The Air Force also continued evaluating strobe lights to reduce bird strikes. Fifty F–111s took part in the program.

End of Production **28 May 1971**

With delivery of two last F–111Es.

Total F–111Es Accepted

94

Acceptance Rates

The Air Force accepted 31 F–111Es during FY 70 (August through December 1969; none during the ensuing 6 months). Deliveries resumed in July 1970, with 63 F–111Es accepted during FY 71.

---

[38] F–111 pilots could not determine approaching stalls by feel, mistaking rudder pedal's vibrations for airframe buffet. Sacramento Air Materiel Area would make the stall warning engineering change. (SMAMA handled all needed modifications and the Phase II structural in-house inspection of all F–111s programmed by the Air Force in August 1971).

[39] The two aircraft remained airworthy prior to crashing. Unprotected from the wind, the crews could not see, communicate, or control the planes. Such losses, in 125,000 flying hours, augured ill of the future, unless something was done about it.

[40] It would likely be the following year before a contract was let, and testing would certainly consume another year or so.

Flyaway Cost Per Production Aircraft[41]

$9.2 million—airframe, $4,756,000; engines (installed), $1,511,000; electronics, $1,945,000; ordnance, $7,000; armament, $1,060,000.

Subsequent Model Series

F–111F, but the delayed F–111D and the FB–111A became operational after the F–111E and before the F–111F.[42]

Other Configurations

None

Operational Status **Mid-1973**

Most of the F–111Es in the USAFE area were combat ready. Nonetheless, like the F–111As, the aircraft had not yet realized their full potential.[43]

Other Uses **1973**

USAF testing of new aircraft was always extensive. Still, the F–111's radical departure from standardized configurations generated a program far more involved than usual. Spin-testing, one of its most crucial aspects, dated back to 1964, but a related accident 8 years later spurred another series of tests.[44] Aided by General Dynamics, the Air Force would test an F–111E for 4 months. Centering on the F–111's stall inhibitor and landing warning systems, the tests ended in May 1973—their results not to be known for several more months.

FB-111A

Weapon System 129A

Previous Model Series

F–111E—only in terms of operational availability.[45]

[41] Plus $2.826,500 of RDT&E cost and $24,771 worth of modification per aircraft, bringing actual F–111E unit cost to $12,130,271.

[42] This out-of-sequence was not rare. Technical problems often delayed a model's production in favor of a later model in the series.

[43] Landing gear problems and cracked struts still hampered F–111A and F–111E operations. A titanium nose wheel developed for the F–111A was yet to be tested; improved aluminum alloy strut pistons would not be available for another year or so.

[44] NASA started spin-testing of an RDT&E F–111A in late 1964, the first contractor stall and spin test occurring 1 year later. Unsuccessful attempts to use a B–52 drag parachute (or one similar to it) slowed the program until mid-1969, when marked progress began. Yet, a 10-month Category II stall and spin prevention program, begun by the Air Force Flight Test Center in August 1972, was marred in September when an F–111A pilot lost control of his aircraft at 35,000 feet. Deployment of the recovery parachute at 20,000 feet did not help because of the aircraft's 220-knot airspeed. The parachute failed and separated from the plane, the crew ejecting safely at 11,500 feet.

[45] An FB–111A prototype actually flew almost a year before the decision to develop a simplified F–111E.

New Features

Longer fuselage (75′6″, against the F–111A's 73′5″), extended wing span of 70 feet (a 7-foot increase), stronger undercarriage and landing gear, extra and bigger fuel tanks, and P–7 engines.[46] The FB–111A also featured the Mark IIB avionic subsystem. This subsystem comprised an improved F–111A attack radar, an inertial navigation system, digital computers, and some advanced displays of the later Mark II that equipped the delayed F–111D. The Mark IIB controlled the new AGM–69A short-range attack missile (SRAM).

Basic Development **1963-1965**

The slow progress in the Advanced Manned Strategic Aircraft (AMSA) program and fear of earlier-than-expected B–52 failures spurred the Air Force to search for an interim bomber.[47] It began considering the F–111A for this role in the spring of 1963—General Dynamics suggesting two strategic versions in November. A series of wind tunnel tests ensued, funded separately from the F–111A development. To hasten availability, on 2 June 1965 the Air Force after much debate settled for the least-modified version of the F–111A. This would be the FB–111A interim strategic bomber. The Air Force also settled for only 263 FB–111As (210 to equip 14 squadrons, each with 15 aircraft; 20,[48] for combat crew training; the others, for support and testing), but wanted them quickly, the first to become operational during fiscal year 1969.[49]

Go-Ahead Decision **1965-1966**

Secretary McNamara publicly announced plans to develop the FB–111A on 10 December 1965[50]—6 months after endorsing the Air Force proposal to replace at the earliest possible date 345 B–

---

[46] The P–7 was a new version of the Pratt & Whitney TF–30 turbofan engine. It had a maximum thrust of 20,350 pounds with afterburner—1,800 pounds more than the P–3 engine of the F–111A and F–111E, but only 100 pounds more than the Navy F–111B's P–12.

[47] Another option was to resume B–58 production (which had ended late in 1962) and to procure 250 of these costly supersonic bombers.

[48] Reduced to 15 in 1969.

[49] The Air Force would have liked more and larger FB–111As, but could spare neither the time nor the money. The latter was a perennial problem of the Air Force's chief goal—the AMSA program.

[50] Early in the year, the OSD had completed a study of the comparative costs and performance of the proposed FB–111A, B–52, and B–58 strategic bombers; also, of the cost effectiveness of a force of some 200 FB–111As.

52s (C through F models) with minimum-modified F–111As.[51] The Secretary, however, did not authorize immediate implementation of the new program. This was postponed until February 1966, when the FB–111A was added to the basic F–111A RDT&E contract of May 1964 and after Congress had approved on 26 January an Air Force reprogramming request for $26 million of development funds.

Additional Requirements **1965-1966**

Development of a minimum-modified F–111A bomber was short lived. In November 1965 (3 months before the 7 February 1966 amendment to the development contract of May 1964) Secretary McNamara decided to delay the FB–111A program 6 months to equip the aircraft with more advanced avionics than originally planned.[52] The Secretary asked the Air Force in January 1966 to begin contract definition on Mark II avionics systems for both the FB–111A and the delayed F–111D—maximum commonality of the two systems being a key requirement. As also requested, the Air Force on 10 February directed the integration of the planned AGM–69A SRAM missile with the FB–111A's Mark II version (Mark IIB).[53]

First Critical Design Review (CDR) **November 1966**

Basic configuration changes (geared toward extra range) were approved in the review at General Dynamics' Fort Worth plant. However, the Air Force asked for and OSD granted extra funding to take care of several other vital SAC needs. Added were weapons bay tanks, turbine starter, horizontal situation display (HSD) and lunar white cockpit lighting. The last two would first enter the 53d

---

[51] Reminiscent of Congress' misgivings in November 1962 (when General Dyanmics, rather than Boeing, was handed the F–111A contract), two factors fueled another round of Congressional concern. One was replacement of the oldest B–52s by a lesser number of unproven FB–111As; the other, Secretary McNamara's surprise announcement of late 1965 to retire (by 30 June 1971) all 80 of the B–58s—SAC's only supersonic bomber.

[52] Even though the B–52 retirement schedule would be adjusted, the Strategic Air Command strongly objected to Secretary McNamara's decision. The FB–111A's whole purpose had been to provide an interim bomber quickly, hence with least possible modification. SAC also argued (to no avail) that, when available, more advanced avionics could be retrofitted in earlier FB–111A productions.

[53] The Air Force on 23 June 1966 awarded the Mark II contract to the Autonetics Division of the North American Rockwell Corporation, which became another of General Dynamics' many F–111 subcontractors. In October the Boeing Company was selected as production contractor for the AGM–69A SRAM missile, planned solely for the future AMSA. Adapting the SRAM development program to the FB–111A schedule would now raise missile development costs to an estimated $170 million. Preparing retained B–52s for eventual use of the SRAM (also announced by Secretary McNamara) would further run up costs and jeopardize the future AMSA.

FB–111A production line—the initial aircraft of the second operational wing.[54]

Initial Problems 1966-1967

One of the major problems of the future FB–111A, also covered in the November 1966 CDR, centered around the aircraft propulsion. The TF–30–P–3 engines[55] of the tactical F–111As (and subsequent F–111Es) had incurable shortcomings and not enough thrust for the heavier FB–111A. The Navy F–111B's new P–12 engine appeared more promising, but it was just being released in November 1966 and would take a while to obtain. Still, by mid-1967, the Air Force had selected the P–12. It would be configured with semi-actuator ejector (SAE) nozzles and be known as the P–5.[56]

First Flight (Prototype) 31 July 1967

A modified RDT&E F–111 (No. 18, still equipped with TF–30–P–1 engines and the tactical F–111A landing gear) served as FB–111A prototype. The aircraft flew for 45 minutes on its maiden flight and achieved Mach 2. Accepted at once by the Air Force, it was left with General Dynamics for further testing.[57]

Other Development Problems 1967-1968

Development of the costly and technically risky SAE nozzles was given up in late 1967. Instead, the Variable Ejector (VE floating tail feathers) with blow-in doors would accompany still another version of the basic TF–30 engine, the P–7.[58] Pending availability of the P–7, FB–111As would receive P–12A engines (USAF version of the Navy P–12, first flown in an FB–111A in October 1968) and these engines would be subsequently brought up to the P–7 configuration.[59] SAC noted, however, that despite the approved airframe changes, the FB–111A's shortened range (inherent in conversions from tactical to strategic aircraft) would not be helped. Moreover, an early 1968 decision to give the aircraft a built-in Triple Plow II air diverter (to prevent engine stall) would curtail

---

[54] Retrofit of earlier FB–111A productions was not planned, but SAC intended to request a retrofit modification later.

[55] Improved P–1s, unavailable until 1967.

[56] Development of the P–12/P–5 engine hinged upon the US Navy effort. Pratt and Whitney, however, lacked a firm production go-ahead—reduction, if not elimination of the Navy F–111B, being already under consideration.

[57] Category I testing, a prime contractor's responsibility, started on 19 July 1967 and lasted through November 1971.

[58] The P–5 with a variable flap ejector nozzle and the P–12, with a fixed shroud and blow-in-door ejector nozzle, were development milestones for the FB–111A's P–7 and the delayed F–111D's P–9 engines.

[59] The programmed modification of 43 P–12A engines began in December 1969, 4 months before completion of the P–7 production.

its range even more.[60] Other unavoidable changes (including redesign of the aft fuselage) would also limit the FB–111A's maximum speed to around Mach 2. The most vexing problem, however, was that the Mark IIB avionic program, which during the first half of 1967 appeared to be on schedule, was beginning to slip.

First Flight (Production Aircraft) **13 July 1968**

The Air Force accepted the aircraft on 30 August and a second FB–111A production on 25 October. Subsystem problems, mainly with the Mark IIB,[61] slowed further deliveries—the Air Force not accepting another FB–111A until 23 June 1969. This third FB–111A differed from the previous two in that it featured a fully developed Triple Plow II air diverter, a complete Mark IIB avionics system, and the new P–7 engines.

Flight Testing

Increased sophistication of the FB–111A, as OSD-directed in November 1965, meant more testing. The Air Force, therefore, raised the number of aircraft for the formal testing program to 7[62]—the first 6 FB–111A productions included, to revert eventually to their original combat purpose. Ensuing FB–111A reductions did not shorten testing (for they had no bearing on the aircraft's configuration), but the shortage of aircraft hindered operational units in raising combat readiness. Category II tests[63] were still going on when Category III testing started (October 1971) and when it ended (31 July 1972).[64]

Program Changes **1968-1969**

A program of 263 planes was projected when the FB–111A development began. This dropped to 126 on 28 November 1968, because of problems with the basic F–111, production delays, and rising

[60] Extension of ferry and combat range would chiefly rest on larger tanks (and air refueling).

[61] Autonetics delivered initial Mark II avionic units to General Dynamics on 21 November 1967. Flight testing, started on 31 March 1968 with a modified F–111A (No. 25), showed good results. Problems cropped up during the first full system test in June, when various components began to interfere with each other.

[62] Use of modified F–111As was confined to few special tests.

[63] Category II testing started on 4 September 1968 (14 months after the beginning of the Category I tests) in the desert at Edwards AFB. The third FB–111A production was also allocated to the Category II tests.

[64] The Category III tests were conducted at Pease AFB in New Hampshire. Immediate (if not unsurmountable) problems developed. Brakes failed to work in the cold as the brake fluid froze. Because of poor insulation, frozen valves prevented transfer of fuel from auxiliary to main tanks.

costs.[65] The second and final cut took place in March 1969, when the total FB–111A purchase dipped to 76.[66]

Enters Operational Service **8 October 1969**

This was the 7th FB–111A production and the Air Force's first new strategic bomber since 1 August 1960 (SAC had then accepted an initial B–58 in similar ceremonies, also held at Carswell AFB). This FB–111A[67] and the next 14 productions would go to a squadron of the 340th Bomb Group at Carswell, responsible for FB–111A combat crew training (CCT). Hence, even though the FB–111A was officially operational, it had yet to reach the combat forces.

Program Slippage **1969–1970**

Problems with the FB–111A's wing longerons and terrain-following radar slowed production. The 4007th CCT Squadron of the 340th Bomb Group was still short 7 aircraft when the Air Force stopped all General Dynamics deliveries in late 1969. Caught up in the mandatory Recovery Program, the few FB–111As already flying were returned to General Dynamics. In April 1970, the first of the CCT FB–111As left Carswell to undergo a 75-day test and structural inspection, receive necessary modifications, and somehow be ready for reassignment to the 4007th in July.[68]

Other Testing **1970–1971**

The Air Force-directed Recovery Program interfered little with the FB–111A testing of the SRAM, begun on 27 March 1970.[69]

---

[65] The reduction followed cancellation of the F–111K (once, practically sold to Great Britain) and the end of the Navy F–111B. Money, however, was the main factor. The cost of 263 FB–111As was estimated at $1.7 billion in 1966. In mid-1969, this amount was pared to $982.6 million—an approximate reduction of $700.00 million. More spectacular was the decrease in aircraft, sinking from 263 to 76 FB–111As, while unit costs soared from $6.45 million to $12.93 million.

[66] The May 1967 production contract for the 493 F–111s, ordered by Secretary McNamara, included 64 of the projected 263 FB–111As. In addition, 48 of the 50 cancelled F–111Ks on this contract were redesignated as FB–111As. During the closing weeks of the Johnson Administration, Deputy Secretary of Defense Paul Nitze announced further amendment of the May 1967 contract to add 14 FB–111As (for a total of 126 aircraft). This was a more than 50 percent reduction, since Nitze indicated no other F–111 strategic bombers would be built. Melvin R. Laird, President Nixon's first Defense Secretary, made the last cut. Some of the money saved would speedup development of the AMSA (redesignated B–1 in April 1969).

[67] Bearing serial number 677193A, it had been actually assigned to the 340th Bomb Group on 25 September.

[68] The last FB–111A production emerged from the Recovery cold-proof tests on 20 January 1971.

[69] Separation of a dummy air-to-surface SRAM missile from an FB–111A (at Mach 0.9 and 25,000 feet altitude) had first occurred on 19 October 1968 at Eglin AFB. First launch of an operational SRAM from an FB–111A occurred in 1974.

Nevertheless, these tests started poorly. In almost 1 year, there were only seven successes out of the 11 launches conducted at the White Sands Missile Range in New Mexico. But the trend shifted in early 1971. The 15 successes out of 19 launches during the entire FB–111A/SRAM test series seemed well worth the $140 million spent in mating the two.[70]

Initial Operational Capability **January 1971**

Four months after the Carswell CCT Squadron received the last of its 15 FB–111As[71]—a final slippage due to the F–111 crash of December 1969 and resulting Recovery Program. Meanwhile, on 16 December 1970, the 509th Bomb Wing at Pease AFB got its first FB–111A. The 509th, after many difficulties,[72] was fully combat ready in October 1971. The 380th Strategic Aerospace Wing (the second of SAC's only two wings of FB–111As) at Plattsburg AFB, N. Y., became combat ready the following year.

End of Production **1 June 1971**

With the Air Force acceptance of the last FB–111A. This aircraft (Serial No. 68–291) was delivered to SAC on 30 June.

Total FB–111As Accepted

76, consisting of 75 productions (the 76th crashed before delivery), plus 1 prototype (an F–111A, modified and charged to the FB–111A program).[73]

Acceptance Rates

The FB–111A prototype (modified F–111A) was accepted in FY 68.

---

[70] Development and production costs of the SRAM started as a low-risk effort with a 1965 bottom estimate of $167.7 million. Nevertheless, in 1971, it was expected to peak at $1.76 billion—$440.6 million for RDT&E and $1.32 billion for production through FY 1975 (as called for by other aircraft's prospective use of the missile).

[71] One year after reaching IOC, the 4007th CCTS (its major training effort completed) relocated from Carswell to Plattsburgh and became part of the 380th Strategic Aerospace Wing. Retaining its original designation, the squadron's strength and number of assigned aircraft declined.

[72] Bad weather (an important factor at both Pease and Plattsburgh during the winter) and supply shortages (resulting in high NORS hours and excessive NORM and cannibalization rates) were two of the culprits. Although the FB–111A's supply and maintenance shortcomings were not unusual for a relatively new weapon system, they were magnified by the concurrent shortage of aircraft. The training program at Pease was hampered by the nonavailability of FB–111As and training sorties. The Category III tests, primarily conducted with men and equipment of the 509th Bomb Wing, received a lower priority as the wing strove for full combat ready status. The Category III testing program, renamed as the operational test and evaluation (OT&E) program on 15 April 1972, finally ended on 31 July with generally satisfactory results.

[73] One of the 75 FB–111A productions crashed on 7 October 1970 and another on 8 January 1971. (Both aircraft had been stationed at Carswell.)

The Air Force accepted the FB–111A productions as follows: three in FY 69 (two in the fall of 1968 and one in June 1969); 6 in FY 70 (between July and December 1969, when all F–111s were grounded); and 66 in FY 71 (between August 1970, when the grounding was lifted, and June 1971).

Flyaway Cost Per Production Aircraft[74]

$9.8 million—airframe, $4,201,000; engines (installed), $1,735,000; electronics, $2,550,000; armament, $1,342,000.

Average Cost Per Flying Hour

$1,479.00

Subsequent Model Series

F–111D—a delayed tactical model of the Air Force's F–111s.

Other Configurations

None

Operational Problems **1971–1973**

Landing gear malfunctions of the FB–111A and other F–111s, persisting through mid-1971, were finally solved by a simple field modification. This did not mean the end of problems, however. As demonstrated by a no-notice Operational Readiness Inspection (ORI) in late 1971, weapons delivery was still marginal, reflecting materiel failures in the Inertial Navigation System of the aircraft's Mark IIB avionics. In mid-1972, with the worst logistics shortages about over, new problems appeared. The most serious was engine flameout following use of the afterburner—probably caused by moisture in the engine sensing line.

Postproduction Modifications **1972–1973**

While taking care of the FB–111A's latest operational malfunctions, the Air Force tried to enhance the aircraft's combat effectiveness. In April 1972 the Sacramento Air Materiel Area began to install new SRAM-carrying equipment on the FB–111A and to replace the pyrotechnique devices used for ejecting the crew-escape module. After being completed on 22 aircraft, the replacement of devices was temporarily suspended, because the original devices lasted longer than first estimated. The SRAM modification, however, were uninterrupted, the last FB–111A being so modified in March 1973. The FB–111A during the same period entered a new SMAMA modification program—LASPAC (Landing Gear, Avionics, Systems Package). LASPAC encompassed the main landing gear retractor actuator, avionics equipment, inspection for cracks, and the reinforcement of wing tips. Seventeen

---

[74] Excluding $2,043,000 of RDT&E costs and $628,811 worth of modication per bomber. In mid-1973 the actual cost of each FB–111A was set at $12.5 million—$400,000 less than anticipated in late 1969.

aircraft had undergone LASPAC by June 1973. At that time, 46 other FB–111As were scheduled for new pyrotechnique devices, along with their LASPAC modification.

Modernization **1972-1973**

Modifications notwithstanding, the FB–111A still needed modernization. As SAC pointed out in early 1971, the aircraft's threat warning system, like the B–52's, was growing obsolete. An F–111 at Eglin had now begun to flight-test an improved threat warning radar, but a lot remained to be done. Modernization of the FB–111A's entire ECM subsystem (as recommended by the OSD and formalized in early 1973) was another must, one component (the QRC–536 transmitter) also being flight-tested at Eglin. If workable, it would jam over a wider frequency range. Replacement of the ECM subsystem's AAR–34 infrared receiver did not fare so well. SAC liked none of the new infrared receiver designs.

Operational Status **Mid-1973**

SAC's FB–111A squadrons possessed most of their authorized aircraft, but they were not all combat ready. The FB–111As, shared by two wings, were still located at Pease and Plattsburgh, where KC–135s were also stationed.

Milestones **1970-1971**

In November 1970 the FB–111A took top honors in bombing and navigation during SAC's combat competition at McCoy AFB, Fla. In April 1971 two Pease FB–111As entered a Royal Air Force-sponsored bombing and navigation meet at Marham RAF station. This marked the aircraft's first oversea deployment.

F-111D

Previous Model Series

FB–111A, for operational availability, but the F–111D's true predecessor was the F–111E.

New Features

Mark II avionics system,[75] environmental control system, and P–9 engines.[76]

Go-Ahead Decision **January 1966**

The decision was made when Secretary McNamara directed the Air Force to begin contract definition on Mark II avionics systems for both the strategic (FB–111A) and tactical F–111s. Insofar as the F–111A was concerned, the Secretary's decision met the Air Force Advanced Development Objective (No. 53) of March 1964.

[75] Sometimes referred to as the Mark IIA avionics subsystem.

[76] The Pratt and Whitney TF30–P–9 turbofan engine had a maximum thrust of 20,840 pounds with afterburner—only 500 more pounds than the P–7 of the strategic FB–111A, but 2,340 pounds more than the tactical F–111E's P–3.

This ADO reflected a November 1963 recommendation of the Air Force Scientific Advisory Board. It called for an improved avionics system (Mark II) to control in any weather the release of various air-to-air missiles against high- and low-altitude targets.

Official Designation **March 1967**

The future Mark II-equipped F–111A was designated F–111D—1 year before endorsement of the earlier F–111E.

Program Approval **May 1967**

The "D" got under way on 10 May, when the definitive contract (for a total of 493 F–111s) replaced the basic production LC of April 1965. A concurrent System Management Directive (SMD) specified the Mark II avionics system for 132 F–111s,[77] starting with the 236th production.[78]

Additional Requirements **26 May 1967**

Another USAF SMD gave the Mark II-equipped F–111D the radar-controlled AIM–7G–1 (Sparrow) air-to-air missile. This would be over and above an improved, infrared, heat-seeking, air-to-air missile,[79] similar to that of the F–111A (and, as it turned out, the F–111E). The request for adaptation of the new (and later cancelled) Raytheon-developed YAIM–7G Sparrow to the Mark II's fire-control radar came after the 23 June 1966 Mark II contract award to Autonetics, a division of the North American Rockwell Corporation.

Engine Change **1968**

The May 1967 acquisition program of necessity gave the future Mark II-equipped F–111A airframe (F–111D) the P–3 engines of the basic aircraft. Concurrent (and quickly successful) efforts to devise a more reliable and higher-thrust engine for the FB–111A interim bomber changed this planning. The Air Force decided in mid-1968 that the future F–111D would be equipped with the P–9, still another version of the Pratt and Whitney TF–30 turbofan. The new engine (first flight-tested with an F–111A on 10 July 1968) entered production in early 1969. The P–9 featured the small afterburner of the P–1 and P–3 engines for greater thrust,[80] the

---

[77] A June 1966 advanced contract change notified General Dynamics of this requirement.

[78] The F–111B, C, K, and FB–111A aircraft were counted in the 493 productions under contract, but not in the USAF tactical production sequence.

[79] The Hughes AIM–4D (Falcon) and the Philco-Raytheon AIM–9D (Navy Sidewinder), were considered, but dropped in favor of the familiar Philco-General Electric AIM–9B (Sidewinder IA) of the F–111A, F–111E, and many other USAF fighters.

[80] The P–9's thrust surpassed the P–3's by over 10 percent—significant, but well below the engine thrust the Air Force would have liked for the F–111D.

nozzle of the FB–111A's P–7 for more efficient thrust control, and the fan and low-pressure compressor of the Navy F–111B's P–12 for operating at higher engine temperatures.

Program Reduction **Mid-1969**

Cost increases in the Mark II system[81] and a stringent budget pared the F–111D program to one wing. The Air Force disclosed on 12 September that, as agreed upon in July by the Senate Armed Services Committee and the Air Force Chief of Staff, it was ordering Autonetics to limit Mark II production to the level called for by 96 aircraft.[82] The balance of F–111Ds under procurement would receive a cheaper avionics package and be known as F–111Fs.

Other Changes **1969-1970**

The Air Force decided in December 1969 to put FB–111A tires on the F–111D's main and nose landing gears. F–111D main landing gear's axles, axle pins, stabilizer rods, as well as attachment pins and nuts, would also be replaced with FB–111A hardware.[83] This would allow the new aircraft to carry more fuel and a heavier weapon load. A less attractive decision in March 1970 cancelled development of the Raytheon AIM–7G Sparrow—leaving the future F–111D armed like other tactical F–111s with 6 air-to-air AIM–9B Sidewinders (at least for the time being) and one 20-mm M–61A1 Gatling gun (mounted on the right inside of the weapon bay).[84]

First Flight (Production Aircraft) **15 May 1970**

By the first F–111D production (Serial Number 68-085), 6 months after USAF preliminary evaluation of the aircraft's avionics system.[85] The first F–111D (equipped with the new P–9 engine, but without a complete Mark II system) was accepted by the Air Force

[81] In early 1968 the Mark II was expected to add $1.5 million to the cost of each F–111D—an off-the-cuff estimate quickly revised to $2.2 million. By mid-1972 actual RDT&E costs of each F–111D already ran over $4 million.

[82] The 96 F–111Ds would equip the 27th TFW's four squadrons (522d, 523d, and 524th TFS, along with the 4429th Combat Crew Training Squadron) with 18 aircraft each, leaving 24 F–111Ds for testing, replacement, and support.

[83] F–111Ds already off the production line (but not released for lack of Mark II avionic systems) would be retrofitted, as would all F–111A and F–111E aircraft. F–111F would also benefit from the Air Force decision—the engineering changes being introduced into the first F–111F production.

[84] Externally, all F–111s could carry 40 different stores (33 conventional weapons, 3 nuclear bombs, fuel tanks, and two types of electronic countermeasure pods—the QRC–160–8 and the QRC–335–4). These stores had to be selected for different loading configurations to carry out the F–111's level and dive-bombing missions.

[85] At the General Dynamics' Fort Worth plant, where Category I testing was underway.

on 30 June. This followed by 1 day the lifting of the 6-month F–111 delivery hold-order, imposed after the F–111A crash of 22 December 1969.

Flight Testing **December 1968-on**

Primarily geared to test the aircraft's new avionics, the whole program slipped. The Category I tests set for October 1967 (an optimistic date to begin with) did not start until December 1968.[86] Development problems deferred Autonetics' delivery of a first and incomplete prototype of the Mark II system to June 1968. General Dynamics flew the prototype on an F–111A for the first time on 2 December—14 months late. Slippage of the Category II tests was worse—26 months. The Air Force further intended to use an F–111A to begin Category II testing. However, the mid-1968 decision to give the F–111D a new engine (and to incorporate in the airframe the Triple Plow II air diverter devised by General Dynamics for the forthcoming F–111E) changed this planning. The Air Force earmarked five early F–111D productions for testing—accepting the first on 30 June 1970. This aircraft had undergone most of the cold-proof, structural tests required by Recovery (the program instigated by the F–111A loss of December 1969). Yet, a few tasks remained to be done. Hence, the Category II tests, forecasted for July 1968, finally slipped to September 1970.

Program Slippage **1970–1973**

The Air Force accepted one F–111D in June 1970, none in the ensuing 12 months. The unavailability of Mark II avionics systems accounted for the delay.[87] Despite every effort, F–111D deliveries, when they resumed in July 1971, proceeded slowly. Only 24 of 96 F–111Ds were available in June 1972— 2 years past the time when the 27th Tactical Fighter Wing should have been operationally ready.[88] That goal was yet to be reached in mid-1973.

Avionics Problems **1966-on**

The revolutionary Mark II system, ordered in June 1966, counted 7

---

[86] In September 1970 (almost 2 years later), additional Category I flight testing was authorized to evaluate the Mark II's Integrated Display Set (IDS) in a new production configuration.

[87] The F–111Ds were not exempted from the Recovery program (which increased General Dynamics workload), but were produced on a schedule independent of the Mark II's availability. By late 1970, General Dynamics had completed most of the F–111D airframes—the last 50 receiving the Recovery inspections during production. Lacking an avionics system, a first increment of 40 airframes was parked at the Fort Worth plant in mid-1970, awaiting the outcome of a new round of Mark II contractual and production arrangements.

[88] The 27th TFW, Cannon AFB, received F–111Es beginning in September 1969. These aircraft went to USAFE's 20th TFW 1 year later, but there were no F–111Ds to take their place at Cannon.

main components.[89] Not surprisingly, development difficulties arose, either with individual or juxtaposed components interfering with each other. Far more unexpected was the seriousness of several such problems. For instance, the Autonetics attack radar needed improvements in its initial design; Norden's Integrated Display Set required extensive changes. While the IDS changes were underway, the radar problems were solved, but not without redesign of the radar doppler unit. This was significant, for the redesigned IDS refused to work with the improved radar and Norden had to come up with even more changes. By late 1969 a complete Mark II avionics system was still not to be had, and the system's escalating cost[90] had reduced the F-111D program to 96 aircraft—against 315 once slated for production. In mid-1970 the integrated display set, plagued by problems from the start, remained the Mark II system's chief setback. Despite a normally binding fixed-price contract with Autonetics, Norden stopped production on 31 October,[91] assembling only 5 more IDSs for Air Force testing. Norden concurrently suggested an immediate year-long development program that would include qualification testing of integrated display sets based on more realistic specifications. The contractor also proposed production and delivery of 98 new, fully proven IDS units over 18 months, beginning in March 1972. Norden delivery of two new IDS prototypes to General Dynamics in December 1970[92] was immediately followed by thorough Air Force tests, which yielded much better results than expected. Lacking a more palatable solution, the Air Force in February 1971 promised Norden an extra $63.2 million (a lot less than asked) to

---

[89] Inertial Navigation Set and Attack Radar, produced by North American Rockwell's Autonetics Division (General Dynamics' subcontractor for the complete Mark II system); Computer, International Business Machines' Federal Systems Division; Converter and Panels, Kearfott Division of Singer-General Precision, Inc.; Integrated Display Set, Norden Division of United Aircraft Corporation; Doppler Radar, Commercial Products Division of Canadian Marconi Company; Horizontal Situation Display, Astronautics Corporation of America; and Stores Management Set, Fairchild Hiller Corporation's Space and Electronics Division.

[90] Redesigns, engineering changes, additional requirements, and the like accounted for the cost overruns. But the economy-dictated F-111D reduction boomeranged—component costs swelled as mass production slumped.

[91] Norden officials claimed that the IDS's original specificatins were beyond the state-of-the-art, the error being shared by upper level subcontractors, the Air Force, and themselves. Norden costs as of late October 1970 reached almost $81 million; the company contract's current value, $47.4 million. Should Norden go on without contractual or legal relief, total losses would climb to some $128 million.

[92] The corporation reorganized its divisions between 19 August and 22 September. The Fort Worth Division became the Convair Aerospace Division.

complete the IDS program, using the revised specifications.[93] Still irked, the Air Force insisted that General Dynamics deliver the first fully Mark II-equipped F–111D in July 1971 and the last 96th in February 1973.[94]

Enters Operational Service **1 November 1971**

It saw first service with the 27th TFW at Cannon. The aircraft (the 6th F–111D produced), accepted by the Air Force on 28 October, had been first flown on 28 September. It was equipped with a full Mark II avionics system, featuring one of Norden's early IDS productions.

Initial Operational Capability **September 1972**

By one of the 27th wing's three tactical fighter squadrons—35 months later than hoped for.

End of Production **28 February 1973**

With delivery of the last F–111D.

Total F–111Ds Accepted

96

Acceptance Rates

The Air Force accepted one F–111D in FY 70, none the following fiscal year. Deliveries resumed in July 1971, totaling 28 in FY 72, and 67 in FY 73.

RDT&E F–111D Unit Cost[95]

$4.3 million, compared with some $2.8 million for each F–111A and F–111E aircraft and almost twice the RDT&E cost of each FB–111A bomber.

Flyaway Cost Per Production Aircraft[96]

$8.5 million—airframe, $3,895,000; engines (installed), $1,229,000; electronics, $2,530,000; ordnance, $6,000; armament, $844,000.

Subsequent Model Series

F–111F

Other Configurations

None. Sixty RF–111Ds programmed for procurement were can-

---

[93] The Air Force formalized the Norden settlement on 19 March 1971.

[94] The Air Force did not like the way General Dynamics and its Convair Division handled the Norden fiasco. General Dynamics support of the delinquent contractor lacked any technical or legal analysis.The primary contractor (bent on stepping aside if any dispute arose during negotiation) suggested the Air Force endorse the Norden proposal.

[95] Excluded from the F–111D's flyaway cost.

[96] A post-FY 73 accounting revision showed a decrease of $87,800 in RDT&E for each F–111D. At the same time, it upped the overall price of every F–111D to $13.5 million—$188,807 below the unit cost once predicted.

celled in September 1969 in favor of cheaper RF–111As (which were in turn cancelled).

Operational Problems **1972–1973**

TAC's few F–111Ds through mid-1972 were crippled by avionics problems.[97] Foremost, was the lack of spares.[98] Also, delivery of field ground equipment was late and depot support poor, SMAMA being unable to handle more than 18 percent of the Mark II repairs. A specialized repair activity (SRA), setup at Cannon in late 1971, brought together the various Mark II contractors with their test equipment and spare parts. The small SRA cut down transit time to and from SMAMA, but achieved little more in 1 year of operation. Category II testing was then suspended,[99] releasing some ground equipment. This lowered the NORS rate, but inexperienced maintenance now prevented any improvement in operational readiness. Meanwhile, the continued shortage of F–111Ds caused concern. The Air Force approved Norden's production speedup of the integrated display set and head-up displays but questioned General Dynamics' slow F–111D deliveries.[100]

Operational Status **Mid-1973**

The 27th TFW increased its monthly average strength of F–111Ds from 30 to 79, but its percentage operationally-ready only went from 28.8 to 53. Maintenance and logistics support improved, but not enough—tight budgets getting in the way. Costly war readiness spares kits were scarce and several problems were yet to be resolved. A serious flaw in the environmental system ducting pushed the F–111D abort rate above that of other F–111s. Finally,

---

[97] One of the most failure-prone of the Mark II line replaceable units was the horizontal situation display, with a field reliability life of 50 hours. Moreover, the core of the Mark II system was Norden's integrated display set (AN/AVA–9), which comprised the primary flight-control instrumentation. The AN/AVA–9 IDS included five line replaceable units—the vertical situation display, multisensor display, signal transfer unit, and two head-up display units. Norden, however, delivered the IDS with only one head-up display until mid-1972, when production finally caught up with requirements. This was after Norden instituted a two-shift, 6-day workweek in order to deliver all IDSs by February 1973—as called for by the contractual settlement of February 1971.

[98] Rarely could relief be gained from other stocks of F–111 spares. Commonality (with FB–111A avionics, in particular), a prime requirement of the Mark II systems envisioned by Secretary McNamara in 1966, had long disappeared. Technical problems, remedial cures and expedients had left the F–111D with a complex, highly integrated, one-of-a-kind, avionics system.

[99] After an interim report indicated the Mark II system could deliver weapons, as required.

[100] General Dynamics took some 30 days to install incoming avionics components (which was perhaps justifiable, considering the Mark II's sophistication), spending 50 workdays to prepare F–111D productions for final acceptance inspection. The Air Force thought the time could be cut.

the F–111D's landing gear still needed working on, as did several of the Mark II's components. It was improbable that the 27th TFW would be operationally ready before January 1974.

F-111F

Previous Model Series

F–111D

New Features

Avionics package (sometimes called the Mark IIF system) combining F–111D[101] and FB–111A navigation and digital computer systems, numerous other FB–111A components (such as the AN/APQ–144 attack radar), and some simpler, less costly avionics of earlier F–111s (the F–111E's stores management set included). The F–111F also featured an improved landing gear, a "Safe Life" wing carry-through box, and the Pratt and Whitney new TF–30–P–100 engine.

Go-Ahead Decision **12 September 1969**

When the Air Force disclosed that "increased cost estimates," forced it to limit Autonetics production of the Mark II electronics and that future F–111s would have "a simpler and less costly system."

Official Designation **September 1969**

A logical outgrowth of the F–111 model sequence. Procurement of stripped-down F–111Ds (already known as F–111Fs) was in the fiscal year 1970 budget that took effect on 1 July 1969. This was the first time the F–111F was formally identified by the Air Force.

Production Approval **19 June 1970**

Approval came several months after the aircraft's endorsement and for only 82 of 219 F–111Fs expected—58 to be purchased in FY 70 and 24 in FY 71. Even so, the fate of the F–111F was yet to be settled.[102]

Contractual Arrangements **1960–1971**

A definitized contract (AF33–657–70–C–1130A), signed by General Dynamics on 1 July 1970, called for 24 F–111Fs—to be paid from FY 71 funds. Like the basic May 1967 production contract (AF33–657–13403) under which the initial 58 F–111Fs would be carried,

---

[101] Excluding the AN/APN–189 Doppler Radar Set of the F–111D's navigation system.

[102] The Air Force in mid-1960 wanted six F–111 tactical wings. This was cut to five in mid-1967 (one wing of F–111As, one of F–111Es, and three of F–111Ds). In 1969 the three F–111D wings dwindled to one, with the remaining two wings due to be equipped with cheaper F–111Fs. At year-end, another money-saving change slashed the F–111 tactical program to four wings.

this second contract was of the fixed-price, incentive-fee type. It had a target profit of 9 percent, a ceiling price of 127 percent of target cost, and an over-target sharing agreement of 80/20. Like the first contract, it also contained a clause for the correction of deficiencies. Furthermore, each of the contract's 24 F–111Fs would carry a 1-year warranty. The terms of the contract were agreed upon, but the contract's total value was not. The Air Force in the fall of 1970 eliminated penetration aids to lower F–111F costs, reducing the contract's ceiling value to $156 million. This was still too high. New price negotiations got under way in March 1971 and soon the Air Force dropped half of the 24 F–111Fs on order.[103]

Engine Problems **1971-1972**

Believing the thrust of the F–111D's P–9 engine did not do the aircraft justice,[104] the Air Force in September 1968 ordered development of the still more powerful P–100,[105] first earmarked for the 107th F–111D. It further decided in September 1969 (when the F–111D program was held to 96 aircraft) that the P–100 would equip subsequent stripped down F–111 productions (F–111Fs). The P–100, initially tested on an F–111A between January and March 1971, worked. Engine and airframe were compatible, which reduced the engine's Category I flight tests by almost 40 percent. Ground tests did not fare so well (the engine failing after 147 hours), but the three engineering changes required were not expected to affect the engine delivery schedule. On 18 June 1971, however, a turbine blade broke during a P–100 production engine's checkout at the Convair plant. This left no alternative but to equip early F–111Fs (due for delivery, beginning in September) with P–9 engines. The Air Force thought only 31 F–111Fs would be involved, but additional technical problems slipped delivery of the new P–100 engines[106] to the spring of 1972. By then, the Air Force had accepted 49 P–9-equipped F–111Fs. These were retrofitted with P–100 engines as soon as possible—Convair completing the task on 3 July 1972.

---

[103] The contract's target and ceiling prices as of 30 June 1973 were 107.3 and 124.5 (Year Dollars in Millions), respectively. General Dyanmics estimate of 12 F–111Fs' price at completion was $102.2 million; the Air Force, $102.4.

[104] Although the P–9's thrust surpassed that of the P–3 of the F–111A and F–111E aircraft, it could not give the F–111D all the maneuverability the Air Force would have liked.

[105] Sixth in the Pratt & Whitney series of TF–30–P turbofan engines appearing at one time or the other on some kind of F–111 aircraft.

[106] The TF30–P–100 engine could generate a 25,100-lb thrust with afterburner—4,260 more pounds than the P–9. It boosted takeoff thrust by 40 percent. To reduce drag, it utilized an adjustable nozzle buried in the engine exhaust section.

Flight Testing **1971**

On 13 October 1971, a modified F–111A started the F–111F Category I flight test program conducted by the Convair Aerospace Division. As for the F–111D, testing focused on the aircraft's avionics, but airframe and engine compatibility were not overlooked. A problem met with during the program was overheating of the aft centerbody fuselage, corrected by an engineering change. By 17 December an F–111F had chalked up 15 flights. This ended a 2-week preliminary evaluation at the Air Force Flight Test Center.

Enters Operational Service **20 September 1971**

With the 347th Tactical Fighter Wing at Mountain Home AFB, Idaho.[107]

Additional Procurement **1971-1972**

The 12 F–111Fs, cancelled in March 1971 for lack of money, were reinstated under a new contract (AF33–657–70–C–1130B) signed on 7 December. A fourth production contract (AF33–657–72–C–0630), signed on 31 July 1972, assured the Air Force of another 12 F–111Fs, to be produced through 1974.[108]

Initial Operational Capability **January 1972**

One squadron of the 347th TFW reached IOC a few months after the F–111F entered operational service. The entire wing became operationally ready in October 1972—1 month ahead of the latest schedule.

Operational Problems **1972-1973**

Significant F–111F difficulties stemmed from the P–100 engine. Afterburner stalls, one of several problems believed to be solved, reoccurred with the onset of cold weather at Mountain Home. Modification of the culprit (a plastic diaphragm in the afterburner turn-on switch, operating poorly in low temperatures) was completed by 11 November 1972. Several other engine deficiencies (tail-feather seal leakage, inlet guide vane cracking, and the like) were also corrected before the end of the year. Meanwhile, the

---

[107] At first the F–111Fs were tagged for the 31st TFW at Homestead AFB. However, the Chief of Staff on 3 December 1970 approved TAC's request to send the aircraft to the 347th.

[108] In addition to the special provisions of the previous ones, these contracts were also fixed-price incentive contracts with firm target prices (adjustable to inflation). As of 30 June 1973, the December 1971 contract showed a target price of $88.3 million, a ceiling price of $102.6 million, and a contractor estimated completion price of $92.6 million, against an Air Force estimate of $94.9 million. The cost figures tied to the July 1972 contract, which also called for only 12 F–111Fs, were much higher. The target price was $136.5 million; the ceiling price, $146.8. General Dynamics estimated price at completion was $136.3 million; the Air Force, $141.6.

inspection of two P–100 engines with 300 hours of flight time disclosed an accumulation of atmospheric dust in the engine's blade cavity. The dust harmed neither the engine's life nor its operation for 450 hours, but it caused other damage, particularly to the second turbine inner air seal. A new blade, with a drilled hole in its tip, let the dust escape, and by 30 June 1973 the P–100's operational life had risen to 600 hours.[109] Remaining problems and improvements awaited a forthcoming engine's update program.

End of Production **December 1974**[110]

When the last of the F–111Fs on order as of mid-1973 was scheduled for delivery.

Total F–111Fs Accepted **30 June 1973**

76 of 94 then programmed—a total finally raised to 106.[111]

Acceptance Rates

The Air Force accepted 70 F–111Fs in FY 72 (September 1971 through June 1972); none, during the first half of FY 73. Deliveries resumed in January 1973 at a monthly rate of one aircraft. This was low enough to keep production flowing for quite a while.

RDT&E Unit Cost[112]

$2.8 million

Flyaway Cost Per Production Aircraft[113]

$10.3 million—airframe, $5,097,000; engines (installed), $2,026,000; electronics, $1,711,000; ordnance, $6,000; armament, $1,529,000.

Subsequent Model Series

None

Other Configurations

None

Operational Status **Mid-1973**

The wing at Mountain Home (with no immediate change of station in view) had fewer supply problems with its F–111Fs than the

---

[109] One month later Pratt & Whitney indicated that the time between overhauls (always too short for hard-to-get new engines) could be extended to about 2,000 hours by cutting the P–100's maximum thrust to 23,000 pounds.

[110] This projection proved to be wrong. Eventually, production completion was set for late 1976.

[111] Congress' desire to keep the production line open outweighed Department of Defense reluctance to release more F–111 money.

[112] This amount (later reduced to $2.7 million) was not included in the F–111F's flyaway cost.

[113] A post-FY 73 cost increase of the F–111F airframe raised the aircraft unit price to $10.9 million. Added to the RDT&E costs, this gave the F–111F a price tag of $13.7 million. This still could vary, however, since production was not completed.

wing at Cannon with more complex F–111Ds. Moreover, the operational rate at Mountain Home exceeded that of the longer-established F–111A and F–111D wings. The F–111F, last in the F–111 program, was the sole F–111 model still under the Air Force Systems Command. With F–111D production over, management had shifted from AFSC to AFLC on 1 May 1973. This was routine procedure for all aircraft out of production.

PROGRAM RECAP

By mid-1973 the Air Force had accepted 533 of a future grand total of 563 F–111s. The 533 comprised 158 F–111As (18 of them RDT&E aircraft); 7 F–111Bs for the Navy (5 RDT&E and 2 productions); 24 F–111Cs (sold to Australia); 2 F–111Ks (salvaged from the cancelled British order); 94 F–111Es; 96 F–111Ds; 76 FB–111A medium-range strategic bombers (1 destroyed before delivery); and 76 F–111Fs (with 30 more to come).

TECHNICAL DATA

F–111A, F–111E, F–111D, and F–111F

Manufacturers	(Airframe)	General Dynamics Corporation, Convair Aerospace Division, Fort Worth, Tex.
	(Engine)	United Aircraft Corporation, Pratt and Whitney Aircraft Division, East Hartfort, Conn.
Nomenclature	(F–111A/E/D/F)	Tactical Fighters.
	(FB–111A)	Medium Range Strategic Bomber.
Popular Name		None

Technical and Operational Characteristics (Best Demonstrated Performances)

Technical	*F–111A*	*F111E*	*F–111D*	*F–111F*
Length/Span (ft)	73.5/63.0	73.5/63.0	73.5/63.0	73.5/63.0
Folded Wing Span (ft)	32.0	32.0	32.0	32.0
Takeoff Weight (lb)	82,632	84,433	85,406	85,161
Engine, Number & Designation	2TF–30–P–3	2TF–30–P–3	2TF–30–P–9	2TF–30–P–100
Max Thrust (sea level static, lb)	18,500[114]	18,500[114]	19,600[114]	25,100[114]
Military Thrust (sea level static, lb)	10,750[114]	10,750[114]	12,000[114]	14,560[114]
Crew (side by side seating)	2	2	2	2
Armament	1M–61A1 Gatling gun	1M–61A1 Gatling gun	1M–61A1 Gatling gun	1M–61A1 Gatling gun
Ordnance[115]				

[114] Achievement of Contractual Guarantees.

[115] Nuclear and Non-Nuclear (6 AIM–9B missiles, special stores, bombs, rockets, and dispensers).

Operational	*F–111A*	*F–111E*	*F–111D*	*F–111F*
Combat Ceiling (ft)	57,900	53,300	55,150	58,500[116]
Basic Nuclear Mission Radius/ Dash (nm)	800/30	800/14	800/16	800/20
Ferry Range (nm)	2,750	2,585	2,500	2,597
Max. Speed (Mach)	2.2	2.4	2.4	2.4[116]
Sustained Speed at Altitude (Mach)	2.2[116]	2.2[116]	2.2[116]	2.2[116]
Sustained Speed at sea level (Mach)	1.2[116]	1.2[116]	1.2[116]	1.2[116]
Takeoff Distance (ft) Basic Nuclear	3,820	4,230	4,020	3,120[116]
Navigation Accuracy (nm/hr)	1.16	1.16	0.39	0.39
Landing Distance (ft) Over 50 ft Obstacle	2,275[116]	2,640	2,750[116]	2,720[116]

[116] Achievement of Contractual Guarantees.

TECHNICAL DATA

FB–111A

Technical and Operational Characteristics
(Best Demonstrated Performances)

Technical	*FB–111A*
Length/Span (ft)	75.6/70.0
Folded Wing Span (ft)	34.0
Takeoff Weight (lb)	107,000
Engine, Number & Designation	2TF–30–P–7
Max Thrust (sea level static, lb)	20,250[117]
Military Thrust (sea level static, lb)	12,290[117]
Crew (side by side seating)	2
Armament	None
Ordnance[118] Maximum Tonnage	20.7

[117] Achievement of Contractual Guarantees.
[118] 50 M–117s; various nuclear and conventional.

Operational	*FB–111A*
Refueling Altitude (ft)	20,000[119]
Basic Nuclear Mission Total Range (nm)	5,669
Basic Nuclear Mission Low Level (nm)	1,236
Sustained Speed at Altitude (Mach)	2.2[119]
Sustained Speed at sea level (Mach)	1.1[119]
Takeoff Distance (ft) Over 50′ Obstacle	7,600

[119] Achievement of Contractual Guarantees

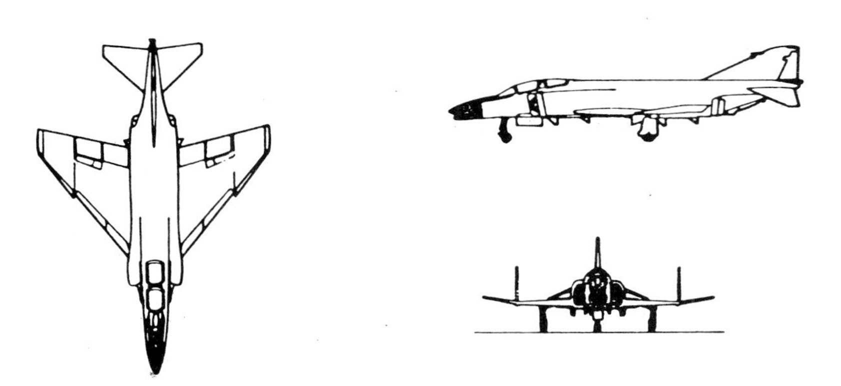

McDONNELL F–4 PHANTOM II

F–4C: The Air Force's two-seater, twin-engined F–4C tactical fighter was very similar to the F–4B, the Navy's first major production type.

RF–4C: Cameras and other reconnaissance gear were fitted in a longer nose—almost as long as the nose of later F–4Es.

F–4D: The F–4D was an improved F–4C. They both looked the same.

F–4E: The F–4E was the definitive Air Force Phantom II. In contrast to the F–4C and F–4D, the F–4E carried a nose-mounted Vulcan gun. All Phantoms had low, sweptback wings that could be folded for ease of storage.

McDONNELL F-4 PHANTOM II

Manufacturer's Model 98DE
Weapon System 327A
Navy Equivalent: F-4B

Basic Development **1953**

McDonnell Aircraft Corporation's[1] drawing of a single-seat twin-engined shipboard fighter attack aircraft for which a 1954 development contract was awarded by the US Navy with the designation AH-1. This aircraft was to emerge as the F4H-1 in 1955, after extensive redesign. In 1962, the F4H-1, powered with General Electric J79-GE-2A engines, was redesignated F-4A.[2] The next production—a two-seater, like the F-4A and later models in the series—received the more powerful J79-GE-8 engine. It became the carrier-based F-4B interceptor, with an additional interdiction capability.

Go-Ahead Decision **March 1962**

Formalized by the Office of the Secretary of Defense, after being publicly announced by Secretary McNamara on 17 January. The Air Force version of the Navy F-4B would include only changes dictated by the mission of the Tactical Air Command.

Letter Contract **March 1962**

The McDonnell F-4 contracts were issued by the Navy for the Air Force.[3] Fixed price incentive contracts (FPIs) followed the LC of March 1962. Air Force requirements were provided to the Navy by means of Military Interdepartmental Purchase Requests (MIPRs). The Air Force issued fixed-price redeterminable contracts of the A type (FPRAs), modified with incentive provisions, to General Electric for the (J79-GE-15) engines of the F-4Cs.

Mockup Inspection **April 1962**

Specific Operational Requirements **29 August 1962**

This was SOR 200, covering the entire tactical mission—close air support, interdiction, and counter air. F-4 configurations for Air Force use, first defined in November 1961, differed from the Navy's air superiority fighter (the F-4B). Fitted for boom air-to-air

---

[1] Became McDonnell-Douglas Corporation on 28 April 1968.

[2] This was in line with the Department of Defense's standardization of aircraft designations on 3 August 1962. The directive was implemented by Joint Regulation on 18 September.

[3] On 22 February 1963 the OSD directed the Air Force to furnish F-4 supplies for both the Air Force and Navy versions. This was the first attempt to merge logistical support of the two services on a major weapon system. The Air Force assumed F-4 purchasing responsibility about 10 years later. This followed completion of Navy F-4 procurement and signing of a 1972 Memorandum of Understanding by the Navy on 24 July, the Air Force on 29 August.

refueling, the Air Force's F–4C (initially designated the F–110A) would carry Sparrow and Bullpup missiles, napalm, as well as conventional and nuclear bombs. If needed, an air cannon (mounted on centerline brackets) could be carried.

F-4C

First Flight (Production Aircraft) **27 May 1963**

The F–4C's first flight exceeded Mach 2. The Air Force accepted the aircraft immediately—65 days ahead of the production schedule. Back in February, the Air Force had received the first of 27 F–4Bs on loan from the Navy. These were used in a training program for instructor pilots and maintenance crews. As the number of F–4Cs grew the B models were returned to the Navy.

Flight Testing **1962**

Category I testing was the longest, extending from April 1962 to July 1964. Category II continued from September 1963 to December 1964. Category III lasted only during August-October 1964.

Enters Operational Service **20 November 1963**

At MacDill AFB, Fla., with the 4453d Combat Crew Training Wing. The 12th Tactical Fighter Wing (also at MacDill) received the first of its new aircraft in January 1964, was fully equipped in July, and operationally ready in October.

Revised Requirements **17 November 1964**

SOR 200 (issued 2 years before) was amended to substitute the AIM–4D Falcon infrared missile for the AIM–9B and –D Sidewinders of early F–4Cs.[4] A number of technical changes were also confirmed or spelled out. Some would affect F–4Cs yet to be produced; a few would be retrofitted in others. Actually, most changes were meant for the upcoming D model of the F–4.

Deployment to SEA **1965**

F–4Cs went to Southeast Asia in early 1965.[5] On 10 July two F–4C crews shot down their first two MIG–17 jet fighters over North Vietnam with Sidewinder missiles. By March 1966, 7 F–4C squadrons were in South Vietnam and 3 in Thailand—war tolls also rising. During 1965 and 1966 the Air Force lost 54 F–4Cs in SEA combat.

---

[4] This change, however, did not reach the F–4C until mid-1968. In any case, F–4Cs (like subsequent models in the series) had a wide choice of weaponry: 4 AIM–7D or –7E Sparrow air-to-air missiles on fuselage; 4 AIM–9B or –9D Sidewinders (removed in mid-1968 but returned a few months later) or 4 AIM–4D Falcon air-to-air missiles on wing pylons; 4 AGM–12B, 2 AGM–12C (Bullpup), 4 AGM–45A (Shrike) or 2 Hill Genie guided air-to-ground rockets on wing stations, plus Navy-developed air-to-surface glide Walleyes (after 1971); also, special or conventional weapons on centerline and wing stations.

[5] One squadron rotated to the Far East in December 1964.

Initial Shortcomings **1965-1966**

The F–4Cs of the first units in SEA lacked the guns of a complete fighter system. Addition of SUU–16A gun pods with M–61A1 20-mm guns compensated for the lack of internal guns, but degraded aircraft performance. A number of F–4Cs had been modified and equipped with a radar homing and warning system.[6] However, retrofitting the aircraft for Wild Weasel duty ran into serious technical problems.[7] This delayed the planned mid-1966 deployment of at least 4 Wild Weasel F–4Cs to SEA.

Operational Problems **1965-1966**

Early F–4Cs sprung wing tank leaks that required resealing after each flight. Eighty-five F–4Cs had cracked ribs (and stringers) on outer wing panels.[8] Critical shortage of spares also arose. Early F–4C operations in SEA were sustained by collocation of units or by designation of hard-core support bases.

Subsequent Model Series

F–4D

Other Configurations

RF–4C—intended to replace the programmed RF–105, cancelled in early 1962.

End of Production **April 1966**

With delivery of the final two F–4Cs.

Total F-4Cs Accepted

583

Acceptance Rates

One F–4C was accepted in FY 63, 128 in FY 64, 280 in FY 65, and 174 in FY 66.

Flyaway Cost Per Production Aircraft[9]

$1.9 million—airframe, $1,388,725; engines (installed), $317,647; electronics, $52,287; armament, $139,706.

Average Cost Per Flying Hour

$924.00

---

[6] The programmed modification (done on 476 of the variety of 2,676 tactical aircraft scheduled in 1966) provided the aircrews with visual and audio signals of enemy radars.

[7] The special electronics gear enabled RHAW-equipped, two-place fighters to act as killer pack leaders for air strikes on radar and surface-to-air missile (SAM) sites.

[8] New F–4s came with a heavy stringer and an additional rib. All F–4Cs in service were repaired by the Air Force.

[9] Excluding $116,289 in modification costs, accrued by mid-1973.

Average Maintenance Cost Per Flying Hour

$545.00

Postproduction Problems **1967-1968**

The Air Force lost six F–4s between June 1966 and December 1967, because of defects in cylinder barrels controlling the ailerons. By mid-1968, an inferior potting compound was discovered in various electric connections and relays of 385 early productions (mostly F–4Cs and RF–4Cs).[10] Despite all efforts, it took more than a year to solve either one of these two problems.

Modification Slippages **1968-1969**

The F–4C's Wild Weasel prototype installation did not begin until June 1968—2 years after the scheduled deployment of Wild Weasel F–4Cs to SEA. Modification of the Wild Weasel aircraft was completed in October 1969, the first of these being sent to the Pacific Air Forces.

Other Modifications **1969-1973**

Several F–4s were lost because of fire in the engine bay. This triggered a major reconfiguration of both engine and bay, that would be standard for all F–4s and RF–4Cs. The project lasted from January through October 1970, at which point the Air Force Logistics Command was directed to begin a new modification. The latter stemmed from F–4 accidents due to aircrew spatial disorientation. The new modification would put a standby, self-contained attitude indicator in the entire F–4 fleet. It would consume at least a year and require careful husbanding of available kits. In addition, F–4Cs would benefit from Rivet Haste,[11] a 1972 improvement program centering on later models of the F–4. Finally, beginning in 1974, the F–4C—like the other F–4s—would undergo structural modifications to stretch its service life.

Operational Status **Mid-1973**

Of 583 F–4Cs produced, only 291 remained.[12] Six squadrons were overseas (4 with USAFE, 2 with PACAF). TAC used 100 other F–4Cs for training. Ten had been transferred to the Air National

---

[10] This compound deteriorated with age, was affected by high temperature and humidity, and eventually reverted to a liquid that leaked out. The aircraft's use in SEA magnified the trouble because the climate speeded the reversion to liquid.

[11] One Rivet Haste goal was to enable all F–4s to fire improved AIM–9 Sidewinders.

[12] Many F–4Cs in SEA were replaced by more efficient F–4Ds after mid-1967. Nevertheless, F–4Cs did bear a heavy share of the war. They flew night harassment missions, day strikes, and for a while were the Air Force's best in air-to-air clashes with the MIGs.

Guard in FY 72. Also, F–4Cs would soon equip the 57th Fighter Interceptor Squadron at Keflavik, Iceland.[13]

Milestones **2 December 1964**

Four F–4Cs set a new unofficial endurance record for jet fighter aircraft. They touched down at MacDill AFB after an 18-hour flight of nearly 10,000 miles, during which they were refueled by KC–135 jet tankers.

RF-4C

Manufacturer's Model 98DF
Weapon System 326A
Navy Equivalent: RF-4B

New Features

Longer nose section to house cameras and other reconnaissance gear: optical, infrared, and electronic sensors; forward-looking radar for ground-mapping and low-level penetration; side-looking radar; and high frequency equipment in lieu of the shorter-ranged UHF.

Specific Operational Requirements **29 May 1962**

This was SOR 196, calling for the RF–4C, an all-weather reconnaissance version of the F–4C (then known as the F–110A). Like the F–4C, this aircraft would be fitted for dropping nuclear weapons visually. However, it would chiefly fly reconnaissance in support of both tactical air and ground forces.[14]

Contractual Arrangements **1962-1970**

Procurement was begun in May 1962 by a Navy LC covering 6 F–4Bs—a time-saving expedient due to the lack of F–4Cs. The Navy planes would be given the reconnaissance configuration by McDonnell and be used by the Air Force for development and evaluation. Ensuing RF–4C contract followed the F–4C procurement pattern, being issued by the Navy as called for by USAF MIPRs. The Air Force personally handled fixed price redeterminable contracts with General Electric (the engine contractor) and fixed price contracts with Texas Instruments for the RF–4C's side-looking radar.

Mockup Inspection **29 October 1962**

The Mockup Review Panel requested nearly 150 configuration changes. Most of them would ease servicing and maintenance of the aircraft's components—for example, better access to cameras

---

[13] The previously selected F–4Es needed leading edge slat modifications.

[14] SOR 196 was amended in July 1962 to delete a component (the QRC–189) of the RF–4Cs electronic intelligence (ELINT) pod. Fifteen of these pods were programmed for the future RF–4Cs of TAC, PACAF, and USAFE.

and to infrared and side-looking radar sensors. The Air Force also endorsed a less sophisticated forward-looking radar.

First Flight (RDT&E Aircraft) **8 August 1963**

The flight occurred 23 days ahead of the McDonnell reconfiguration schedule. The Air Force took delivery of the aircraft in the same month. A second reconfigured Navy F-4B (featuring high and low panoramic and frame cameras) began flying on 30 September; a third (equipped with forward-looking radar, inertial navigation, and radar altimeter), on 18 November.

First Flight (Production Aircraft) **18 May 1964**

Almost 1 month sooner than expected. The aircraft differed from the reconfigured Navy planes. It featured the changes introduced in the tactical F-4C, basic reconnaissance modifications, and almost all needed components. It nevertheless lacked fully qualified sensors and equipment.[15]

Flight Testing **1963-1966**

None of the aircraft used in the first Category I tests (February 1963-August 1966) had a complete sensor package. Moreover, 17 RF-4C components were yet to be qualified by the end of 1963. The Category II tests (October 1964-December 1965) slipped due to late instrumentation of the test aircraft. Category III testing (October-December 1965) also lagged because the planes still carried only partially qualified equipment.

Enters Operational Service **24 September 1964**

The RF-4C entered operational service at Shaw AFB with TAC's combat training group. True operational capability, however, took until August 1965, when TAC's 16th Tactical Reconnaissance Squadron (TRS) became combat ready. Even then, early RF-4Cs continued to lack components and to carry unqualified equipment.

Oversea Deployments **1965**

Deficiencies notwithstanding,[16] a nine-plane force first deployed to SEA on 31 October 1965. Hurried deployment of 11 more RF-4Cs

---

[15] The October 1962 Cuban crisis and early SEA operations had disclosed serious reconnaissance deficiencies. This led the Air Force to re-evaluate the entire reconnaissance process. Redefining of RF-4C requirements and publishing a Systems Package program (19 December 1963) resulted in configuration changes and the usual cost hikes. In the meantime, the need for special sensors (to transmit air-ground data) had not been overlooked, but their steep price stood in the way.

[16] These comprised sensors that did not meet specifications, shortages of tools and spare parts, and too few skilled maintenance men. On the positive side, the RF-4Cs already featured infrared sensors; Tan Son Nhut AB could eke out support; and all command levels were aware of these problems.

to Tan Son Nhut AB followed on 28 December.[17] Additional RF–4Cs arrived in July 1966, and by October 1967 four squadrons were formed. One of these replaced an inactivated RF–101 unit at Udorn AB.[18]

Inherent Shortcomings **1966–1968**

The RF–4C's infrared sensor (AN/AAS–18), later replaced by the AN/AAS–18A, had to be improved. The KS–72 cameras of the RF–4Cs needed lighting to record ground objects at night. Reconnaissance crews therefore released photo flash cartridges that were ejected from the aircraft fuselage just forward of the empannage. The flashes, however, alerted the enemy. In-flight film processing and casette ejection also proved impractical.[19] The RF–4C, in addition, shared with the F–4C the frequent groundings due to dripping potting compound. Lastly, airframe vibrations (first detected during the Category II tests and already suspected of causing sensor malfunctions) continued to distort images of the optical sensors in the camera bays.

SEA Commitments **1966–1971**

Despite its short range and other failings, the RF–4C posted an impressive record during the most intense years of the war. Fierce defenses in North Vietnam accounted for many losses. But, all things considered, these losses were low.

Modernization **1972-on**

Fund shortages and the search for finer equipment slowed both modification and modernization of the RF–4C. Since 1968 TAC had given a high priority to refairing of the RF–4C nose section for better sensor resolution. Yet, modification of the entire fleet did not begin until mid-1972 and was programmed to take 4 years. Similarly, improvement of the RHAW system, added to tactical and recon F–4s, only started in January 1973. By mid-year, 253 of these aircraft were modified, the RF–4Cs included in this group exchanging their APR–25/26s for the superior ALR–46s. Lack of money, however, would stretch modification of the remaining aircraft over several years. Another major project gave some RF–4Cs[20] new side-looking radar (SLR)[21] by mid-1973. It was nonethe-

[17] Almost concurrently, early RF–4Cs of Shaw's 16th TRS joined the USAFE, the 16th being re-equipped with 20 fully-configured new productions.

[18] The planes of the inactivated squadron beefed up other RF–101 units.

[19] Immediate postflight film processing and readout were provided by photo processing vans deployed to SEA in early 1965. Later models (WS–430B vans) began to arrive in August 1967.

[20] The handful of aircraft, all earmarked for the USAFE, reached West Germany in June.

[21] The new, but interim SLR was part of a system involving installation of additional components to WS–430B processing vans and associated ground equipment. The entire system was to be fully operational in September 1973.

less an interim effort to bolster all-weather reconnaissance until 1976, when a more efficient SLR was expected.

Subsequent Model Series

None

Other Configurations

RF-4E—similar to the RF-4C, except for some subsystem changes and two J79-GE-17 engines in lieu of the less powerful -15s. All RF-4Es would go to foreign military sales.

End of Production **December 1973**

As scheduled in mid-1973

Total RF-4Cs Accepted **30 June 1973**

499 (including the 6 reconfigured Navy F-4Bs used for testing), against 505 ordered and funded.

Acceptance Rates

Four RF-4Cs were accepted in FY 64, 56 in FY 65, 124 in FY 66, 110 in FY 67, 68 in FY 68, 44 in FY 69, 58 in FY 70, 17 in FY 71 (second half), 6 in FY 72 (first half),[22] and 12 in FY 73 (one per month).[23]

Flyaway Cost Per Production Aircraft[24]

$2.3 million[25]—airframe, $1,679,000; engines (installed), $276,000; electronics, $293,000; armament, $73,000.

Unit R&D Costs

$61,200—cumulative through mid-1973 and included in the RF-4C's flyaway cost.

Average Cost Per Flying Hour

$867.00

Average Maintenance Cost Per Flying Hour

$545.00

Operational Status **Mid-1973**

The Air National Guard began receiving RF-4Cs in fiscal year 1971—having 58 in mid-1973 against the Air Force's 324. The Air Force planned to keep the bulk of its RF-4Cs for many more years.

---

[22] During 1971 no RF-4Cs were produced for the Air Force, but it did accept 86 RF-4Es for the FMS. These were over and above eight similar aircraft, produced and accepted in the last 4 months of 1970.

[23] Procurement of RF-4Cs for the Air Force was expected to end in fiscal year 1972 (when the last 12 aircraft were funded). Yet, since the late 60's, Presidential budgets had supported a "one per month" RF-4C rate to keep production lines open longer.

[24] Subject to change, the aircraft being still in production in mid-1973.

[25] $55,217 spent for Class V modification, excluded.

Other Countries

Of 94 RF–4Es produced, 6 were purchased by Israel. West Germany bought the remainder, receiving its 88th aircraft in June 1972.

F-4D

Manufacturer's Model 98EN

Weapon System 327B

Previous Model Series

F–4C

New Features

An improved bombing capability by supplying radar slant range to the bombing computer. Better air-to-air range from a stabilized lead computing gunsight. Redesigned equipment cooling system and number 1 fuel cell.[26] From the start, F–4Ds featured AIM–4D Falcon infrared air-to-air missiles.[27]

Contractual Arrangements **1964–1966**

The Navy procured the F–4D for the Air Force as it had the F–4C. Purchase of the first 52 F–4Ds, funded by Congress in fiscal year 1964, was initiated by a March 1964 letter contract. Procurement ended 2 years later in favor of the subsequent F–4E. Navy fixed-price contract (N00019–67–C–0095), definitized in August 1966, covered both the last F–4Ds (funded in fiscal year 1966) and the first F–4Es.

First Flight (Prototype) **June 1965**

First Flight (Production Aircraft) **8 December 1965**

The Air Force accepted the aircraft in the same month.

Flight Testing **1965-1966**

Category I, June 1965-March 1966; Category II, March 1966-October 1966. To save time, the 8-month Category II testing also evaluated the F–4D under simulated combat conditions. This eliminated formal Category III tests.

---

[26] Specified in a first 20 February 1964 amendment of SOR 200, these improvements were not retrofitted in the F–4Cs.

[27] These replaced the AIM–9 Sidewinders of the preceding F–4C (as called for by SOR 200's third amendment of November 1964). Even though no Sidewinders remained on the F–4Cs as of mid-1968, they were returned to the aircraft by April 1969 and added to the D in June. From mid-1969 on, the F–4Ds could fire both Sidewinders and Falcons as well as the basic all-weather, radar-guided Sparrow III air-to-air missiles. (Four Sparrows were carried semi-submerged under the fuselage.) Other F–4D weaponry resembled that of the earlier F–4C, including the Walleye (first carried by the D).

Enters Operational Service **April 1966**

TAC assigned its first 16 F–4Ds to the Fighter Weapons School at Nellis AFB. It was 21 June before the aircraft reached a combat unit (the 33d TFW at Eglin).

Initial Shortcomings **1966**

The nonavailability of certain components and incomplete testing of others slowed the beginning of F–4D production. Early deliveries lacked multiple and triple ejection racks and carried deficient fire-control systems, weapon release computers, and ECM equipment. Limited space to house these items posed another problem.

Urgent Modifications **1966–1967**

The F–4D, like many SEA-bound fighters, required special equipment.[28] It urgently needed a RHAW system. Moreover, some F–4Ds also had to be modified for Combat Eagle and Wild Weasel duty. Modifications lagged from the outset. Combat Eagle was delayed almost a year, because no new Walleye missiles were available. Wild Weasel fared no better, due to time-consuming difficulties in installing the new APS–107 radar in the RHAW system. Furthermore, new problems arose once the aircraft arrived overseas.

Oversea Deployments **May 1967**

In spite of modification slippages, an initial F–4D contingent reached Southeast Asia on schedule. The 555th TFS at Ubon received the first of these aircraft. Other Thailand-stationed F–4C squadrons exchanged their aircraft in October and were combat-ready in late November. In January 1968, three F–4C squadrons at Da Nang were also re-equipped.

Operational Problems **1967–1968**

The sophisticated APS–107 radar of RHAW-equipped F–4Ds promised greater accuracy than the APR–25/26 system of other RHAW fighters. It was also due to work with Navy-developed AGM–78A and B standard antiradiation missiles (SARMs).[29] Yet, the APS–107's operational debut in SEA proved unreliable and erratic. The Walleye, pioneered by the F–4D in August 1967, was likewise a

---

[28] One of the F–4D's first modifications under Project Skyspot (previously Combat Proof) gave a ground-directed bombing capability to SEA aircraft, operating at night or in bad weather. The airborne segment of the Skyspot system utilized the Motorola-developed SST–181 X band radar transmitter; the ground portion, the AN/MSQ–77 radar.

[29] The OSD released the AGM–78B for production in March 1968, with initial operational capability scheduled for 1 year later. Also being developed for use with the F–4 were 2 flak-suppression missiles—the XAGM–79A and XAGM–80A self-guided standoff weapon. They contained an altimeter fuze for airburst and bomblet dispersion.

disappointment at first.[30] The aircraft itself had problems, having retained most of the F–4C's deficiencies.

End of Production **February 1968**

With Air Force acceptance of 7 F–4Ds, the last 3 of which reached TAC in April.

Subsequent Model Series

F–4E

Other Configurations

None

Total F-4Ds Accepted

793—excluding 32 accepted by the Air Force for the FMS program.

Acceptance Rates

Sixty-eight F–4Ds were accepted in FY 66, 519 in FY 67,[31] and 206 in FY 68.

Flyaway Cost Per Production Aircraft

$1.7 million[32]—airframe, $1,018,682; engines (installed), $260,563; electronics, $262,101; ordnance, $6,817; armament, $133,430.

Average Cost Per Flying Hour

$896.00

Average Maintenance Cost Per Flying Hour

$545.00

Postproduction Changes **1969-1973**

As a war-rushed product (almost 800 aircraft built in less than 2 years), the F–4D proved successful. Nonetheless, it bore many F–4C failings and received similar modifications. As forerunner to the F–4E (ordered in mid-1966), the F–4D benefited from Rivet Haste, Pave Spike, and several other E modifications. The F–4E in turn shared some D improvements.

Other Special Improvements **1969-1973**

The most significant improvements came during the second half of 1969. In July, 90 F–4Ds were programmed for the new Wild Weasel APR–38 advanced avionics system. The first D fitted with the new system flew on 27 November 1972.[33] Again, as early as November

---

[30] Fifty percent of the AGM–62A Walleyes received at Ubon malfunctioned. This triggered a USAF investigation in late 1967 of the contractor's quality control and production line test procedures.

[31] Monthly production soared to 50 during January-June 1967.

[32] Excluding $233,458 in Class V modification costs, accrued by mid-1973. This brought the price of each F–4D to more than $1.9 million.

[33] Barring unexpected problems, this Advanced Wild Weasel System would probably be installed later into several of the more modern F–4Es.

1969 a LC to Philco-Ford started Project Pave Knife. It put a removable pod-mounted laser designator on 6 F–4Ds.[34] The first 3 of them (with support equipment and personnel) arrived at Ubon during March 1971. Immediate combat evaluation proved Pave Knife's worth. Although no additional pods were procured, 6 other F–4Ds were given the Pave Knife configuration. Moreover, in early 1972 all 12 planes enjoyed low-light-level television and better laser warmup. A third decision in December 1969 expanded the number of F–4Ds featuring the long-range navigation weapon delivery system.[35] Moreover, these planes were further enhanced by mid-1971. Another key decision in late 1969 proved difficult to carry out. For better acquisition, lock-on, and launch of electro-optical weapons, the Air Force wanted scan converter television displays put on 344 F–4Ds.[36] The Air Force also wanted an October 1971 IOC. In handling this $15 million modification project, Hazeltine (the contracting company) faced technical difficulties from the start and could not deliver qualified scan converters on schedule. Yet, by the end of 1972—after the number of F–4Ds involved had been cut to 285—the project appeared to be getting off the ground, as testing of still unqualified converters disclosed few reliability problems. Nevertheless, the new system would undergo more improvements prior to the final 200-hour mean time before failure tests in July 1973.

Redeployments **1971-1972**

The Ds were the first of the F–4s to go home under the United States SEA withdrawal program.[37] F–4Ds of the 12th TFW's 389th TFS, in South Vietnam since March 1966, started leaving Phu Cat Air Base in late October 1971.[38] However, Constant Guard III sent 4 F–4D squadrons to Takhli RTAFB, in May 1972—TAC's biggest single unit deployment ever during a crisis.

Modernization **Mid-1973**

In spite of concurrent modifications, the F–4D would still lack the

---

[34] Twelve F–4Ds (4 to begin with and 8 in early 1969) had previously received a less sophisticated but related modification under Paveway. Illuminators were mounted on the aircraft canopy to guide MK–84 bombs equipped with KMU-351B laser guidance kits.

[35] A previous LORAN system never went past the Igloo White F–4Ds. The system worked poorly and occupied too much aircraft space.

[36] The D's scan converter (also programmed for the F–4E) would resemble that of the F–111D's Mark II Integrated Display Set.

[37] The Ds were also first in joining the F–105Fs deployed to South Korea in early 1968—following North Korea capture of the U.S.S. *Pueblo*.

[38] The inactivated squadron left quite a record—downing 6 MIGs in early combat over North Vietnam and flying more than 13,000 sorties during its last 3 years in SEA.

lower speed and higher attack angle of the slat-equipped F–4E.[39] Yet, desirable as it was, retrofit of the D appeared remote. There would be no modernization money for such project until at least past 1974.

Operational Status **Mid-1973**

The USAF inventory stood at 515 F–4Ds (against total procurement of 793), 14 of which were used for testing. Altogether, 15 of 19 fully-equipped F–4D squadrons were overseas.[40] Wherever the place, the Air Force planned to retain most Ds for many years.

Other Uses **December 1969**

The Air Force used the F–4D to flight test the AGM–65A Maverick, a new tactical air-to-ground missile for hard targets, such as tanks and field fortifications. The first launch resulted in a direct hit on an M–41 tank.[41]

Other Countries **1968-1969**

Thirty-two of the Air Force F–4Ds were sold to Iran in 1968. Deliveries, started in 1968, were completed in 1969.

F–4E

Manufacturer's Model 98GV–1
Weapon System 327C
Navy Equivalent: F–4J

Previous Model Series

F–4D

New Features

General Electric Vulcan armament system (M61A1, 20-mm gun) mounted in the aircraft's nose;[42] AN/APQ-120C fire-control system; two J–79–GE–17 turbojet engines (17,900-lb thrust with afterburner); and slotted stabilator. Also (beginning with the 1972 productions), leading edge slats (LES);[43] and fittings for mounting armorplate over certain aircraft systems and armor on the rear of the fuselage.

---

[39] The thin aluminum, hydraulically operated slats were 9 feet long and 15 inches wide. Two (one retractable; the other, semifixed) were mounted on the edge of each wing. The slat kits, manufactured by McDonnell-Douglas were costly—$93 million for 350, ordered in April 1973. The Air Force intended to use them for the early F–4Es.

[40] All F–4Ds were expected to leave Thailand before the end of 1973, but the number stationed in Korea was due to rise.

[41] The Air Force liked the new missile and bought 3,000 of them in FY 1973. $112 million (for twice that many) was included in the FY 1974 defense budget.

[42] The nose was much like the RF–4C's and 5 feet longer than that of the tactical F–4C and D.

[43] F–4Es produced before 1972 would be retrofitted with LES.

Basic Development **1964**

Followed the 17 June completion by the Air Force of a DOD-directed study. It probed the known limitations of the F–4C and yet-to-be-flown F–4D. It covered every facet of the tactical mission and—as requested—the cost effectiveness of various means to improve air-to-air, all-weather, and low-altitude performance. The study's chief recommendations were: (1) delete installation of an infrared search and track set (the gain would not justify the cost); (2) substitute the cheaper and more versatile Hughes AIM–4D infrared Falcon for the Navy (Philco-developed) AIM–9D Sidewinder; (3) do without data link equipment (too costly for limited tactical use); and (4) defer any final decision until the coherent-on-receive doppler system (CORDS) was tested.[44] If CORDS did not work, give up the whole project and end the F–4 program with the forthcoming F–4D.[45]

Go-Ahead Decision **22 July 1966**

By the Secretary of Defense some 18 months after CORDS's initial flight test. The first F–4E was set for production in August 1967; the 35th was to include the new APQ–120 and Hughes CORDS.

Contractual Arrangements **1966–1973**

A Navy LC in late July 1966 and a Navy fixed price contract in August started the F–4E procurement, as requested by the Air Force. Ensuing fixed price and incentive contracts were issued by the Navy until fiscal year 1973, when the Air Force took over. It then ordered 76 more F–4Es for the FMS and another 48 for itself.

Development Problems **1966–1967**

Hughes successfully flight-tested the CORDS in February 1965. However, the system soon became so erratic that McDonnell (the prime contractor) had to put off Hughes's production contract. Programmed for the 35th F–4E, CORDS would at best appear on the 120th.

First Flight **30 June 1967**

Immediately accepted by the Air Force, this first F–4E was neither a prototype nor a typical production. It had undergone contractor-conducted Category I tests since April, and was tagged for continued testing. Yet, it was not actually a test aircraft, being accounted for as the first F–4E production.

---

[44] CORDS, a component of the AN/APQ–120's microminiaturized radar, promised better detection of low-flying aircraft, even of ground moving targets.

[45] A later and less drastic conclusion suggested use of another, but related, system. This quickly became academic, since CORDS made a brilliant (if ephemeral) debut.

Enters Operational Service **3 October 1967**

Although TAC had only received a first few F–4Es,[46] testing began at the Nellis Fighter Weapon Center on 23 October. Soon afterwards, the 33d Wing at Eglin (TAC's first F–4E combat unit) got its initial aircraft.

Flight Testing **1967–1970**

The F–4E testing program was extensive and unconventional. Category I started on the ground in April 1967. It formally ended in August 1968 but lingered through December 1969. Category II, initiated in November 1967, was completed in June 1968, with follow-on tests extending through May 1970. Category III (officially called combat evaluation) was expedited because of the aircraft's urgent need in Southeast Asia. For the same reason, these tests began in November 1967, concurrent with the beginning of Category II (a not too common procedure). TAC cut short the F–4E combat evaluation in July 1968, as the aircraft's oversea deployment became imminent. Also, the lack of modified engines (to cure demonstrated stalls and flameouts) made further testing meaningless. All told, testing showed that the F–4E excelled the F–4D. Despite failings, the new J–79–GE–17 turbojet seemed basically sound. The aircraft's inside gun worked well. Still, flight testing of the few early APQ–120s available pinpointed deficiencies. Most likely, the problems turned up by the F–4E evaluation would hamper the plane for a time in actual combat.

Revised Requirements **1968**

Although still needed, CORDS failed to work out. Headquarters USAF cancelled it on 3 January and directed fresh effort towards an F–4E look-down capability—without major modification of radar and fire-control. The Air Force forbade any production commitment until the new component had definitively proved out.[47] Further, in May 1968, the Air Force stopped the installation of the trouble-ridden APS–107, flown by the RHAW F–4Ds. F–4Es already equipped would be retrofitted with the APR–36/37, which would be on forthcoming F–4Es.

Oversea Deployments **13 November 1968**

These F–4Es (18 by January 1969) were the first of many sent to Southeast Asia. To meet PACAF's most urgent requirements, they were fitted with Skyspot radar beacons, together with the APX–76 and strike/documentation camera systems. Special modifications let them carry more ECM pods at the same time. They

---

[46] Eleven were on hand by the close of October.

[47] Hughes again attacked the problem, while Westinghouse studied it from a different angle. Prototype development, if approved, was not expected before mid-1970.

could also fire AIM–9B Sidewinders as well as the AIM–4D Falcons and AIM–7 Sparrows (both provided during production). However, the target identification system approved for 4 of the first F–4Es was missing.[48] By mid-1971 only 72 F–4Es were in SEA—the deployment program having slipped.[49] Meanwhile, a few F–4Es went to Europe, first appearing on USAFE inventory in July 1969.

Engine Problems **1968–1972**

Early F–4Es (beginning with those going overseas) were modified to prevent engine stalls and flameouts. Yet engine problems of all sorts remained. Like previous F–4s, the Es delivered through November 1969—before necessary changes reached the production lines—had to be modified to avoid engine bay fires. Moreover, the J–79–17 at first did not live up to its billing. The new engine could not exceed 2.15 Mach by mid-1970—the Air Force citing General Electric for not reaching the specified 2.24 Mach. Meanwhile, engines remained hard to obtain. In the summer of 1969, engine failure rate rose, while engine life expectancy declined to 608 hours. A 4-month strike in October did not help matters. Depot stocks sunk so low that TAC raided assets at McDill to deploy an Eglin squadron to SEA on time. Ensuing progress was short-lived. In early 1972, just before the Constant Guard F–4 deployments, spare engines were again scarce; engine overhaul money, limited. Another problem also loomed. Engine stalls appeared likely as LES-equipped F–4Es (delivered after April) began flying at lower speed and higher attack angle. Finally (despite several years of effort by G.E., the Navy, and the Air Force), engine smoke trails in every model of the F–4 persisted—alerting the enemy from miles away.

Other Problems **1968–1972**

Early F–4Es had no or incomplete AN/APQ–120 fire-control systems. Even though the APQ–120 passed through several modifications, it was still imperfect in late 1972. Aerospace ground equipment for both the new APQ–120 and the M–61A1 gun was initially

---

[48] This was the AN/ASX–1 Target Identification and Electro-Optical (TISEO) System. It had been requested by Southeast Asia Operational Requirement (SEAOR) 118 on 8 April 1967. By mid-1970 the TISEO had not yet been flight-tested, but when proved out progress came swiftly. The Air Force definitively decided on this system for the F–4E in March 1971, three months before winding up Pave Scope flight tests of TISEO and the Mark 84 weapon (Pave Scope sought to integrate target acquisition aids with electro-optical weapons on a tactical fighter). McDonnell got a preproduction TISEO in December and a production version in April 1972. The Air Force received the first TISEO-equipped F–4E production in June—83 more would be forthcoming.

[49] The 4th and 421st TFSs at Da Nang each had 18 F–4Es; the 34th TFS and 469th TFG at Korat, 36.

short. Then, too, troubles existed in several new missiles and in the overall F–4E weapon system.[50] In January 1969, the Air Force began to correct deficiencies arising when the AIM–7E Sparrow was combined with any model of the F–4. Its project to mate AIM–7F missiles with the F–4E had made little headway by December 1972. On the other hand, the Air Force had modified the AIM–9B Sidewinder and shipped the first newly configured AIM–9Es to SEA in early 1969. These missiles were used by all F–4s, as were the AGM–45A Shrike antiradiation missiles (retrofitted with improved warheads and new rocket motors).

Attrition **1972**

The F–4, by 1 January 1972, ranked second to the F–105 in SEA combat losses—362 (all models), most of them downed by the enemy.[51] Later, in F–4Es alone, the Air Force lost eight in 2 months of intensive combat.

Redeployments **1972**

By 30 January, F–4 strength in SEA stood at only 11 squadrons—8 in Thailand, 3 in South Vietnam. Massive North Vietnamese attacks, on the heels of the United States withdrawal, swiftly brought back US air power (a move that later proved to be both successful and crucial). In the Constant Guard I deployment,[52] F–4Es were among the first to depart from the United States. The 334th and 336th squadrons of TAC's 4th Tactical Fighter Wing left Seymour Johnson AFB, N. C., in early April. Under Constant Guard II, the Homestead-based 308th TFS and the 58th TFS from Eglin departed Florida later in the month. These Constant Guard I and II F–4Es went to Thailand—36 each to Ubon and Udorn. Alternately flying day and night missions, the F–4E squadrons struck enemy targets around the clock. By 30 June they had lost 8 aircraft.

Modernization **1973**

The Air Force decided to go ahead with Pave Spike in May, having made sure in 1972 that the program's technical problems would not disrupt SEA operations.[53] Pave Spike, estimated to cost $81

---

[50] A weakness common to all F–4s was the egress system. A new ejection seat, installed in fiscal year 1969, worked better at low speed and low altitude. Sequence controls prevented both crewmen from being ejected at the same time. Even so, TAC believed that the new ejection seats could be improved. Hence, modifications were either in progress or planned.

[51] This total did not include RF–4C losses since October 1965.

[52] All Constant Guard movement orders specified a deployment of not more than 179 days.

[53] Optic jitter, pod head hangup at supersonic speeds, and erroneous ballistic computation plagued the contractor-maintained test pods. Ground equipment was also inadequate.

million,[54] called for Westinghouse to produce 156 (AN/ASQ–153) pods, and for modification of 317 aircraft (106 F–4Ds and 211 F–4Es).[55] These modified aircraft and pods would provide a self-contained day tracking and laser target designator for delivery of laser-guided weapons. Another long-range project had been launched in April 1973. It would improve the structure of all F–4s and RF–4Cs (late F–4Es productions were excluded, their structural integrity requirements being covered by the Leading Edge Slat Program). The structural improvement program (prompted by the January loss of an early F–4E) would cost $5 million, but it would stretch the aircraft's service life from 3,000 to at least 4,500 hours. The Air Force figured the structural modifications would begin in May 1974 (upon delivery of the first kits) and end in June 1977. The work would be done during regular depot maintenance.

Subsequent Model Series

None

Other Configurations

F–4F, flown by the Federal German Luftwaffe; and *F–4E (J)*, being produced for the Japanese Air Self Defense Forces.

End of Production **1976**

In June 1972, the Air Force expected to receive the last of its 740 F–4Es in December 1974. Additional procurement (48 in FY 73, and 24 in FY 74) changed all this. Now, the USAF portion of F–4E production would most probably end with acceptance of the 812th aircraft, due for delivery in the spring of 1976. An upturn in F–4E sales also promised to extend FMS production by several years.

Total F–4Es Accepted **30 June 1973**

734,[56] against 812 ordered and funded.[57]

Acceptance Rates

The Air Force accepted one F–4E in FY 67, 145 in FY 68, 242 in FY

---

[54] Including funds already earmarked for modifying 38 F–4Ds and procuring 19 Pave Spike pods. The total likewise covered equipment to support 12 squadrons, a special repair activity, and the remaining 137 pods (planned for delivery beginning in early 1975). Costs for up-grading the first 19 pods (authorized for production in late 1972) were also part of the estimate.

[55] The first modified F–4D arrived at Ubon on 29 December 1972, 1 month ahead of any production pod. Although 4 of the 19 operationally acceptable but unperfected Pave Spike pods were delivered in January 1973, all 19 pods were not yet available by mid-1973.

[56] Thirty-four F–4Es were diverted to the Israeli Air Force. Israel would pay back the 34 planes from future FMS production—the USAF total purchase of 812 F–4Es remaining intact.

[57] USAF F–4E procurement, ordered and funded, totaled 99 in fiscal year 1966; 191, FY 67; 245, FY 68; 145, FY 69; 24 FY 71; 36, FY 72; 48, FY 73, and 24, FY 74.

69, 186 in FY 70, 105 in FY 71, 25 in FY 72 (December 1971 through May 1972), and 30 in FY 73 (all during the first 6 months of 1973).

Flyaway Cost Per Production Aircraft[58]

$2.4 million—airframe, $1,662,000; engines (installed), $393,000; electronics, $299,000; ordnance, $8,000; armament, $111,000.

Unit R&D Costs

$22,700—cumulative through mid-1973 and included in the F–4E's flyaway cost.

Average Cost Per Flying Hour

$896.00

Average Maintenance Cost Per Flying Hour

$545.00

Operational Status **Mid-1973**

Of 734 F–4Es accepted, 614 remained, with 78 still due. There were 438 F–4Es in 22 squadrons. Ten of these units served overseas—mostly with the USAFE. The Air Force planned to use F–4Es a long time. However, F–15s (also by McDonnell-Douglas) might replace some F–4Es after 1975.

Other Countries **Mid-1973**

While few F–4s were funded under the MAP (18 in FY 69), many went to the FMS—mostly F–4Es,[59] some slightly modified. The F–4F program, estimated at $750 million, fell under the latter category. It would give the Luftwaffe 175 F–4Fs. The first 2 were to be delivered in August 1973 at Jever AB, West Germany, by the Air Force's 2d Aircraft Delivery Group. As for the F–4E (J),[60] it was also a modified E to be used solely for air defense. Twelve of the 128 F–4E (J) interceptors due by 1980 were operational in mid-1973.[61] Meanwhile, stateside production of FMS F–4Es grew. As of 30 June, the Air Force had accepted a total of 89 F–4Es for Israel and 36 for Iran. Delivery of F–4Es to Greece was set for April 1974; to Turkey, later in the year.

---

[58] Excluding $7,995 in Class V modification costs, accrued by mid-1973. This gave each F–4E a price tag of $2,480,995. But this could change, the aircraft being still in production.

[59] The exceptions were 36 early F–4Cs (all delivered to Spain by the fall of 1972) and the 32 F–4Ds, sold to Iran in the late sixties.

[60] The F–4E (J) would be made in Japan, by licensing agreement between McDonnell and the Mitsubishi Heavy Industries. The F–4F would be produced in the United States; its J–79–17 engines and inertial navigation systems in West Germany (under licensing agreements with US manufacturers).

[61] Two of these came off McDonnell lines, 8 had been assembled in Japan from "knockdown kits," and 3 had already been produced by Mitsubishi.

Other Uses **1969**

As planned since early 1967, the Air Force re-equipped its aerial demonstration team with F–4Es during the summer of 1969. The Thunderbirds expected almost the impossible of their aircraft. Structural cracks quickly developed, requiring reinforcement of the outer wing panels. F–4Es also took part in Red Baron II, a 2-year project begun in mid-1968. It would compare the merits of USAF planes with what was known of current or programmed Soviet aircraft.

Items of Special Interest **July 1970**

Under Peace Reef—devised in April 1970, after Australia deferred acceptance of 24 F–111Cs—the Air Force leased that country 24 F–4Es. The first six were delivered on 9 September, after the Air Force furnished ground equipment and a 1-year supply of spares. The last of the 24 leased F–4Es were returned by Australia in June 1973.

June 1972

The NATO dual-based, F–4E-equipped 4th TFW was the first to receive the new AGM–65 Maverick (initially flight-tested by an F–4D). By 30 June, 24 of the wing's F–4Es were fitted to carry the missile, and aircrew training was underway.

PROGRAM RECAP

By mid-1973 the Air Force had accepted 2,609 tactical and reconnaissance F–4s of divers kinds, against 2,693 ordered and funded. Except for 18 of these, diverted to MAP, all were for the Air Force's own use. Total deliveries counted 583 F–4Cs, 499 RF–4Cs (with 6 more to come), 793 F–4Ds, and 734 F–4Es (78 less than programmed). The Air Force in addition had already received 16 F–4Ds and 94 RF–4Es for the FMS. And an increase in Phantom foreign sales was a sure thing.

TECHNICAL DATA

F-4C, F-4D, F-4E, and RF-4C

Manufacturers	(Airframe)	McDonnell-Douglas Corporation, St. Louis, Mo.
	(Engine)	General Electric Company, Evandale, Ohio.
Nomenclature	(F-4C/D/E)	Tactical Fighters.
	RF-4C)	Tactical Reconnaissance Aircraft.
Popular Name		Phantom II

Characteristics	*F-4C*	*F-4D*	*F-4E*	*RF-4C*
Engine, Number & Designation	2J79-GE-15	2J79-GE-15	2J79-GE-17	2J796GE-15
Length/Span (ft)	58.2/38.4	58.2/38.4	63.0/38.4	62.9/38.4
Crew	2	2	2	2
Performance				
Type Mission	HI-LO-HI	HI-LO-HI	HI-LO-HI	High Alt Recon
Takeoff Weight (lb)	51,688	51,482	53,814	52,823
Payload	(4)SP III+1 (MK-26 + 2 370-gal tanks	4SP III+1 MK-28 + 2 370-gal tanks	4 AIM-7E + 1 MK-28+ 2 370-gal tanks	1,398 lb Recon Equip
Takeoff to clear 50′	3,800 ft	3,770 ft	4,490 ft	3,990 ft (max. power)
Combat Radius (nm)	421	396	367	673
Avg Cruise Speed (kn)	501	501	506	510
Max. Speed	2.16 Mach	2.16 Mach	2.24 Mach	2.2 Mach
Combat Weight (lb)	38,606	38,706	41,135	40,267
Combat Ceiling (ft)	55,400	54,950	57,200	55,200
Max. Rate of Climb at sea level (fpm)	45,800	45,700	41,300	44,800
Max. Speed at Specified Altitude (kn/ft)	1186/40,000	1186/40,000	1221/40,000	1204/40,000
Landing Weight (lb)	33,888	34,205	36,831	33,598
Ground Roll at Sea Level (ft)	3,125	3,150	3,680	3,100
Ferry Range (nm)	1,528	1,469	1,401	1,418

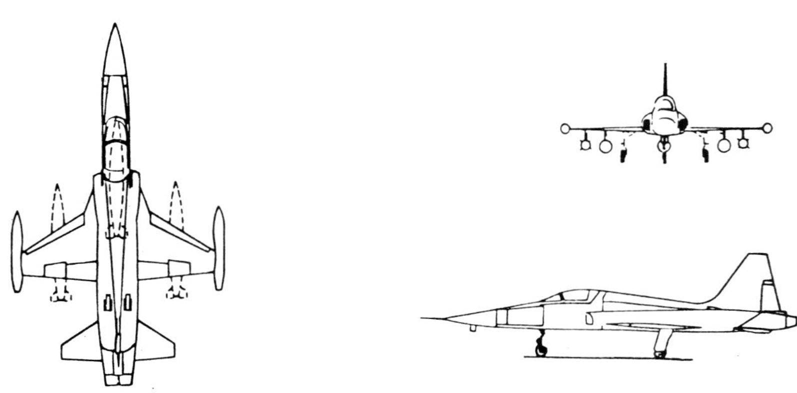

NORTHROP F–5 FREEDOM FIGHTER

F–5A: The small F–5A logged in one year more than 1.75 million miles without any accident.

F–5B: The two-place F–5B trainer entered service ahead of the basic F–5A.

F–5E: The F–5E retained the simplicity of its predecessors, but it was a bit bigger and quite more powerful.

NORTHROP F–5 FREEDOM FIGHTER

Manufacturer's Model N–156F
Weapon System SS–420A

Basic Development **1955**

The N–156 concept was generated by a 1954 governmental study of European and Asian needs for a lightweight and inexpensive fighter of high performance, and Northrop began designing its N–156C in 1955. After 2 years of private development, the contractor obtained USAF interest in a trainer version, the N–156T, which resulted in the 1961 production of the T–38. Northrop developed the single-seat N–156F Freedom Fighter in parallel with the T–38.

First Flight (N–156C Prototype) **30 July 1959**

Powered by two General Electric YJ85–GE–1 turbojet engines, the first N–156C prototype exceeded Mach 1 on its maiden flight. Two other protypes were built, one of which was equipped with more powerful engines (two J–85–GE–13s) and completed to F–5A standard. The three flying prototypes were funded by the Air Force under a research and development contract formalized in July 1959.

Go-Ahead Decision **23 April 1962**

The Secretary of Defense approved the Air Force selection of the Northrop N–156C as the FX aircraft (subsequently identified as the F–5) for support of the Military Assistance Program.

Specific Operational Requirements 199

The original FX configuration, specified in SOR 199, provided only minimum fighter capability. Additional requirements were directed by the Secretary of Defense, following his approval of the Air Force selection. These changes, calling essentially for the addition of two internal 20-mm guns and provisions for nose fuel tank and cameras, were incorporated in a mid-1964 revision of SOR 199.

F–5A

Contractual Arrangements **October 1962**

Production was initiated by a $20 million fixed price firm (FPF) contract. A second contract was signed on 27 August 1963. The two initial orders called for a total of 170 F–5A and B aircraft. Like subsequent contracts, they were negotiated under the sole source method of procurement.

First Flight (F–5A Prototype) **May 1963**

First Flight (Production Aircraft) **October 1963**

First Acceptance **January 1964**

Flight Testing **1962–1965**

Category I testing took place October 1962-May 1965, first using an N–156C aircraft. Categories II and III followed in February 1964-October 1964. These tests were conducted simultaneously, after an initial delay of 4 months caused by the added requirement of installing internal guns on the single-seat F–5A. A mixture of F–5A and B aircraft participated in all tests.

Enters Operational Service **August 1964**

The first aircraft saw operational service with TAC's 4441st Combat Crew Training School (CCTS) at Williams AFB.

Significant Operational Problems

None. In its first year of operation, the F–5 logged more than 1.75 million miles without any accident.

Subsequent Model Series

F–5B—trainer variant of the F–5A. The F–5B actually entered operational service ahead of the basic F–5A.

Other Configurations

RF–5A

End of Production **March 1972**

Production ended with delivery of the last F–5A.

Total F–5As Accepted

621—almost all for recipient countries of the Military Assistance Program; the others, for the foreign military sales program.

Flyaway Cost per Production Aircraft

$756,000—airframe, $578,000; engines (installed), $155,000; electronics, $11,000; ordnance, $2,700; armament, $9,300.

Average Cost Per Flying Hour

$326.00

Average Maintenance Cost Per Flying Hour

$187.00

Items of Special Interest

Originally developed to provide unsophisticated allied air forces with a modern, versatile tactical aircraft, the F–5 was tested in Southeast Asia to determine its potential under combat conditions. The tests and evaluation, which became known as Project Skoshi Tiger, were directed by the Air Force in mid-1964 and were conducted by a 12-aircraft unit of TAC's 4503d Tactical Fighter Wing. The aircraft used were diverted from MAP production, modified for air-refueling, and equipped with armor plate, jettisonable pylons, additional avionics and camouflage paint. The 4503d unit was deployed to Da Nang in October 1965, and within 4 months flew more than 2,500 hours in close support, air- to-air, interdiction, and reconnaissance missions over South Vietnam and the Laotian panhandle. During February 1966 the unit moved to Bien Hoa AB, and the 4503d pilots began flying interdiction, armed reconnaissance, and MIG CAP missions over North Vietnam. In March, the 4503d unit built its size to 18 aircraft, became the 10th Fighter Commando Squadron, and was assigned to the 3d Tactical Fighter Wing at Bien Hoa. At the same time, the Air Force directed the Tactical Air Command to initiate immediately a training program for F–5 pilot replacements. The 4441st CCTS at Williams AFB began this training on 15 April, although the base's training facilities were already saturated by the school's undergraduate program.

Other Countries

Modernization of the South Vietnamese Air Force with F–5 aircraft began in March 1967. The in-country aircraft, modified for the Air Force's Skoshi Tiger tests,[1] were first transferred under the service-funded program of 31 March 1966—a program similar to the one implemented during the Korean conflict. Iran, Greece, and Korea were the initial countries to receive F–5 aircraft under the Military Assistance Program. The Philippines, Nationalist China, and Turkey were next. Norway and Libya were the first to buy F–5s through the Foreign Military Sales Program; Iran and Nationalist China followed. By mid-1972, the MAP and FMS programs had provided at least 15 nations with F–5 aircraft.

F–5B

Manufacturer's Model N–156F
Weapon System SS–420A

Previous Model Series

F–5A

New Features

Two seats in tandem for dual fighter/trainer duties. The internal guns of the single-seat F–5A were not installed on the F–5B.

Contractual Arrangements **October 1962**

Procurement of the F–5B was initiated with that of the A model series. The first two contracts issued by the Air Force called for a production ratio of one two-seater for every nine single-seat F–5As.

First Flight (Production Aircraft) **24 February 1964**

The Air Force began accepting F–5Bs during the following month.

[1] These tests led to the F–5A's nickname of "Tiger." The F–5A's successor was dubbed "F–5E Tiger II." The F–5A was eventually called "F–5A Tiger I."

Enters Operational Service **30 April 1964**

The F–5B became operational 4 months before the F–5A, with the 4441st CCTS at Williams AFB.

Significant Operational Problems

None

Subsequent Model Series

F–5E

Other Configurations

None

End of Production

Originally due to phaseout in April 1973, F–5B production was extended in May 1972 on the basis that future F–5E sales might boost FMS requirements for the F–5B trainer. No firm commitment for additional productions was made at the time, however.

Total F–5Bs Accepted

By mid-1973, the Air Force had accepted 84 of 88 F–5Bs destined for the Military Assistance Program (Grant Aid). It had also received, between fiscal years 1967 and 1970, 13 FMS F–5Bs (2 bought by Libya, 6 by Norway, and 5 by Iran). Two more, sold to Jordan, were expected in early 1974.

Flyaway Cost Per Production Aircraft

$1.2 million—airframe, $856,000; engines (installed), $218,000; electronics, $22,000; ordnance, $6,000; other (including armament), $81,000.

Average Cost Per Flying Hour

$326.00

Average Maintenance Cost Per Flying Hour

$187.00

Items of Special Interest

During the F–5 training course, which lasted 45 days, students flew 38 sorties, participated in 56 events, and gathered 40 hours of flying time in addition to 182 hours of academic and ground training. The first foreign students to enter the F–5 training program—from Iran, Greece, and Korea—completed training in March 1965. A longer training course was developed for pilots due to enter combat operations. The course, specially designed for the South Vietnamese Air Force (VNAF), featured 92 hours of flying time in 103 training days. The first VNAF group of 33 A–1 qualified pilots commenced conversion to F–5s in October 1966.

RF–5A

Manufacturer's Model N–156F
Weapon System SS–420A

Previous Model Series

F–5A

Development Directive **October 1963**

The directive called for a daylight tactical reconnaissance version of the single-place F–5A for support of the Military Assistance and Foreign Military Sales programs. The photographic reconnaissance capability of the new F–5 configuration would be patterned on that of the MAP's RF–104G aircraft.

New Features

Four KS–92A cameras—all located in the airplane's nose.

First Flight **May 1968**

First Delivery **June 1968**

The first country to purchase RF–5As through the FMS was Norway, which received 16 of the first 32 RF–5As accepted by the Air Force through 1969. The other first RF–5As were allocated to MAP. Libya and Morocco were the next FMS customers on line.

End of Production **June 1972**

Production ended with delivery of the last RF–5A.

Total RF–5A Accepted

89

Flyaway Cost Per Production Aircraft

$890,000—airframe, $676,000; engines (installed), $175,000; electronics, $33,000; ordnance, $2,700; $3,300.

F–5E

Manufacturer's Model F–5–21

Previous Model Series

F–5B

New Features

Maneuvering flaps; landing-edge extensions at wing roots; hikeable nose gear; extra internal fuel (10 percent more than the F–5A and F–5B); integrated fire-control system; and J–85–GE–21 engines (with afterburner), yielding 5,000-lb thrust, a 20-percent increase over the J–85–GE–13 of the earlier F–5s.

Basic Development **1969**

Northrop developed the F–5E from the F–5A—the intervening F–5B being nothing more than a two-seat version of the basic tactical fighter.

Program Slippage **1969–1970**

Several factors accounted for the delay of almost 2 years which pre-empted the F–5E's acquisition. First, neither the Secretary of Defense nor the Air Force would endorse Northrop's unsolicited proposal for an advanced version of its F–5 until flight tests had demonstrated the inherent advantages of an improved engine. The new fighter had to retain the simplicity of earlier F–5s—for it would also be operated and maintained by nations with little modern technological experience. Yet, its primary purpose would be to fly air superiority missions against enemy aircraft as advanced as the Soviet-built MIG–21 Fishbed. F–5B testing of a prototype J–85–GE–21 had clearly established by August 1969 that the new engine could boost performance over that of earlier F–5 configurations. Nevertheless, further delay was to occur. Before appropriating FY 70 funds for the so-called Advanced International Fighter,[2] Congress required a competitive selection of the contractor. Hence, the Air Force had to solicit proposals from other aerospace corporations. This took more time than dealing solely with Northrop, as first intended.

Competition and Selection **February–November 1970**

The Air Force solicited proposals from eight aerospace corporations on 26 February. Four (including Northrop) responded in March, each with a variation of a fighter it had produced.[3] After a 6-month USAF evaluation of the four proposed aircraft, the Secretary of Defense approved the contractor in November 1970.

Go-Ahead Decision **20 November 1970**

The Air Force publicly announced selection of Northrop as prime contractor for the International Fighter Aircraft.

Initial Contract **8 December 1970**

This was a definitive fixed-priced-incentive contract calling for development and production of 325 aircraft—officially designated F–5Es on 28 December 1970. The contract's terms set a 120-percent ceiling on costs and a 70/30 government/Northrop share-ratio on additional costs between 100–120 percent. The Air Force believed at the time Northrop's cost estimates were too low. It expected that the program (including $96.1 million for research, development, test and evaluation, plus $54.1 million worth of initial spare parts) would reach $695 million. This total would still fall below the program's cost ceiling but above Northrop's target costs. In any case, Northrop's incentive award would await the last delivery, tentatively scheduled for January 1977.

---

[2] Applied by the Air Force in December 1969, the name was finally changed a few months later to International Fighter Aircraft (the F–5E also carried the nickname of Tiger II).

[3] McDonnell-Douglas offered a stripped version of its F–4E; Lockheed, an F–104 variation; Ling-Temco-Vought, a variant of its F–8; and Northrop, the advanced version of the F–5 (previously proposed).

Program Change **November 1971**

The F–5E program's urgency prompted the Air Force to increase the F–5Es allocated for development from 5 to 6.[4] This would accelerate flight testing.

Development Problems **1971–1972**

Difficulties pushed up costs, justifying USAF belief that the F–5E estimates were unrealistic. To keep weight down, Nortrop used expensive titanium in the aft fuselage section (the engine/exhaust shroud area).[5] Solving these problems, moreover, slowed the program slightly.

Testing **1972–1974**

Following engine static tests in May 1972, the Air Force approved the J–85–GE–21. When malfunctions occurred in August, the Air Force suspended F–5E flight tests from 21 September–16 December, pending General Electric's correction of the most serious deficiencies. Reapproval of the J–85–GE–21 followed completion of new static tests on 25 April 1973. The Air Force now estimated that the F–5E flight tests would extend through February 1974.

First Flight (Production Aircraft) **11 August 1972**

The flight took place four months earlier than the target date set in November 1970 and 6 weeks before flight testing had to be stopped. During a 50-minute flight from Edwards AFB, the first F–5E attained an altitude of 20,000 feet and 230 knots air speed. The aircraft (rolling out of Northrop's facility at Hawthorne, on 23 June 1972) was not accepted by the Air Force until April 1973.

Enters Operational Service **4 April 1973**

TAC's 425th Tactical Fighter Training Squadron at Williams AFB, where operational testing had begun, put the F–5Es into service. TAC wanted a fully equipped squadron of 20 F–5Es to support its foreign pilot training program by October 1973.

Total F–5Es Accepted **Mid-1972**

The Air Force accepted 13 F–5Es in FY 73[6]—6 for testing and 7 for TAC training. It planned in mid-1972 to give TAC 13 more F–5Es and to allocate foreign nations the remainder of the 325 F–5Es under contract since December 1970. South Vietnam, South Korea,

---

[4] Northrop planned to refurbish and include all test aircraft in the operational inventory upon completion of the development tests.

[5] Cancellation of the Boeing supersonic transport program also affected the F–5E's program price. This was due to Northrop's having used its anticipated SST subcontracts in computing a production base for estimating fighter aircraft costs.

[6] Optimistic late 1970 delivery schedules projected 26 aircraft in FY 72, 71 in FY 73, 120 in FY 74, and 108 in FY 75.

and Thailand would get the first of these aircraft through the Military Assistance Service Fund/Military Assistance Program.[7] The Air Force also planned an amendment of the December 1970 contract to fill FMS orders for 226 F-5Es, purchased by Taiwan, Saudi Arabia, and Iran.

End of Production **Unknown**

Date would depend upon orders from foreign governments.

Subsequent Model Series

F-5F. Northrop proposed a two-seat version of the F-5E. The Air Force, with Congressional approval, decided on 15 May to allocate $3.1 million ($1.9 million of FY 73 funds and $1.2 million of FY 74 funds) to further look into the Northrop proposal. Meanwhile, TAC would keep using the two-seat F-5B for training.

Other Configurations

None

Flyaway Cost Per Production Aircraft[8]

$2.1 million[9]—airframe, $1,625,000; engines (installed), $426,000; electronics, $47,000; ordnance, $5,000; armament, $17,000.

Milestones **May-June 1973**

One production F-5E flew at the Paris Air Show as part of a world trip to promote foreign military sales.

---

[7] The Military Assistance Service Fund supported combat in SEA by Asian allies who were otherwise assisted through the Military Assistance Program.

[8] Including $703,000 of R&D costs.

[9] The F-5E program was originally funded every fiscal year—$2.5 million each for the first small lot of F-5Es, $2.1 million for the second. These costs were higher than Northrop had hoped for, but cheaper than the Air Force had expected. And, in spite of an agreed-upon price escalation of 3.6 percent (compounded annually), the F-5E unit cost went down as production grew.

PROGRAM RECAP

As of mid-1973 the Air Force had accepted 621 F–5As and production of this model was discontinued. It had also taken delivery of 97 F–5Bs, against 106 on order, and further procurement was a possibility. Production of the RF–5A was completed with 89 deliveries—all allocated to the Military Assistance or the Foreign Military Sales Programs. Against 325 F–5Es under contract since December 1970, only 13 had been accepted by 30 June 1973. These 13 F–5Es, and 13 more to come, were the only ones earmarked for USAF use. Final F–5E deliveries were scheduled for January 1977, but additional foreign sales might keep the program going even longer. Production of the two-seat F–5F had not started. Yet, there was little doubt that it would soon materialize.

TECHNICAL DATA

F–5A/B and RF–5A

Manufacturer		Northrop Corporation, Norair Division, Hawthorne, Calif.
Nomenclature	(F–5A)	Supersonic Tactical Fighter.
	(F–5B)	Supersonic Tactical Fighter/Trainer.
	(RF–5A)	Supersonic Tactical Reconnaissance Aircraft.
Popular Name		Freedom Fighter

Characteristics	*F–5A*	*F–5B*	*RF–5A*
Length/Span[10]	47.1/25.3 ft	46.5/25.3 ft	47.1/25.3 ft
Engines, Number & Designation	2GE–J–85–13	2GE–J–85–13	2GE–J–85–13
Max. Takeoff Weight	19,736 lb	19,736 lb	19,736 lb
Takeoff Ground Run	6,750/2,550 ft	6,750/2,550 ft	6,750/2,550 ft
Average Cruise Speed	480 kn	480 kn	480 kn
Max. Speed	1.4 Mach	1.35 Mach	1.4 Mach
Range (tanks dropped)	1,400 nm	1,400 nm	1,400 nm
Combat Ceiling	50,000 ft	50,000 ft	50,000 ft
Rate of Climb (Max.)	28,700 fpm	28,700 fpm	28,700 fpm
Radius H-L-H[11]		475	
Crew	1	2	1
Ordnance—Max. Tons[12]	2.95	2.95	2.95
Guns (internal)	2 M–29s (Colt-Browning)	None	2 M–39s (Colt-Browning)

[10] Span included a 50-gal nondroppable tank at each wing tip.
[11] Full internal and external fuel plus 1,990-lb payload.
[12] Including combination of missiles (AIM–9B Sidewinder AAMs, AGM–12B Bullpup ASMs), rockets (LAU–3/As and LAU–10/As) and bombs (MK–84s, MK–83s, M–117s, BLU–1/Bs, MK–82s, and MK–81s).

TECHNICAL DATA

F–5E

Manufacturer	Northrop Corporation, Aircraft Division, Hawthorne, Calif.
Nomenclature	Air Superiority Fighter Aircraft.
Popular Name	International Fighter

Characteristics

Length/Span (ft)	48.2/26.7 (excluding AIM–9E Sidewinder missiles on wing tips)
Engines, Number & Designation	2J85–GE–21
Max. Takeoff Weight (lb)	24,018
Takeoff Ground Run (ft)	1,800 (at 15,292 lb)/5,100 (at 24,018 lb)
Average Cruise Speed (kn)	500
Max. Speed	1.51 Mach
Ferry Range (nm), w/3 275-gal tanks	1,555 (AIM–9 missiles on wing tips)
Combat Ceiling (ft)	52,500
Rate of Climb (fpm)	33,500
Radius (nm)[13]	415 (w/1 275-gal tank)
Crew	1
Ordnance—Max. Tons[14]	3.08
Guns (Internal)	2 M–39s (Colt-Browning)

[13] Combat Air Patrol (subsonic intercept); AIM–9 missiles on wing tips.
[14] Combination of missiles (AIM–9E Sidewinders), rockets (LAU–3/As and LAU–59/As), bombs (MK–84s, MK–1117A1s, CBU–24/49s, BLU–27/Bs, BLU–32/Bs, and MK–82s), and ammunition (20-mm).

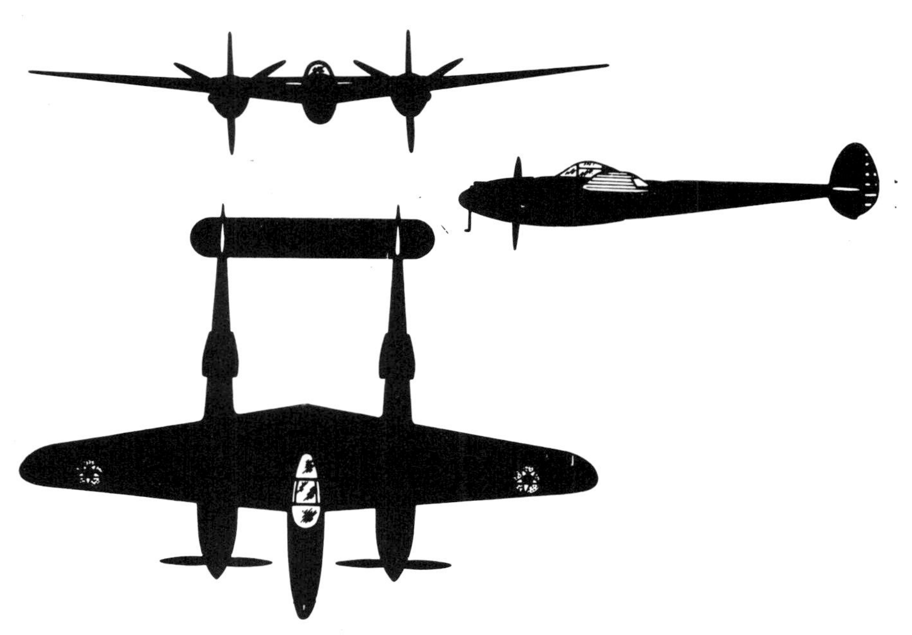

LOCKHEED P–38 LIGHTNING

First flown across the Nation from California, to a crack-up landing at Mitchel Field, Long Island, on 11 February 1939 (with Lt. Ben Kelsey as pilot).

APPENDIX I

WORLD WAR II FIGHTERS IN THE POST-WAR PERIOD

LOCKHEED P-38 LIGHTNING

One of the best known WW II fighters, produced in various configurations and used in a variety of roles. Redesignated F–38 in mid-1948, a few Lightnings (F–38J and F–38L) survived the post-war years until 1949, when they were declared surplus.

First Flight	February 1939
First Deliveries	June 1941
Total P–38s Accepted	9,395
Flyaway Cost Per Production Aircraft	$134,284

TECHNICAL DATA

	P–38J	P–38L
Length/Span (ft)	52/37.10	52/37.10
Empty Weight (lb)	12,780	12,800
Gross Weight (lb)	21,600	21,600
Engine, Number & Designation	2V–1710–89/91	2V–1710–111/113
Max. Speed (kn) (at 25,000 ft)	359.5	359.5
Service Ceiling (ft)	44,000	44,000
Range (nm)	391	391
Armament	1 20-mm gun 2 0.50-in machine-guns 2 1,600-lb bombs	1 20-mm gun 2 0.50-in machine-guns 2 1,600-lb bombs
Crew (enclosed cockpit)	1	1

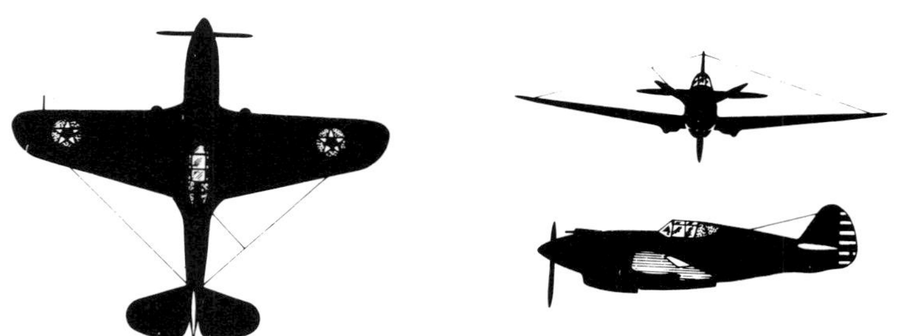

CURTISS P–40 WARHAWK

Curtiss developed the P–40 from its P–36. The experimental P–40 flew for the first time on 14 October 1938.

CURTISS P-40 WARHAWK

Evaluated at Wright Field, Ohio, in May 1939 in competition with other pursuit prototypes. Immediately selected for procurement under a first contract worth nearly $13 million—the largest order placed at the time for a US fighter. The entire P–40 fleet, however, was phased out prior to 11 June 1948, when the newly formed United States Air Force renamed all pursuit aircraft as fighters.[1]

First Deliveries	May 1940
Total P–40s Accepted	12,302
Flyaway Cost Per Production Aircraft	$60,552

Technical Data[2]

	P–40	P–40N–20
Length/Span (ft)	31.9/37.4	33.4/37.4
Weights: Empty (lb)	5,376	6,000
Gross (lb)	7,215	8,850
Engine, Number & Designation	1V–1710–33	1V–1710–81
Max. Speed (kn at ft)	310/15,000	328/10,500
Service Ceiling (ft)	32,750	38,000
Range (nm)	826	208.6
Armament	2 0.50-in machine-guns	6 0.50-in machine-guns 1 500-lb bomb
Crew (enclosed cockpit)	1	1

---

[1] Allocation of the F prefix to the Douglas A–24 attack bomber was an exception. A few F–24s remained in the USAF inventory until 1950.

[2] First and last models.

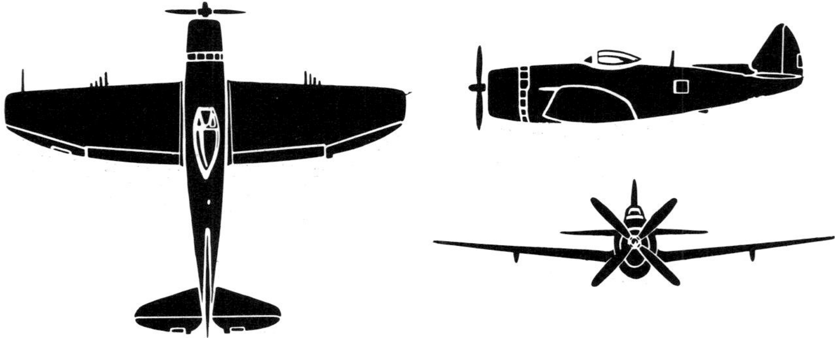

REPUBLIC P–47 THUNDERBOLT

Toward the end of WW II, better than 40 percent of all AAF fighter groups serving overseas were equipped with the rugged P–47s.

REPUBLIC P-47 THUNDERBOLT

Single-engined, single-seat escort fighter and fighter-bomber. Conceived, tested, produced, and put into action wholly within the period of World War II. P–47 Thunderbolts (F–47Ds and F–47Ns) equipped SAC, TAC and ADC squadrons for a number of postwar years. They subsequently reached the Air National Guard and did not completely pass out of service until 1955. The F–47 was the Air Force's last radial-engine fighter.

First Flight (prototype)	6 May 1941
First Deliveries	1942
Total P–47s Accepted	15,686
Flyaway Cost Per Production Aircraft	
First 733	$113,246
Others	$83,000

Technical Data

	P–47D–25	P–47N
Length/Span (ft)	36.1/40.9	36.1/42.7
Empty Weight (lb)	10,000	11,000
Gross Weight (lb)	19,400	20,700
Engine, Number & Designation	1R–2800–59	1R–2800–77
Max. Speed (kn at ft)	372/30,000	405/32,500
Service Ceiling (ft)	42,000	43,000
Range (nm)	413	696
Armament	8 0.50-in machine-guns 2 1,000-lb bombs	8 0.50-in machine-guns 2 1,000-lb bombs
Crew (enclosed cockpit)	1	1

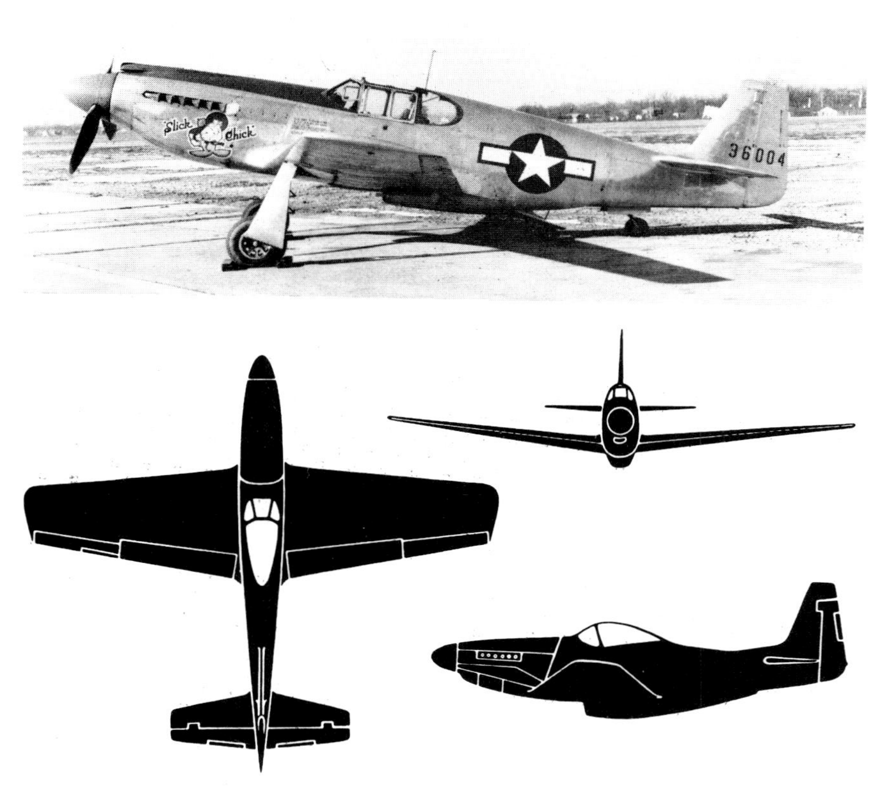

NORTH AMERICAN P–51 MUSTANG

The single-engine, low-wing P–51 monoplane flew its first long escort mission on 13 December 1943—490 miles to Kiel and back—which was the record to date.

Following the capture of Iwo Jima in February 1945, the P–51s added to their already secure reputation as the world's best escort by aiding the B–29s in their mounting assault on Japanese targets.

NORTH AMERICAN P-51 MUSTANG

The P–51 was developed in record time to satisfy a British World War II requirement. The first prototype, minus engine, rolled out at Inglewood, California, only 117 days after work on the design had begun. The United States adopted the plane for its own use in 1942, ordering 2,000 P–51Bs. These were a ground attack variant of the Royal Air Force P–51 single-seat fighter. The P–51B was followed in the AAF inventory by the P–51D, its numbers exceeding all other P–51 models combined.

P–51s of one kind or another saw service far beyond WW II. Two models (F–51B and F–51K) equipped active operational forces until 1951. Moreover, two other types of the redesignated P–51 (F–51D and F–51H) were flown by Air Reserve and Air National Guard units for several more years.

The F–51 was one of the first USAF fighters to participate in the Korean War, arriving in the fall of 1950. Twenty-two ANG units also served there, flying combat F–51s and their reconnaissance counterparts (RF–51Ds and RF–51Ks). The obsolete and tired F–51 finally withdrew from combat on 26 January 1953. The ANG retired its last propeller-driven F–51s in 1957.

First Flight (prototype)	October 1940
First Flight (Production Aircraft) ...	October 1941
Enters Operational Service (P–51Bs)	December 1943
Total P–51s Accepted	14,068
Unit Cost (1945)	$50,985

Technical Data

	P–51B	P–51D/K	P–51H/M
Length/Span (ft)	32.3/37	32.3/37	33.4/37
Empty Weight (lb)	6,985	7,125	6,585
Gross Weight (lb)	11,800	11,600	11,054
Engine, Number & Designation	1 V–1650–3	1V–1650–7	1V–1650–9
Max. Speed (kn at ft)	382/30,000	379/25,000	434/25,000
Service Ceiling (ft)	41,800	41,900	41,600
Range (nm)	348	826	739
Armament	4 0.50-in machineguns 2 1,000-lb bombs	6 0.50-in machineguns 2 1,000-lb bombs	6 0.50-in machineguns 2 1,000-lb bombs or (10) 5-in rockets
Crew (enclosed cockpit)[3]	1	1	1

[3] Pilot and instructor in tandem in TP–51.

NORTHROP P–61 BLACK WIDOW

The two-engine P–61, which saw service during the last year of the war, was an all-metal monoplane with a twin fuselage and a twin tail, somewhat resembling the P–38 but much larger.

The most notable feature of the P–61 was the large quantity of radar and communications equipment it carried in order to permit effective night operation.

The P–61 proved to be highly maneuverable, more so than any other AAF fighter.

NORTHROP P-61 BLACK WIDOW

The first American plane designed as a night fighter, its need becoming apparent in early 1940, when the RAF fought off German night attacks. The P–61 quickly supplanted the interim P–70s in all AAF night fighter squadrons, but had a short post-WW II career. Only 116 (F–61s) remained in the USAF inventory by December 1948, and only 2 by July 1950.

First Flight (XP–61)	26 May 1942
First Deliveries	July 1943
Total P–61s Accepted	704[4]
Average Unit Cost	About $190,000

Technical Data P–61B

Length/Span (ft)	49.7/66
Empty Weight (lb)	22,000
Gross Weight (lb)	29,700
Engine, Number & Designation	2R–2800–65 piston radials
Max. Speed (kn at ft)	317.8/20,000
Service Ceiling (ft)	33,100
Ferry Range (nm)	2,608.6
Armament	4 0.50-in machineguns, forward firing 4 20-mm guns, in remote-controlled top turret 4 1,600-lb bombs, under wings
Crew	3 (pilot, radar operator and gunner)

[4] Including prototypes and test aircraft, but excluding 36 reconnaissance models. These were accepted as F–15As, redesignated RF–61Cs in 1948, and phased out by 1952.

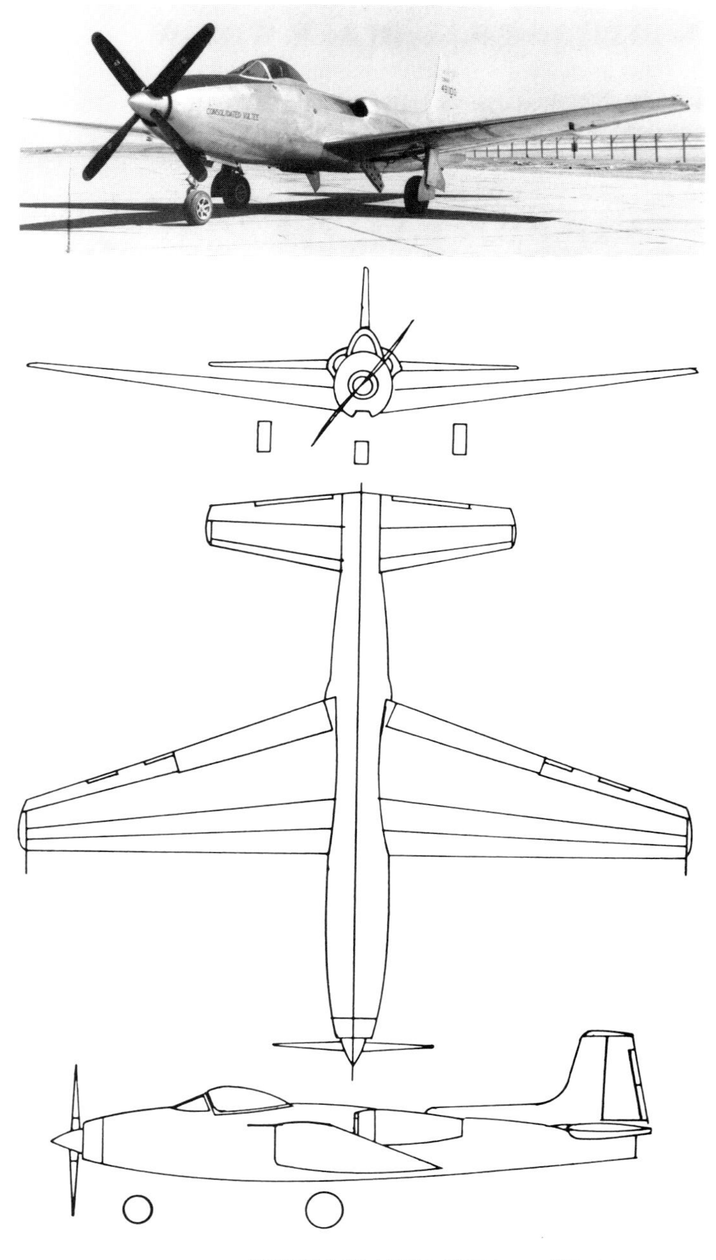

CONSOLIDATED-VULTEE XP-81

First American turboprop-powered aircraft to fly, its most significant features were the incorporation of a turboprop engine in the nose and a turbojet engine in the rear.

The two test aircraft completed a total of 89 hours and 45 minutes of flying time.

APPENDIX II

POST-WW II EXPERIMENTAL AND PROTOTYPE JET FIGHTERS

CONSOLIDATED-VULTEE XP-81

Low-wing monoplane to satisfy AAF escort fighter requirements of September 1943.

Initial Contract Date	18 January 1944
First Flight (experimental)	7 February 1945
Quantity on Order	2 XP–81s, 11 YP–81s
Total Aircraft Accepted	2 XP–81s
RDT&E Costs	$4.6 Million
Status (11 YP–81s)	Cancelled

Technical Data

Length/Span (ft)	44.10/50.6
Loaded Weight (lb)	24,650
Engine, Number & Designation	2J–33–GE & XT–31[1]
Max. Speed (kn)	440
Crew	1

[1] The high-fuel consumption of early jet fighters prompted Convair to equip the XP–81 with a turboprop and jet combination. A Rolls-Royce Merlin V–1650 engine, manufactured by Packard, replaced the yet to be available General Electric TG–100 (XT–31) turboprop during the initial tests.

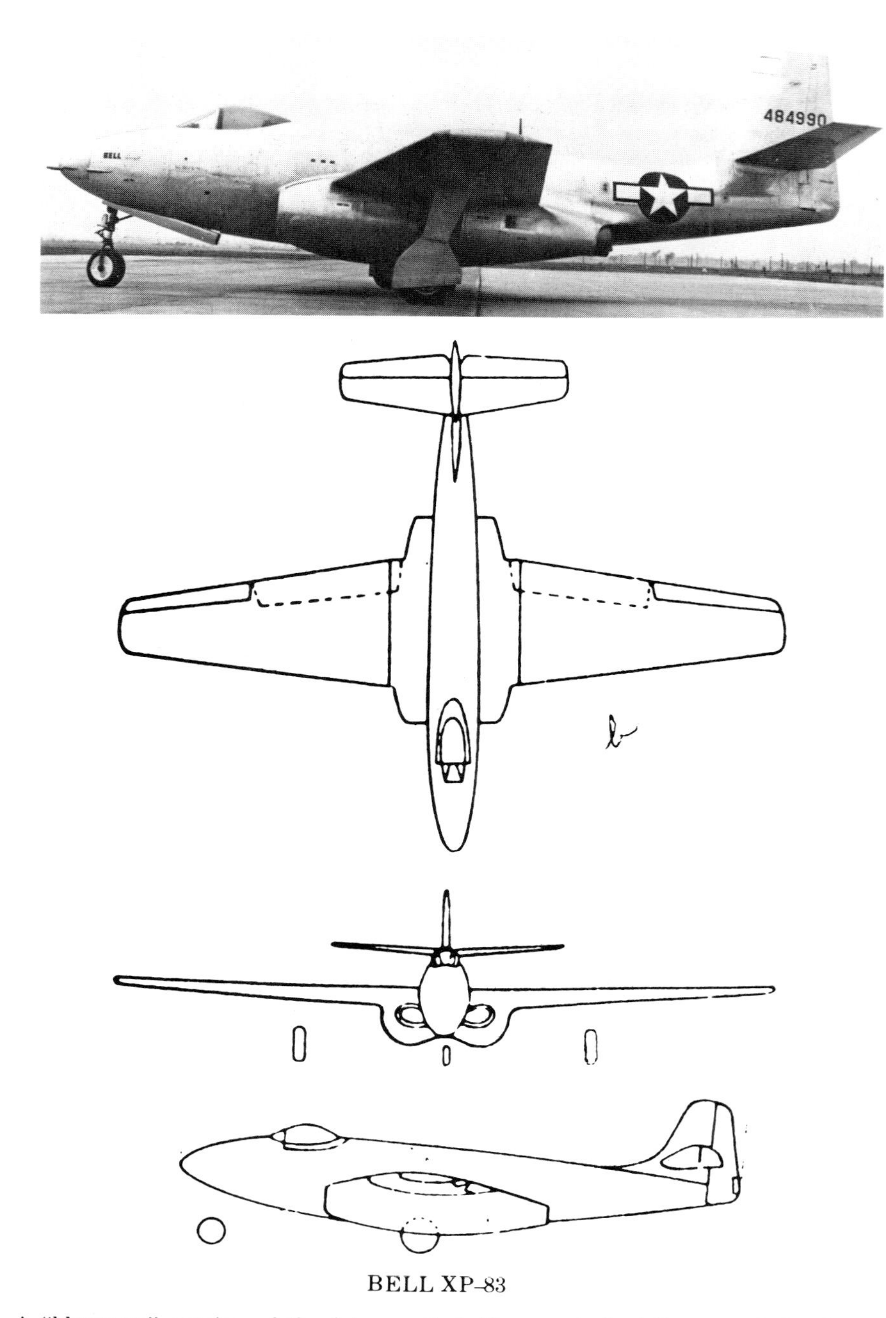

BELL XP–83

A "blown-up" version of the jet-propelled Airacomet, first flown on 1 October 1942. The XP–83 featured heated wings and a pressure cabin. Its engines were mounted under the wings, by the fuselage side. It would normally be armed with six .50-caliber machineguns.

The XP–83's bulky shape allowed the proposed escort to carry huge quantities of fuel internally. External fuel tanks would increase the XP–83's range even further.

BELL XP-83

A development of the Bell Aircraft Corporation's disappointing P–59 Airacomet jet fighter. The proposed P–83 pressurized escort fighter did not see service.[2]

Initial Contract Date	11 March 1944
First Flight (experimental)	25 February 1945
Quantity on Order	2 XP–83s
Total XP–83s Accepted	2
RDT&E Costs	$4.2 Million

Technical Data

Length/Span (ft)	44.10/53
Loaded Weight (lb)	24,090
Engine, Number & Designation	2J–33–GE–5
Max. Speed (kn)	468
Crew	1

[2] The fact that a plane did not go into production did not necessarily mean the design was bad. Numerous experimental projects were dropped merely because the war was over. Tight budgets became the rule even after the start of the Korean War, when most funds were spent on operational forces. Moreover, there was an amazing surge in technology that brought forth complex weapon systems of staggering cost. Research and development had to continue, but many factors entered into the selection of later Air Force weapons.

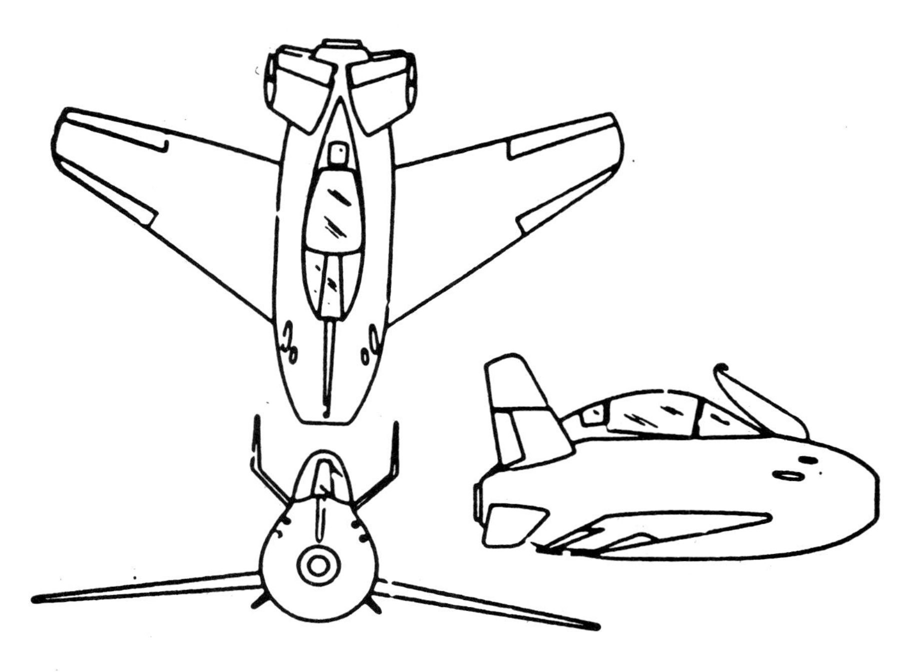

McDONNELL XF-85 GOBLIN

Perhaps no aircraft ever was better nicknamed as the little, short Goblin.
It took four years to develop the XP-85. But, inspite of its small size and high speed, the plane performed well.

McDONNELL XP-85 GOBLIN

Developed as the XP–85, this folding-wing escort pursuit fighter was intended to be carried into combat by the huge B–36.[3] The project survived,[4] but use of the Goblin was abandoned after test drops from a B–29.

Inital Contract Data	October 1945
First Flight (experimental)	23 August 1948
Quantity on Order	2 XP–85s
Total Accepted (XF–85s)	2
RDT&E Costs	$3.1 Million

Technical Data

Length/Span (ft)	14.10/21.2
Loaded Weight (lb)	4,836
Engine, Number & Designation	1XJ–34–WE–22
Max. Speed (kn)	451.5
Crew	1

[3] Although not new, the idea of a bomber carrying its own defending fighter was still fraught with danger. If the bomber was destroyed before the fighter was launched, both would be lost. If the bomber was shot down after the launching, the fighter lacked the range to make it back home. Finally, retrieving the fighter in the heat of battle would be no small feat.

[4] It shifted to reconnaissance, with the successful launch in May 1953 of an RF–84 from a modified B–36.

CURTISS XF-87 BLACKHAWK

It took 34 months to develop the big, sleek Blackhawk—last of the Curtiss-built planes.

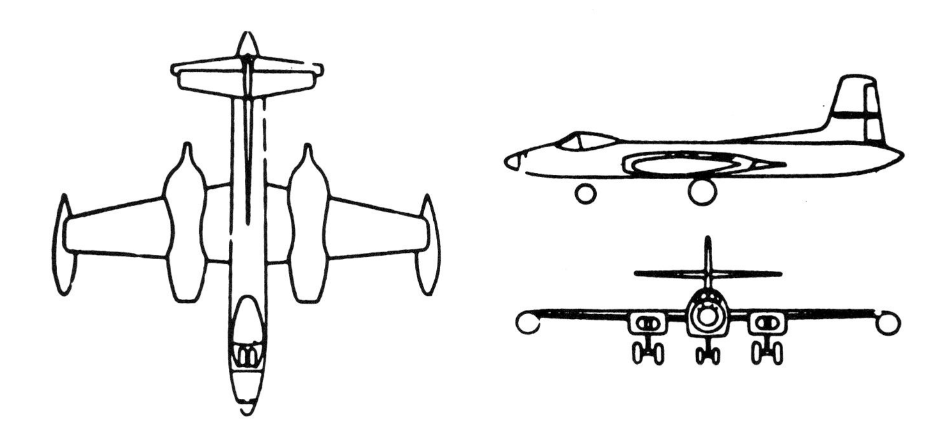

CURTISS XF-87 BLACKHAWK

High-altitude jet fighter, capable of seeking out and destroying enemy aircraft and ground targets in all weather.[5] The low-wing, cantilever XF–87 monoplane was fitted with two wing-mounted jet units in elongated nacelles. It gave way to the XF–87A Blackhawk, 80 productions of which were tentatively ordered, but later cancelled in favor of the Northrop F–89. The XF–87A was never flown.

Initial Contract Date	26 December 1945
First Flight (experimental)	15 February 1948
Quantity on Order	2
Total Accepted	2
RDT&E Costs	$11.3 Million

Technical Data

Length/Span (ft)	65.6/60
Loaded Weight (lb)	49,687
Engine, Number & Designation	4J–34–WE–7
Max. Speed (kn)	451.5
Crew	2 (pilot and radar observer)

[5] As called for by the military characteristics of 23 November 1945. A subsequent set of military characteristics required the aircraft to operate at night as well as in inclement weather. This would be the XF–87A, a modified XF–87, equipped with J–33 engines. A reconnaissance version of the Blackhawk was also seriously considered.

McDONNELL XF–88 VOODOO

Four years of development accounted for the XF–88 that later became the F–101—the two shared the same nickname.

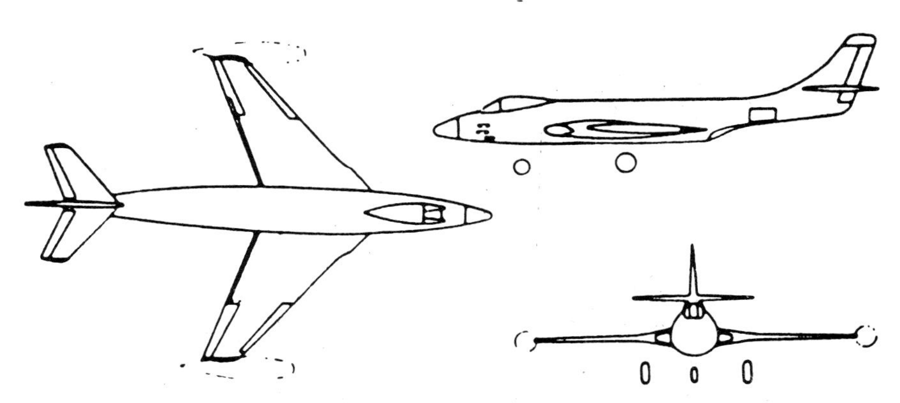

McDONNELL XF-88 VOODOO

A penetration fighter, reconfigured by May 1951, and redesignated F–101 on 30 November. The Voodoo program did fairly well after a bad start. When production ended in 1961, 705 F–101s of various types had been built.

Initial Contract Date	13 June 1946
First Flight (experimental)	20 October 1948
Quantity on Order	2
Total Accepted	2
RDT&E Costs	$6.6 Million

Technical Data

Length/Span (ft)	54.2/39.8
Loaded Weight (lb)	18,500
Engine, Number & Designation	2J–34–WE–13
Max. Speed (kn)	556.6
Crew	1

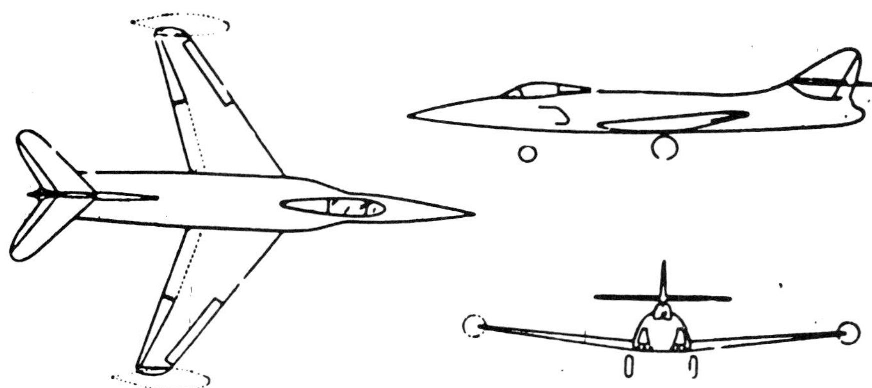

LOCKHEED XF–90

After 37 months of development and 13 months of flight tests, the one-man XF–90 never went to production.

LOCKHEED XF-90

A heavy penetration fighter, the needle-nosed XF–90 broke the sonic barrier 15 times. Nonetheless, the engines did not give the expected thrust, even with afterburners. The XF–90 lost out to McDonnell's reconfigured XF–88 Voodoo in the Air Force design competition of May 1951.

Initial Contract Date	20 June 1946
First Flight (experimental)	4 June 1949
Quantity on Order	2
Total Accepted (XF–90s)	2
RDT&E Costs	$5.1 Million

Technical Data

Length/Span (ft)	56.2/39.2
Loaded Weight (lb)	26,900
Engine, Number & Designation	2J–34–WE–11/22
Max. Speed (kn)	616.5
Crew	1

REPUBLIC XF–91

A novel feature was the proposed use of built-in rocket engines to augment the thrust of the XF–91's basic turbojet.

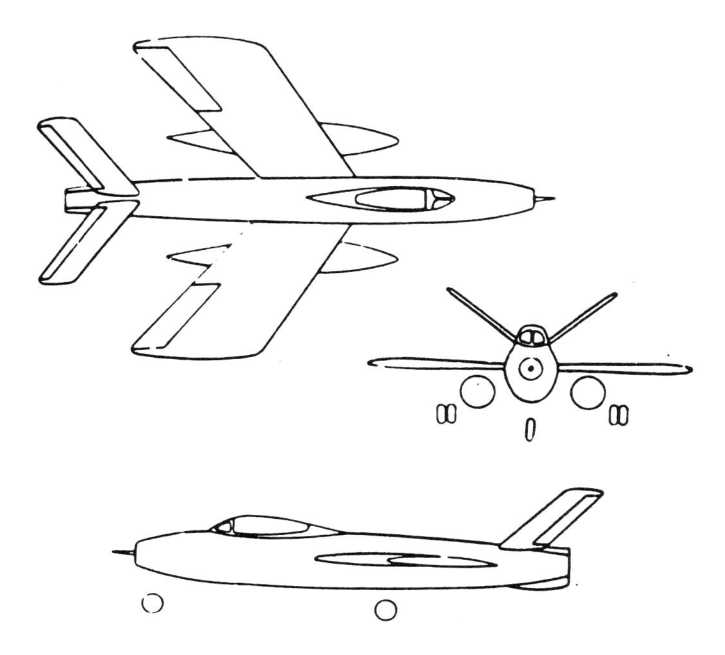

REPUBLIC XF-91 THUNDERCEPTOR

First developed as a penetration fighter, then considered as an interim interceptor. The Republic interceptor design was characterized by variable incidence (adjustable wing angle of attack) and inversely tapered wings. The Air Force's decision in 1951 to speed up the Convair interceptor program halted further development of the experimental F–91A interceptor. Work stopped in October, following the mockup inspection. The two XF–91s, already available, had completed performance capability tests utilizing turbojet and afterburner power. The Air Force used the two planes as high-speed armament test vehicles, after augmenting their engines with rocket motors—a proposed built-in feature of the cancelled XF–91A.

Initial Contract Date	March 1946
First Flight (experimental)	9 May 1949
Quantity on Order	2
Total Accepted (XF–91s)	2
RDT&E Costs	$11.6 Million

Technical Data

Length/Span (ft)	43.3/31.3
Loaded Weight (lb)	28,516
Engine, Number & Designation	1J–47–GE–3
Max. Speed (kn)	642.5
Crew	1

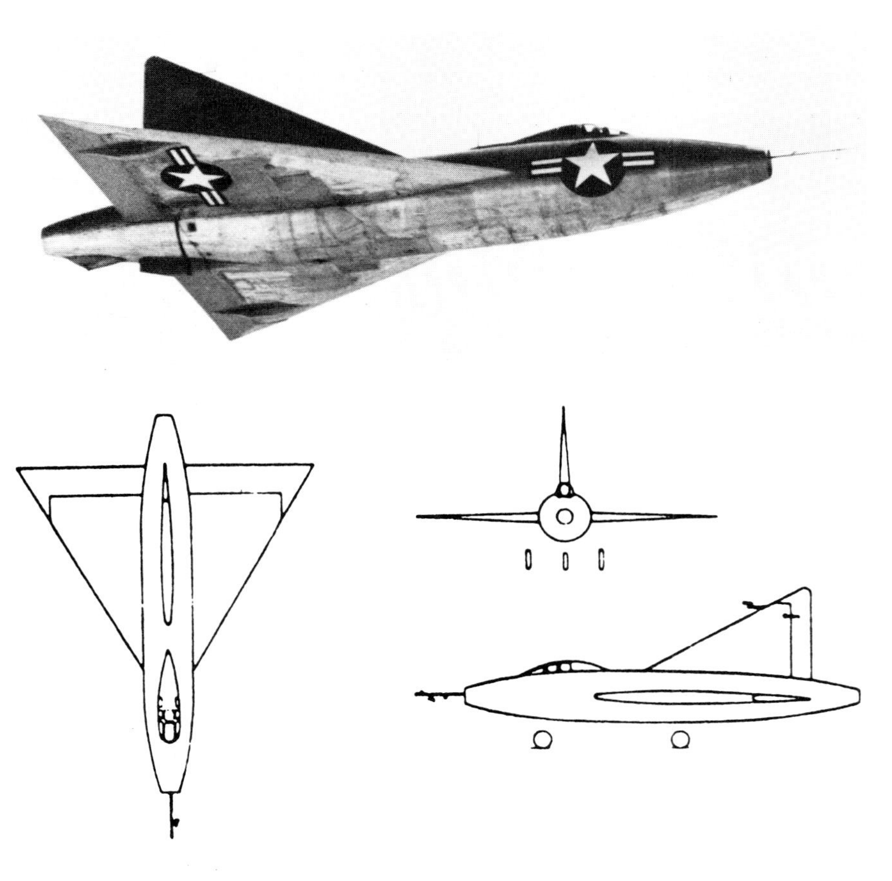

CONSOLIDATED VULTEE XF-92A

In the **XF-92A** the Allison J-33-A23 turbojet took the place of the 18 rocket engines proposed for the **XF-92**—a rocket-propelled, piloted missile that was never built.

CONSOLIDATED-VULTEE XF-92A

The first American delta-wing aircraft flown. Dr. Alexander Lippisch, World War II leader of the German delta-wing program, assisted in its design. The XF-92 was the forerunner of the Convair F-102 interceptor.[7]

Initial Contract Date	16 May 1949
First Flight (XF-92A)	18 September 1948
Quantity on Order	3—XF-92As[8]
Total Accepted (XF-92As)	1[9]
RDT&E Costs	$4.3 Million

Technical Data

Length/Span (ft)	42.5/31.3
Loaded Weight (lb)	13,000
Engine, Number & Designation	1J-33-A-23/29
Max. Speed (kn)	547
Crew	1

[7] Consolidated-Vultee merged with General Dynamics, becoming the Convair Division of that corporation on 29 April 1954.

[8] The first XF-92A flew in October 1949. The other two were cancelled.

[9] The Air Force handed over the plane to NACA in 1952.

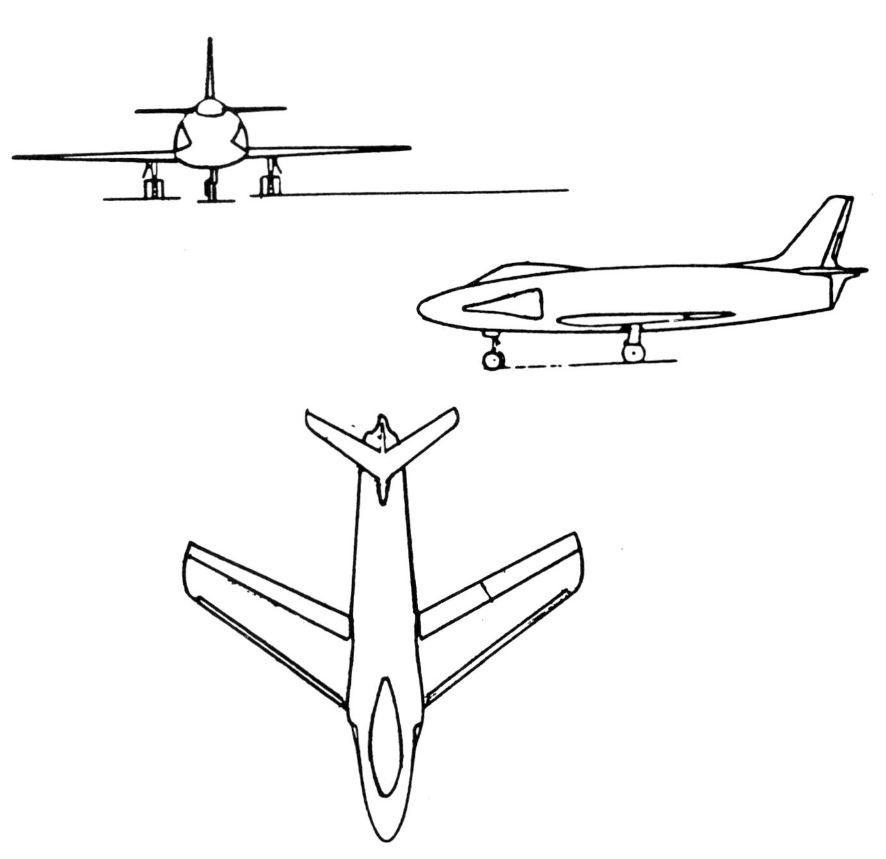

NORTH AMERICAN YF-93A

The F–86C was redesignated as the F–93A in September 1948; committed to production in February 1949; and cancelled in June.

NORTH AMERICAN YF-93A

This plane was meant to become the F–86C, with 118 productions on order since 9 June 1948. But its design departed so drastically from the basic F–86 Sabre, it was redesignated F–93A. This led to the cancelling of the productions and the subsequent order of two prototypes. During the Air Force competition of May 1951 the North American YF–93A (like the Lockheed XF–90 penetration fighter) lost out to McDonnell's reconfigured Voodoo.

Initial Contract Date	February 1949
First Flight (prototype)	25 January 1950
Quantity on Order	2
Total Accepted (YF–93As)	2[10]
RDT&E Costs	$11.5 Million

Technical Data

Length/Span (ft)	44.1/38.9
Loaded Weight (lb)	25,500
Engine, Number & Designation	1J–48–P–3/6
Max. Speed (kn)	615.6
Crew	1

[10] NACA later used the two USAF YF–93As in high-speed tests.

XF-95A

YF-96A

YF-97A

NORTH AMERICAN XF-95A

The XF–95 appeared on the contractor's drawing boards in March 1949. Its story proved a complete reversal of the North American YF–93A's. The single-seat XF–95A, successfully flown in September 1949, was basically a F–86 with a nose radar and engine afterburner. Although in the operational inventory less than a year, the F–86A was considered the best USAF jet fighter. Hence, the Air Force quickly endorsed the North American YF–95A and redesignated it F–86D. Some 2,500 F–86Ds were built, a few remaining in the active forces until April 1958.

REPUBLIC YF-96A

A swept-wing fighter-bomber, proposed by Republic in November 1949, when USAF development funds were at the lowest ebb. The Republic drawing, based on a standard F–84E fuselage, gave hope that available tooling could be used at considerable savings. The Air Force in consequence returned one F–84E to the contractor for prototype development. This so-called YF–96A was flown on 3 June 1950, but it took the Korean War to prompt its production. The Air Force then requested that the plane be given a better engine and a more logical designation. A new prototype flew in February 1951, 5 months after being relabeled the YF–84F. More than 2,300 of this swept-wing, single-seat fighter-bomber were eventually built.

LOCKHEED YF-97A

Lockheed began work on this prototype in early 1949, using a converted F–94A. The YF–97A flew in January 1950, becoming the first straight-wing aircraft (other than experimental) to exceed the speed of sound. Hard-pressed to get a better interim interceptor, the Air Force in February 1950 placed a tentative production order for 110 F–97As (renamed F–94Cs in September). The program for this third, biggest, and last of the F–94 model series did not fare as well as expected.

XF-103

YF-107A

REPUBLIC XF-103

The experimental and never flown F–103 originated in early 1948 with the Republic AP–44A design for an all-weather, high-altitude defense fighter. The contractor sent its design to the Air Force in January 1951, and in September received a Phase I development contract for the highly sophisticated plane, listed on Air Force books as Weapon System 204A.

A full-scale mockup on 2 March 1953 brought a major configuration change,[11] an 18-month extension of the Phase I contract, and further state-of-the-art studies of titanium fabrication, high-temperature hydraulics, escape capsules, and periscopic sights. The Air Force also decided to keep the program going with scarce research and development money. This would include prototype and flight testing, usually covered by procurement support funds. Republic finally obtained a contract for three XF–103s in July 1954. However, progress inched along, hindered by low titanium priority, difficulties in the making of titanium alloy, engine development problems, and critical funding.

The XF–103 program was pared to one plane and two flight engines early in 1957. In September the contract for the Mach 3, 80,000-ft altitude delta-wing XF–103 was cancelled,[12] development being too slow to justify further expense. The program had cost $104 million over 9 years.

NORTH AMERICAN YF-107A

This plane was conceived in 1953 as the second model of the F–100 Sabre series. It was due to differ from the basic F–100A tactical fighter by being able to also serve as a bomber. But new requirements in December 1954 generated such extensive changes that the projected F–100B designation was dropped—the proposed plane being renamed F–107A before the prototype flew.[13] The promising F–107A tempted the Air Force in mid-1956 to cancel the Republic contract for the F–105, which had run into production problems. It held off, however, because even under ideal conditions the F–107A could not be available as soon as the F–105. NASA finally used the USAF YF–107As in supersonic research. One was later returned for permanent display in the Air Force Museum.

---

[11] The mockup inspection called for replacement of the canopy by a flush cockpit with periscope.

[12] So was the contract for the Wright MX–1787 dual-cycle turbojet-ramjet.

[13] The F–100B was skipped. The F–100A was followed by the F–100C, which embodied numerous features of the original F–100B design.

Initial Contract Date	29 February 1956
First Flight (experimental)	10 September 1956
Quantity on Order	12 (prototypes and test aircraft)
Total Accepted (YF–107As)	3
RDT&E Costs	None[14]

Technical Data

Length/Span (ft)	61/36
Takeoff Weight (lb)	38,000
Engine, Number & Designation	1 J–75–P–9 with afterburner
Max. Speed (kn)	Over Mach 2
Service Ceiling (ft)	Above 50,000
Crew	1

NORTH AMERICAN XF–108 RAPIER

First known as the LRIX (long-range interceptor, experimental), development of the XF–108 followed USAF GOR 114, dated 6 October 1955. The North American letter contract of 6 June 1957 called for an all-weather, two-man, two-engine, long-range interceptor, with a combat speed of at least Mach 3 and swift maneuver at 70,000 feet. The aircraft would carry two or more air-to-air missiles with nuclear or conventional warheads. The armament bay was to house a number of weapon combinations.

The Air Force expected a lot from the complex new plane.[15] It wanted an early 1963 operational date, 1,000-nm cruise speed with 5 minutes of combat at Mach 3, and a cruise speed of Mach 3 for 350-nm and 10 minutes of combat time (also at Mach 3). Finally, the F–108 should be able to fly to a specified point at supersonic speed, loiter for about an hour, and speed on to the target.

A mockup inspection on 26 January 1959 disclosed few needed changes. Nonetheless, the XF–108 (nicknamed the Rapier on 15

---

[14] The YF–107A program from the start was paid with procurement support funds. Total cost (flight testing included) had reached $105.8 million, when production of the nine planes remaining on order was cancelled.

[15] Many subcontractors were involved. Hughes Aircraft Corporation would provide the aircraft's fire-control system and GAR–9 missiles; Convair, the wing; Marquardt, the air induction control system; Hamilton Standard, the air conditioning and pressurization; Federal Division of the International Telephone & Telegraph Co., the mission and traffic control system; and Electronic Speciality Co., the antenna system. The Air Force would take care of the engine, the General Electric J–93 turbojet (first developed as the X–279E).

May 1959) never flew. The Air Force in 1957 had programmed for more than 480 F–108s, but the pinch in funds wiped out the whole project on 23 September 1959.[16] Total RDT&E expenditures then stood at $141.9 million.

XF-108 RAPIER

[16] The Air Force believed the F–108 would have been a good mobile missile launcher to intercept enemy aircraft far away from their intended targets. This was a role the B–70 bomber (being also built by North American and later consigned to the XF–108's fate) could not perform.

F-110A

YF-12A

McDONNELL F-110A[17]

This was to be the Air Force's first version of the Navy F4H Phantoms. The OSD decision on 3 August 1962 to standardize all Department of Defense aircraft designations, changed this planning. McDonnell's F4H-1 for the Navy became the F-4A, while the Air Force's first configuration of the basic F4H-1 was the F-4C.

LOCKHEED YF-12A

As a variation of the Lockheed A-11, the YF-12A interceptor (like SAC's SR-71s) originated in November 1959. This was 1 month after the OSD had cancelled the stainless steel XF-108, but let work continue on several of the aircraft's components.[18]

The Lockheed A-11 had a long narrow fuselage, twin engines, and a fixed delta-wing. Its first flight came in July 1962, only 32 months after the development contract was awarded. President Lyndon B. Johnson revealed the plane's existence on 29 February 1964. Designated YF-12A, this interceptor version of the almost all-titanium A-11[19] was unveiled at Edwards AFB on 30 September. The Air Force in October (SOR 220) set forth performance standards surpassing those first imposed on the North American Rapier. Specifically, it required from this IMI (improved-manned-interceptor) a combat radius up to 1,200 nm, Mach 3+ speed, and swifter maneuver at high altitude.

On 1 May 1965, two F-12A prototypes established nine world speed and altitude records that were unbroken 7 years later.[20] Nonetheless, the OSD discontinued development of the F-12 program on 27 November 1967, but ordered in the same month a new airborne warning and control system (AWACS). The OSD believed that the future AWACS and so-called F-106Xs (later cancelled in favor of a further modernization of existing F-106s) would be more

---

[17] After being earmarked in turn for several projects (all abandoned), the F-109 designation was never used. The General Dynamics F-111, endorsed by the OSD in September 1961, was the last plane identified under the individual service scheme.

[18] The Hughes ASG fire-control system and GAR-9 missiles (later designated XAIM-47As), flight-tested in 1960 with a modified Convair B-58 Hustler.

[19] A titanium alloy airframe would withstand the high temperatures at more than three times the speed of sound. This was a metallurgic first in the world of aviation. Also noteworthy were the YF-12A's ASG-18 pulse doppler fire-control system and XAIM-47A missiles. In contrast to other interceptor subsystems, they were designed to operate with little or no ground control.

[20] These records had previously been held by a Russian E-166 aircraft (1,665.89 mph and sustained horizontal flight at 74,376.49 ft).

cost-effective. The F–12A would have been expensive (between $15 and $18 million if 100 were ordered). Only three prototypes were built—the third being converted to a two-place SR–71 trainer, designated SR–71C.

The 4786th Test Squadron was the sole USAF unit involved with the YF–12A. When it ceased operations at Edwards AFB on 5 May 1972, USAF participation in a joint test program with NASA also ended. They had worked together on this project since mid–1969.

Technical Data

Length/Span (ft)	107.5/55.7
Gross Weight (lb)	136,000
Engine, Number & Designation	2 65,000-lb thrust J–58 turbojets w/ afterburners
Ceiling (ft)	80,000
Max. Speed	Mach 3+
Crew	2

McDONNELL-DOUGLAS YF-15 EAGLE

As an air superiority replacement for the F–4, the F–15 (first known as the F–X) originated in late 1965. In a simpler but still advanced configuration, with a projected 1970 IOC, the F–X had been first discussed in the fall of 1964. (The appearance of a Soviet prototype fighter a short time before led to this discussion.) But many factors hindered progress.[21] Not until December 1969 and after several rounds of design proposals[22] did the OSD give the go-ahead. Once approved, however, the F–15 development was fast.

Displayed at the contractor's St. Louis plant on 26 June 1972 (when it was christened the Eagle), the YF–15 made a 50-minute first flight over Edwards AFB on 17 July. Rigorous flight tests in the 20-aircraft program followed, numbering 1,000 as of November 1973. By then, the YF–15 had flown above 60,000 feet at Mach 2 + speed.

---

[21] The war in Southeast Asia, the calls for new planes (F–5 and A–7), tight budgets, and the OSD drive to convince the Navy and Air Force to use similar tactical aircraft ("commonality").

[22] The Air Force first sent requests for proposals (RFP's) to 13 aerospace companies on 18 December 1965. It again solicited bids for F–X design studies on 11 August 1967, but only from seven companies. Two (General Dynamics and McDonnell-Douglas) received study contract awards in December. The others (Fairchild-Hiller, Grumman, Lockheed, and North American) stayed in the race at their own expense—Boeing had dropped out. By 1969 the field had been narrowed down to Fairchild-Hiller, North American, and McDonnell-Douglas. They all submitted technical proposals in mid-1969, and cost proposals on 30 August. Revised cost proposals, forwarded by the three late in the year, established McDonnell-Douglas as the undisputed winner.

Initial Contract Date (Total System Development)	January 1970
Critical Design Review	April 1971
First Flight (prototype)	July 1972
Production Approval	February 1973
Quantity on Order:	
Prototypes/Test Aircraft	20
Production Aircraft	30[23] (against 729 programmed)
Projected IOC	1975
Total Aircraft Accepted (as of 30 June 1973)	7 (prototype/test aircraft)
RDT&E Estimated Costs	$1.7 billion
Procurement Unit Cost (estimated)	$8.2 million

Technical Data

Length/Span (ft)	64.11/42.8
Takeoff Weight (lb)	40,000
Engine, Number & Designation	2 23,000-lb thrust P&W F100 turbofans w/afterburners
Max. Speed	Mach 2+
Cruise Radius (nm) (Designed Mission)	200
Crew	1 (2 in the TF-15 trainer)
Armament	AIM-7 Sparrow, AIM-9 Sidewinder, M61A1 Vulcan 20-mm cannon, plus options

[23] Sudden engine problems caused the number to be temporarily held at 30.

YF-15 EAGLE

SELECTED BIBLIOGRAPHY

This encyclopedia, covering nearly 30 years of aviation technology in fighter aircraft, relies chiefly on Air Force data drawn from thousands of official documents. Secondary sources (commercial publications, newspapers, etc.) were consulted solely to reconcile minor conflicting information. By far the bulk of the author's research rests on Air Staff seminannual historical reports, major command histories, and historical records of some lower units. Other valuable source material were the many special studies of the Air Force Logistics Command and the Aerospace Defense Command. These documents are in the archives of the Albert F. Simpson Historical Research Center, Maxwell AFB, Ala. Those of special value are listed below.

Air Staff Directorate Histories

Development and Acquisition, DCS/Research and Development, 1 April 1970-on

Maintenance, Supply and Services, DCS/Materiel, until 10 April 1951

Maintenance Engineering, DCS/Materiel, 10 April 1951 to 30 June 1961

Maintenance Engineering, DCS/Systems and Logistics, 1 July 1961 to 14 March 1973

Maintenance, Engineering and Supply, DCS/Systems and Logistics, 15 March 1973-on

Military Assistance, DCS/Systems and Logistics, 1 May 1965 to 22 December 1968 (Assistant for Mutual Security until 1 May 1965)

Military Assistance and Sales, DCS/Systems and Logistics, 23 December 1968-on

Operational Requirements, DCS/Operations, 20 April 1959 to 31 January 1963

Operational Requirements, DCS/Programs and Requirements, 1 February 1963 to 2 May 1965

Operational Requirements and Development Plans, DCS/Research and Development, 3 May 1965-on

Procurement and Production Engineering, DCS/Materiel, until February 1955

Procurement and Production, DCS/Materiel, 1 February 1955 to 30 June 1961

Procurement Management, DCS/Systems and Logistics, 1 July 1961 to February 1963

Procurement Policy, DCS/Systems and Logistics, February 1963-on

Production, DCS/Systems and Logistics, 1 February 1963 to 14 January 1965

Production and Programming, DCS/Systems and Logistics, 15 January 1964 to 14 February 1969
Production and Programming, DCS/Research and Development, 15 February 1969 to 13 November 1969
Production, DCS/Research and Development, 14 November 1969 to 31 March 1970
Reconnaissance (Assistant for), DCS/Research and Development, 3 May 1965 to 14 April 1968
Reconnaissance and Electronic Warfare, DSC/Research and Development, 15 April 1968-on
Requirements, DCS/Development, until 20 April 1959

Major Command and Division Histories

Aerospace Defense Command, 15 January 1968-on
Air Defense Command, until 15 January 1968
Air Force Logistics Command, 1 April 1961-on
Air Materiel Command, until 1 April 1961
Air Force Systems Command (AFSC), 17 March 1961-on
  Aeronautical Systems Division (AFSC), 1 July 1961-on
Air Research and Development Command (ARDC), until 17 March 1961
  Air Development Force (ARDC), 2 April 1951 to 6 June 1951
  Wright Air Development Center (ARDC), 2 April 1951 to 6 June 1951
  Wright Air Development Division (ARDC), 15 December 1959 to 31 March 1961
Pacific Air Forces, 1 July 1957-on
Strategic Air Command, 21 March 1946-on
Tactical Air Command, 21 March 1946 to 1 December 1948; 1 December 1950-on (TAC was subordinate to Continental Air Command between December 1948 and December 1950.)

Special Studies

Alling, Frederick, *The F–102 Airplane, 1950–1956.* AMC Historical Study 310 (1957).
Boylan, Bernard L, *Development of the Long-Range Escort Fighter.* USAF Historical Study 136 (RSI, Air University), September 1955.
De Haven, Ethel, *The Voodoo Story, 1945–1957.* AMC Historical Study 309 (1957).
Goldberg, Alfred and Little, Robert D., *History of Headquarters USAF, 1949–1950.* Ofc/AF Hist, 1954.
Goldberg, Alfred, ed., *History of Headquarters USAF, 1950–1951.* Ofc/AF Hist, 1955.
Jensen, Edna., *Case History of XP–80, et al.* AMC Historical Study, August 1948.

Johnson, L. L., The Century Series Fighters, *A Study in Research and Development*. Rand Study RM 2549, 20 May 1960.

Lemmer, George F., *Strengthening USAF General Purpose Forces, 1961–1964*. Ofc/AF Hist, January 1966.

Marmor, Arthur K., *The Search for New USAF Weapons, 1958–1959*. Ofc/AF Hist, April 1961.

McMullen, Richard F., *Aircraft in Air Defense, 1945–1960*. ADC Historical Study 12 (1960).

McMullen, Richard F., *History of Air Defense Weapons, 1946–1962*. ADC Historical Study 14 (1962).

McMullen, Richard F., *The Air National Guard in Air Defense, 1946–1971*. ADC Historical Study 38 (1971).

Miller, Dorothy, L., *Case History of the F–84 Airplane*. AMC Historical Study 35 (1950).

Miller, Martin J. and Bagwell, Margaret C., *Case History of the F–82E, F, and G Airplane and Related Engines*. AMC Historical Study, January 1951.

Nalty, Bernard C., *The Quest for an Advanced Manned Strategic Bomber, USAF Plans and Policies, 1961–1966*. Ofc/AF Hist, August 1966.

Schultz, Helen., *F–89*. AMC Historical Study 37 (1952).

Smith, Robert A. and Brassel, John C., *F–84F History, November 1949–November 1954, A Study in Economic Mobilization*. AMC Historical Study (1955).

Williams, Fenton L., *Project Pull Out F–86 Modification Program 1954–1955*. AMC Sacramento AMA Historical Study (1956).

Wolk, Herman S., *USAF Plans and Policies, R&D for Southeast Asia, 1965–1967*. Ofc/AF Hist, June 1969.

Reports

Annual Report of the Secretary of the Air Force in Annual Report of the Secretary of Defense. FY 56 thru FY 70.

Army Air Forces Statistical Digest. World War II thru 1946.

Hearings before House Subcommittee Nr. 2 of the Committee on Armed Services, *Department of Defense Decision to Reduce the Number and Types of Manned Bombers in the Strategic Air Command*, 89th Cong. 2d sess, 1966.

Hearings before House Subcommittee of the Committee on Appropriations, *Department of Defense Appropriations for 1964*, 88th Cong, 1st sess, 1963.

Hearings before House Subcommittee of the Committee on Appropriations, *Department of Defense Appropriations for 1966*, 89th Cong, 1st sess, 1965.

Hearings before Senate Committee on Armed Services, *Authorization for Military Procurement, Research and Development, Fiscal Year 1970, and Reserve Strength*, 91st Cong, 1st sess, 1969.

Semiannual Report of the Secretary of the Air Force in Semiannual Report of the Secretary of Defense. Jan 55 thru Jun 55.
USAF Aircraft and Missile Characteristics Summary (Black Book). 1962-on.
USAF Management Summary, Major Force Program, Resume. 30 Nov 73
USAF Management Summary, Research and Development. 1965 thru 1970.
USAF Production Digest. 1956 thru 1971.
USAF Standard Aircraft Characteristics (Green Book). 1950-on.
United States Air Force Statistical Digest. 1947 thru June 1950 and FY 51 thru FY 74.

Orders, Manuals, and Other Publications

Department of Defense Model Designation of Military Aircraft, Rockets, and Guided Missiles. Jul 68, Jul 70, Apr 74.

Air Force Pamphlet 190–2–1. Releasable Data on USAF Aerospace Craft. 1 Jun 60.
Air Force Pamphlet 190–2–2. A Chronology of American Aerospace Events from 1903 through 1964. 1 Sep 65.
USAF Research and Development Quarterly Review. 1950 thru 1960.
AFLC Technical Manual (T.O. 00–25–30). Unit Costs of Aircraft, Guided Missiles and Engines. 30 Jun 71, 30 Jun 72, 30 Jun 73.
AFLC Technical Order 00–25–30. Unit Costs of Aircraft, Guided Missiles and Engines. 30 Apr 68, 1 Jul 69, 30 Jun 70.
AMC Technical Order 00–25–30. Unit Costs of Aircraft, Guided Missiles and Engines. 25 Aug 58, 20 Feb 60.

Periodicals

Air Force Magazine. Air Force Association, Washington. Monthly. Nov 58-on.
Air University Review. Air University, Maxwell AFB, Ala. Quarterly. 1963-on.
Armed Forces Journal. Washington. Weekly. July 1968-on.
Aviation Week and Space Technology. New York. Weekly. 1956-on.

Books

Art, Robert J. *The TFX Decision: McNamara and the Military.* Boston: Little, Brown and Co., 1968.
Bridgman, Leonard, ed. and compiler. *Jane's All the World's Aircraft.* London: Sampson Low, Marston & Co., Ltd.
Brown, Heyn, Freeman, Bowyer, and Berry, compilers; Bruce Robertson, editor. *United States Army and Air Force Fighters 1916–1961.* U.S.A. Aero Publishers, Inc.

Emme, Eugene M. *Aeronautics and Astronautics: An American Chronology of Science and Technology in the Exploration of Space, 1915–1960*. Washington: GPO, 1961.

Futrell, Robert Frank. *The United States Air Force in Korea 1950–1953*. New York: Duell, Sloan and Pearce, 1961.

Green, William. *The World's Fighting Planes*. New York: Doubleday and Co., 1965.

Goldberg, Alfred, ed., *A History of the United States Air Force, 1907–1957*. (Princeton, NJ: VanNostrand, 1957).

Swanborough, Frederick G., and Bowers, Peter. *United States Military Aircraft Since 1909*. London and New York: G. P. Putnam's Sons, 1963.

GLOSSARY

AAF	Army Air Forces
ADC	Air Defense Command, Aerospace Defense Command
ADO	Advanced Development Objective
AFB	Air Force Base
AFCS	Automatic Flight Control System
AFLC	Air Force Logistics Command
AFR	Air Force Reserve
AMC	Air Materiel Command
AMI	advanced manned interceptor
AMSA	Advanced Manned Strategic Aircraft
AMTI	airborne moving target indicator
ANG	Air National Guard
APG	Air Proving Ground
APGC	Air Proving Ground Command
ARDC	Air Research and Development Center
ATC	Air Training Command
AWACS	airborne warning and control system
AWCS	automatic weapons control system
BROFICON	broadcast fighter control
CADC	central air data computer
CAP	combat air patrol
CAS	close air support
CCM	counter-counter measures
CCT	combat crew training
CCTS	combat crew training squadron
CDR	critical design review
CONAC	Continental Air Command
CONUS	Continental United States
CORDS	coherent-on-receive doppler system
CPFF	cost-plus-a fixed fee
CSAF	Air Force Chief of Staff
CSD	constant speed drive
CSTI	control surface tie-in
DEF	development engineering inspection
DOD	Department of Defense
ECCM	electronic counter-counter measures
ECM	electronic counter-measures
ECS	electronic control system
ELINT	electronic intelligence
FAI	Fédération Aéronautique Internationale
FEAF	Far East Air Forces
FFAR	folding fin aerial rocket

FICON	Fighter-Convair
FIS	fighter-interceptor squadron
FMS	foreign military sales
FPF	fixed-price firm
FPI	fixed-price incentive
FPIF	fixed-price incentive firm
fpm	feet per minute
FPRA	fixed-price redeterminable contract of the A type
ft	foot, feet
FY	fiscal year
GFAE	government-furnished aeronautical equipment
GOR	General Operational Requirements
HSD	horizontal situation display
HSI	horizontal situation indicator
HVAR	high velocity aircraft rocket
ICI	initial capability inspection
IDS	integrated display set
ILS	instrument landing system
IOC	initial operational capability
IRAN	inspection and repair as necessary
IOC	initial operational capability
kn	knot
LABS	low altitude bombing system
LARA	low altitude radar altimeter
LASPAC	Landing Gear, Avionics, Systems Package
lb	pound
LC	letter contract
LES	leading edge slat
LORAN	long-range navigation
MAP	Military Assistance Program
MAS	Military Assistance Sales
MASF	Military Assistance Service Fund
MDAP	Mutual Defense Assistance Program
MEISR	Minimum Essential Improvement in System Reliability
Mfr	manufacture, manufacturer
MIPR	Military Interdepartmental Purchase Request
MTBF	mean time between failures
NACA	National Advisory Committee for Aeronautics
NADAR	signal data recorder
NASA	National Aeronautics and Space Administration
NATO	North Atlantic Treaty Organization
nm	nautical mile
No	number
NORAD	North American Air Defense Command

NORM	not operationally ready-maintenance
NORS	not operationally ready-supply
ORI	operational readiness inspection
OSD	Office of the Secretary of Defense
OST	operational suitability test
OT&E	operational test and evaluation
PACAF	Pacific Air Forces
PCS	pitch control system
RAAF	Royal Austrialian Air Force
RAF	Royal Air Force
RAFS	Royal Air Force Station
RCAF	Royal Canadian Air Force
R&D	research and development
RDT&E	research, development, test and evaluation
RFPs	request for proposals
RHAW	radar homing and warning
SAC	Strategic Air Command
SAE	semi-actuator ejector
SAGE	Semi-Automatic Ground Environment
SAM	surface-to-air missile
SARM	standard antiradiation missile
SDR	System Development Requirement
SEA	Southeast Asia (Republic of Vietnam, Thailand, Laos, and Cambodia)
SEAOR	Southeast Asia Operational Requirement
SL	sea level
SLAR	side-looking airborne radar
SLIM	Simplified Logistics and Improved Maintenance
SLR	side-looking radar
SMAMA	Sacramento Air Materiel Area
SMD	System Management Directive
SOR	Specific Operational Requirements
SRA	Specialized repair activity
SRAM	short-range attack missile
TAC	Tactical Air Command
TACAN	tactical air navigation
TFG	tactical fighter group
TFR	terrain following radar
TFS	tactical fighter squadron
TFW	tactical fighter wing
TFX	Tactical Fighter Experimental
TISEO	Target Identification and Electro-Optical System
TRS	tactical reconnaissance squadron
U.K.	United Kingdom
UN	United Nations

USAFE	United States Air Forces in Europe
VAX	attack aircraft, experimental
VNAF	South Vietnamese Air Force
V/STOL	vertical and short takeoff and landing
VTOL	vertical takeoff and landing
WS	weapon system
ZELMAL	Zero Length Launch and Mat Landing

INDEX

☆ U.S. GOVERNMENT PRINTING OFFICE : 1985 O—485-057